For Reference

Not to be taken from this room

Child Abuse

SOURCEBOOK

FIFTH EDITION

Child Abuse
SOURCEBOOK

FIFTH EDITION

Basic Consumer Health Information about Child Abuse or Neglect and the Physical, Sexual, and Emotional Abuse of Children, Including Abusive Head Trauma, Bullying, Munchausen Syndrome by Proxy, Statutory Rape, Incest, Educational Neglect, Exploitation, and the Long–Term Consequences of Child Maltreatment, Featuring Facts about Risk Factors, Prevention Initiatives, Reporting Requirements, Legal Interventions, Child Protective Services, and Therapy Options

Along with Information for Parents, Foster Parents, and Adult Survivors of Child Abuse, a Glossary of Related Terms, and Directories of Additional Resources

OMNIGRAPHICS

615 Griswold, Ste. 520, Detroit, MI 48226

Bibliographic Note
Because this page cannot legibly accommodate all the copyright notices, the Bibliographic
Note portion of the Preface constitutes an extension of the copyright notice.

* * *

OMNIGRAPHICS
Angela L. Williams, *Managing Editor*
* * *

Copyright © 2019 Omnigraphics

ISBN 978-0-7808-1699-2
E-ISBN 978-0-7808-1700-5

Library of Congress Cataloging-in-Publication Data

Names: Omnigraphics, Inc., issuing body.

Title: Child abuse sourcebook: basic consumer health information about child neglect
and the physical, sexual, and emotional abuse of children, including abusive head
trauma, bullying, munchausen syndrome by proxy, statutory rape, incest, educational
neglect, exploitation, and the long-term consequences of child maltreatment,
featuring facts about risk factors, prevention initiatives, reporting requirements,
legal interventions, child protective services, and therapy options; along with
information for parents, foster parents, and adult survivors of child abuse, a glossary
of related terms, and directories of additional resources.

Description: 5th Edition. | Detroit, MI: Omnigraphics, Inc., [2019] | Revised edition
of Child abuse sourcebook, [2016]

Identifiers: LCCN 2019009457 (print) | LCCN 2019010722 (ebook) | ISBN
9780780817005 (ebook) | ISBN 9780780816992 (hard cover: alk. paper)

Subjects: LCSH: Child abuse--United States. | Child abuse--United States--
Prevention. | Abused children--United States.

Classification: LCC HV6626.52 (ebook) | LCC HV6626.52.C557 2019 (print) | DDC
362.76--dc23

LC record available at https://lccn.loc.gov/2019009457

Table of Contents

Part II: Physical and Sexual Abuse of Children

Part III: Child Neglect and Emotional Abuse

Part IV: Adult Survivors of Child Abuse

Part V: Child Abuse Preventions, Interventions, and Treatments

Preface

About This Book

According to the Administration for Children and Families (ACF), over 700,000 children are abused in the United States annually. Child maltreatment can create visible welts, bruises, and broken bones, or it can be invisible, producing deep emotional scars and life-long mental-health challenges. Children who have been the victims of abuse or neglect can experience alterations in brain chemistry, difficulty with social interaction, physical injuries, and even death.

Child Abuse Sourcebook, Fifth Edition provides updated information about child neglect and the physical, emotional, and sexual abuse of children, including facts about severe punishment, abusive head trauma, Munchausen syndrome by proxy, rape, incest, exploitation, medical neglect, educational neglect, bullying, and aggression through technology. The book explains the differences between situations that require legal intervention and those considered to be parental choices, even when controversial. Facts about child protective services (CPS) and interventions by the court system are also included. Parenting issues that may relate to child abuse risks, including domestic violence, postpartum depression, military service, substance abuse, and disciplinary strategies, are addressed, and information for adult survivors of child abuse is provided. The volume concludes with a glossary, a state-by-state list of contact information for reporting suspected child maltreatment, and a directory of resources for finding additional help and information.

How to Use This Book

This book is divided into parts and chapters. Parts focus on broad areas of interest. Chapters are devoted to single topics within a part.

Part I: Child Maltreatment explains the types of intentional actions that U.S. state laws typically recognize as forms of abuse. These include physical abuse, sexual abuse and exploitation, emotional abuse, neglect, and abandonment. Related issues, including bullying and exposure to violence, are also explored. The part concludes with a discussion regarding the physical, psychological, behavioral, and societal consequences of child maltreatment.

Part II: Physical and Sexual Abuse of Children concerns itself with modes of maltreatment that result from physical actions, including family violence, harsh corporal punishment, abusive head trauma (shaken baby syndrome), and Munchausen syndrome by proxy. It also reports on the physical and behavioral indicators of sexual abuse and provides facts about incest and abuse in dating relationships, and it discusses statutory rape laws.

Part III: Child Neglect and Emotional Abuse provides information about forms of abuse that are generally less visible than physical abuse. These can result from the failure of a parent or guardian to take appropriate action on a child's behalf—such as refusing to seek medical care or education—or from other behaviors that negatively impact a child's mental development or psychological wellbeing.

Part IV: Adult Survivors of Child Abuse explains the long-term consequences of experiencing maltreatment during childhood, and it discusses the outcomes that may emerge in adulthood. Mental-health issues related to the vestiges of child abuse are also addressed, and the link between child abuse and adult suicide risk is explored.

Part V: Child Abuse Preventions, Interventions, and Treatments reports on various strategies, laws, and regulations intended to reduce the incidence of child abuse. It explains how child protective services can intervene in suspected abuse cases, and it describes therapy options for children and adults who have been impacted by abuse.

Part VI: Parenting Issues and Child Abuse Risks describes some of the most common family challenges that place children in dangerous situations, including domestic violence, mental-health issues, parental substance abuse, and inappropriate forms of discipline. It provides tips for improving parenting skills and also offers suggestions for parents, and foster and adoptive parents.

Part VII: Additional Help and Information includes a glossary of terms related to child abuse and child protective services, a state-by-state list of contact information for reporting suspected child maltreatment, and a directory of organizations involved in efforts to end child abuse and heal its effects.

Bibliographic Note

This volume contains documents and excerpts from publications issued by the following U.S. government agencies: Administration for Children and Families (ACF); Assistant Secretary for Planning and Evaluation (ASPE); Centers for Disease Control and Prevention (CDC); Child Welfare Information Gateway; *Eunice Kennedy Shriver* National Institute of Child Health and Human Development (NICHD); National Criminal Justice Reference Service (NCJRS); National Human Genome Research Institute (NHGRI); National Institute of Justice (NIJ); National Institute on Mental Health (NIMH); National Institute of Neurological Disorders and Stroke (NINDS); National Institutes of Health (NIH); Office for Victims of Crime (OVC); Office of Juvenile Justice and Delinquency Prevention (OJJDP); Office on Women's Health (OWH); Substance Abuse and Mental Health Services Administration (SAMHSA); U.S. Department of Justice (DOJ); U.S. Department of Education (ED); U.S. Department of Health and Human Services (HHS); U.S. Department of State (DOS); U.S. Department of Veterans Affairs (VA); and U.S. National Library of Medicine (NLM).

It may also contain original material produced by Omnigraphics and reviewed by medical consultants.

About the Health Reference Series

The *Health Reference Series* is designed to provide basic medical information for patients, families, caregivers, and the general public. Each volume takes a particular topic and provides comprehensive coverage. This is especially important for people who may be dealing with a newly diagnosed disease or a chronic disorder in themselves or in a family member. People looking for preventive guidance, information about disease warning signs, medical statistics, and risk factors for health problems will also find answers to their questions in the *Health Reference Series*. The *Series*, however, is not intended to serve as a tool for diagnosing illness, in prescribing treatments, or as a substitute for the physician/patient relationship. All people concerned about medical symptoms or the possibility of disease are encouraged to seek professional care from an appropriate healthcare provider.

A Note about Spelling and Style

Health Reference Series editors use *Stedman's Medical Dictionary* as an authority for questions related to the spelling of medical terms and the *Chicago Manual of Style* for questions related to grammatical structures, punctuation, and other editorial concerns. Consistent adherence is not always possible, however, because the individual volumes within the *Series* include many documents from a wide variety of different producers, and the editor's primary goal is to present material from each source as accurately as is possible. This sometimes means that information in different chapters or sections may follow other guidelines and alternate spelling authorities. For example, occasionally a copyright holder may require that eponymous terms be shown in possessive forms (Crohn's disease vs. Crohn disease) or that British spelling norms be retained (leukaemia vs. leukemia).

Medical Review

Omnigraphics contracts with a team of qualified, senior medical professionals who serve as medical consultants for the *Health Reference Series*. As necessary, medical consultants review reprinted and originally written material for currency and accuracy. Citations including the phrase "Reviewed (month, year)" indicate material reviewed by this team. Medical consultation services are provided to the *Health Reference Series* editors by:

Dr. Vijayalakshmi, MBBS, DGO, MD
Dr. Senthil Selvan, MBBS, DCH, MD
Dr. K. Sivanandham, MBBS, DCH, MS (Research), PhD

Our Advisory Board

We would like to thank the following board members for providing initial guidance on the development of this series:

- Dr. Lynda Baker, Associate Professor of Library and Information Science, Wayne State University, Detroit, MI

- Nancy Bulgarelli, William Beaumont Hospital Library, Royal Oak, MI

- Karen Imarisio, Bloomfield Township Public Library, Bloomfield Township, MI

- Karen Morgan, Mardigian Library, University of Michigan-Dearborn, Dearborn, MI

- Rosemary Orlando, St. Clair Shores Public Library, St. Clair Shores, MI

Health Reference Series *Update Policy*

The inaugural book in the *Health Reference Series* was the first edition of *Cancer Sourcebook* published in 1989. Since then, the *Series* has been enthusiastically received by librarians and in the medical community. In order to maintain the standard of providing high-quality health information for the layperson the editorial staff at Omnigraphics felt it was necessary to implement a policy of updating volumes when warranted.

Medical researchers have been making tremendous strides, and it is the purpose of the *Health Reference Series* to stay current with the most recent advances. Each decision to update a volume is made on an individual basis. Some of the considerations include how much new information is available and the feedback we receive from people who use the books. If there is a topic you would like to see added to the update list, or an area of medical concern you feel has not been adequately addressed, please write to:

Managing Editor
Health Reference Series
Omnigraphics
615 Griswold, Ste. 520
Detroit, MI 48226

Part One

Child Maltreatment

Chapter 1

Defining Child Maltreatment

Chapter Contents

Section 1.1

Understanding Child Abuse and Neglect

This section includes text excerpted from "Child Abuse and Neglect Prevention," Centers for Disease Control and Prevention (CDC), April 10, 2018.

Children under the age of 18 may be exposed to abuse and neglect by a parent, caregiver, or another person in a custodial role (e.g., clergy, coach, or a teacher). There are four common types of child abuse and neglect.

- Physical abuse
- Sexual abuse
- Emotional abuse
- Neglect

The Centers for Disease Control and Prevention (CDC) research and programs work to understand the problem of child abuse and neglect and prevent them before they begin.

Data and Statistics Related to Child Abuse in the United States

Listed below are statistical facts on child abuse in the United States.

- There were 676,000 victims of child abuse and neglect reported to child protective services (CPS) in 2016.
- A non-CPS study estimated that one in four children experience some form of child abuse or neglect in their lifetime, and one in seven children have experienced abuse or neglect in the last year.
- About 1,750 children died from abuse or neglect in 2016.
- The total lifetime economic cost of child abuse and neglect is estimated at $124 billion each year.

Risk and Protective Factors of Child Abuse

A combination of individual, relational, community, and societal factors contribute to the risk of child abuse and neglect. Although children are not responsible for the harm inflicted upon them, certain characteristics have been found to increase their risk of being abused and/or neglected. Risk factors are characteristics that are associated with child abuse and neglect—they may or may not be direct causes.

Risk Factors for Victimization

Individual risk factors for victimization include:

- Children younger than four years of age
- Special needs that may increase caregiver burden (e.g., disabilities, mental-health issues, and chronic physical illnesses)

Risk Factors for Perpetration

Individual risk factors for perpetration include:

- Parents' lack of understanding of children's needs, child development, and parenting skills
- Parental history of child abuse and/or neglect
- Substance abuse and/or mental-health issues, including depression in the family
- Parental characteristics, such as young age, low education, single parenthood, having a number of dependent children, and low income
- Nonbiological, transient caregivers in the home (e.g., mother's male partner)
- Parental thoughts and emotions that tend to support or justify maltreatment behaviors

Family-related risk factors include:

- Social isolation
- Family disorganization, dissolution, and violence, including intimate partner violence (IPV)
- Parenting stress, poor parent-child relationships, and negative interactions

Risk factors associated with community include:

- Community violence

5

- Concentrated neighborhood disadvantage (e.g., high poverty, residential instability, high unemployment rates, and high density of alcohol outlets) and poor social connections

Protective Factors for Child Maltreatment

Protective factors buffer children from being abused or neglected. Protective factors have not been studied as extensively or rigorously as risk factors. However, identifying and understanding protective factors are equally as important as researching risk factors.

There is scientific evidence to support the following protective factors.

Family protective factors include:

- Supportive family environments and social networks

- Concrete support for basic needs

- Nurturing parenting skills

- Stable family relationships

- Household rules and child monitoring

- Parental employment

- Parental education

- Adequate housing

- Access to healthcare and social services

- Caring adults outside of the family who can serve as role models or mentors

Community protective factor includes:

- Communities that support parents and take responsibility for preventing abuse

Essentials for Childhood Framework: Creating Safe, Stable, Nurturing Relationships and Environments for All Children

Young children experience their world through their relationships with their parents and other caregivers. Safe, stable, nurturing relationships and environments are essential to preventing child abuse and neglect.

The *Essentials for Childhood Framework*, as provided by the CDC, includes strategies to promote relationships and environments that can help create neighborhoods, communities, and a world in which every child can thrive. It is intended for communities committed to both promoting the positive development of children and families and preventing child abuse and neglect. The framework has four goal areas and suggests strategies based on the best available evidence to achieve each goal. The four-goal areas include:

- Goal 1: Raise awareness, and commit to promoting safe, stable, nurturing relationships and environments to prevent child abuse and neglect

- Goal 2: Use data to inform actions

- Goal 3: Create the context for healthy children and families through norms change and programs

- Goal 4: Create the context for healthy children and families through policies

States Implementing the Framework

The CDC's Division of Violence Prevention (DVP) is funding five state health departments in California, Colorado, Massachusetts, North Carolina, and Washington to implement the four goals in the *Essentials for Childhood Framework,* using a collective impact process. The CDC also offers technical assistance and training to many other states that do not receive CDC funding but are engaged at varying levels in implementing the *Essentials for Childhood Framework*. State health departments:

- Coordinate and manage existing and new partnerships with other child abuse and neglect prevention organizations and nontraditional partners involved in assuring safe, stable, nurturing relationships and environments for children

- Work with partners to identify and align strategies across sectors

- Identify, coordinate, monitor and report on the strategies implemented by multi-sector partners

- Document the state-level impact of these efforts

Section 1.2

Legal Definitions of Child Abuse and Neglect

This section includes text excerpted from "Definitions of Child Abuse
and Neglect," Child Welfare Information Gateway, U.S. Department
of Health and Human Services (HHS), April 2016.

Child abuse and neglect are defined by federal and state laws. At
the state level, child abuse and neglect may be defined in both civil and
criminal statutes. At the federal level, the Child Abuse Prevention and
Treatment Act (CAPTA) defines "child abuse" and "neglect" as "any act or
failure to act on the part of a parent or caretaker, which results in death,
serious physical or emotional harm, sexual abuse, or exploitation, or an
act or failure to act which presents an imminent risk of serious harm."

Types of Abuse

Nearly all states, the District of Columbia (DC), American Samoa,
Guam, the Northern Mariana Islands, Puerto Rico, and the United
States Virgin Islands provide civil definitions of child abuse and
neglect in statute. States recognize the different types of abuse in
their definitions, including physical abuse, neglect, sexual abuse, and
emotional abuse. Some states also provide definitions in statute for
parental-substance abuse and/or for abandonment as child abuse.

Physical Abuse

Physical abuse is generally defined as any non-accidental physical
injury to the child and can include striking, kicking, burning, or biting
the child, or any action that results in a physical impairment of the
child. In approximately 38 states and American Samoa, Guam, the
Northern Mariana Islands, Puerto Rico, and the Virgin Islands, the
definition of abuse also includes acts or circumstances that threaten
the child with harm or create a substantial risk of harm to the child's
health or welfare. In 7 states, the crime of human trafficking, including labor trafficking, involuntary servitude, or trafficking of minors,
is included in the definition of child abuse.

Neglect

Neglect is frequently defined as the failure of a parent or other person with responsibility for the child to provide needed food, clothing,

shelter, medical care, or supervision to the degree that the child's health, safety, and well-being are threatened with harm. Approximately 25 states, the DC, American Samoa, Puerto Rico, and the Virgin Islands include failure to educate the child as required by law in their definition of neglect. 10 states and American Samoa specifically define medical neglect as failing to provide any special medical treatment or mental healthcare needed by the child. In addition, 4 states define medical neglect as the withholding of medical treatment or nutrition from disabled infants with life-threatening conditions.

Sexual Abuse / Exploitation

All states include sexual abuse in their definitions of child abuse. Some states refer in general terms to sexual abuse, while others specify various acts as sexual abuse. Sexual exploitation is an element of the definition of sexual abuse in most jurisdictions. Sexual exploitation includes allowing the child to engage in prostitution or in the production of child pornography. In 21 states, the definition of sexual abuse includes human trafficking—including sex trafficking or trafficking of children—for sexual purposes.

Emotional Abuse

Almost all states, the DC, American Samoa, Guam, the Northern Mariana Islands, Puerto Rico, and the Virgin Islands include emotional maltreatment as part of their definitions of abuse or neglect. Approximately 33 states, the DC, Guam, the Northern Mariana Islands, and Puerto Rico provide specific definitions of emotional abuse or mental injury to a child. Typical language used in these definitions is injury to the psychological capacity or emotional stability of the child as evidenced by an observable or substantial change in behavior, emotional response, or cognition." These definitions also point to injury as evidenced by "anxiety, depression, withdrawal, or aggressive behavior."

Parental Substance Abuse

Parental substance abuse is an element of the definition of child abuse or neglect in some states. Circumstances that are considered abuse or neglect in some states include:

- Prenatal exposure due to the mother's use of an illegal drug or other substance (14 states—including Arizona, Arkansas, Colorado, Illinois, Indiana, Iowa, Louisiana, Massachusetts,

9

Minnesota, North Dakota, Oklahoma, Oregon, South Dakota, and Wisconsin—and the DC)

- Manufacture of a controlled substance in the presence of a child or on the premises occupied by a child (12 states, including Colorado, Indiana, Iowa, Montana, Ohio, Oklahoma, Oregon, Pennsylvania, South Dakota, Tennessee, Virginia, and Washington).

- Allowing a child to be present where the chemicals or equipment for the manufacture of controlled substances are used or stored (3 states, including Arizona, Arkansas, and Washington).

- Selling, distributing or giving drugs or alcohol to a child (7 states—including Arkansas, Florida, Hawaii, Illinois, Minnesota, Ohio, and Texas—and Guam).

- Use of a controlled substance by a caregiver that impairs the caregiver's ability to adequately care for the child (8 states).

Abandonment

Approximately 17 states and the DC include abandonment in their definitions of abuse or neglect, usually as a type of neglect. Approximately 19 states, Guam, Puerto Rico, and the Virgin Islands provide definitions for abandonment that are separate from the definition of neglect. In general, it is considered abandonment of the child when the parent's identity or whereabouts are unknown, the child has been left by the parent in circumstances in which the child suffers serious harm, or the parent has failed to maintain contact with the child or to provide reasonable support for a specified period of time.

Chapter 2

Acts of Omission: An Overview of Child Neglect

Chapter Contents

Section 2.1

An Overview of Child Neglect

This section includes text excerpted from "Acts of Omission: An
Overview of Child Neglect," Child Welfare Information Gateway,
U.S. Department of Health and Human Services (HHS), July 2018.

Neglect accounts for over three-quarters of confirmed cases of child
maltreatment in the United States—far more than physical or sexual
abuse. It continues, however, to receive less attention from practitioners,
researchers, and the media. Some reasons may be that neglect is not well
understood, and it is difficult to identify, prevent, and treat effectively.

Child Neglect: Scope of the Problem

According to the latest Children's Bureau *Child Maltreatment*
report, more than 514,000 children were neglected in 2015, accounting for 75.3 percent of all unique victims of child maltreatment. In
addition, neglect was either the sole cause or one of the contributors
to nearly 73 percent of the 1,670 deaths related to child maltreatment
in 2015.

These statistics include only children that were brought to the
attention of state child protective services (CPS) agencies. The National
Incidence Study (NIS) of Child Abuse and Neglect, which generates
broader estimates by gathering data from sources beyond CPS agencies, generally shows higher numbers of maltreatment than those
shown in the *Child Maltreatment* reports. The most recent version,
NIS-4, uses data from 2005 to 2006 to show that more than 2.2 million
children were neglected, accounting for about 77 percent of all children
harmed or endangered by maltreatment. Although the rates of all
types of maltreatment have declined in recent years, rates of neglect
have decreased much less than the other types. The persistently high
rates of neglect and its serious consequences point to the need for more
effective prevention and early intervention in cases of neglect.

Defining Child Neglect

Both federal and state laws provide basic definitions of child abuse
and neglect. The federal Child Abuse Prevention and Treatment Act
(CAPTA), as amended by the CAPTA Reauthorization Act of 2010,
defines "child abuse" and "neglect" as the following:

- Any recent act or failure to act on the part of a parent or caretaker, which results in death, serious physical or emotional harm, sexual abuse, or exploitation

- An act or failure to act, which presents an imminent risk of serious harm

The Justice for Victims of Trafficking Act of 2015 expanded the federal definition of "child abuse and neglect" and "sexual abuse" to include a child who is identified as a victim of sex trafficking or other severe forms of trafficking.

Neglect is commonly defined in state law as the failure of a parent or other person with responsibility for the child to provide needed food, clothing, shelter, medical care, or supervision to the degree that the child's health, safety, and well-being are threatened with harm. Some states specifically mention types of neglect in their statutes, such as educational neglect, medical neglect, and abandonment; in addition, some states include exceptions for determining neglect, such as religious exemptions for medical neglect and financial considerations for physical neglect.

Child neglect is generally thought of as the inability of a parent or caregiver to meet a child's basic needs, potentially placing the child at risk of serious harm. For definitions, many state laws focus on the omission in care by parents or caregivers, but holding parents or caregivers accountable for the harm that results from failing to care for their children is challenging for child-welfare workers who may feel uncomfortable labeling failure to provide necessary care as "neglect." Definitions and accountability are complicated by multiple and interacting factors, such as the following:

- Whether care is adequate to meet a child's needs
- If harm is actual or potential
- Variety in the types of neglect
- Whether the neglect was intentional

These factors create difficulties in developing standard definitions of neglect, and the varied definitions contribute to a lack of consistency in research on neglect and responses to the research.

Types of Neglect

Although state laws vary regarding the types of neglect included in definitions, summarized below are the most commonly recognized categories of neglect.

- **Physical neglect** is abandoning the child or refusing to accept custody and not providing for basic needs, such as nutrition, hygiene, or appropriate clothing.

- **Medical neglect** is the act of delaying or denying recommended healthcare for the child.

- **Inadequate supervision** is the act of leaving the child unsupervised (depending on the length of time and the child's age/maturity), not protecting the child from safety hazards, not providing adequate caregivers, or engaging in harmful behavior.

- **Emotional neglect** is the act of isolating the child, not providing affection or emotional support, or exposing the child to domestic violence or substance use.

- **Educational neglect** is the act of failing to enroll the child in school or homeschool, ignoring special-education needs, or permitting chronic absenteeism from school.

Reasons for Neglect

To fully understand the reasons for neglect, it is important to move beyond considerations of child neglect only as a function of parent or caregiver characteristics. Considerations should include the following four levels of the socioecological model. To better understand the influences on individual families, it is important to explore the context for these different areas in the lives of families. Examples of factors in each of the levels of the socioecological model that contribute to and protect against child neglect include the following:

- **Child/individual**—Physical, emotional, intellectual, and other personal characteristics of the parent or child; current or past trauma; nurturing and attachment capacity of the parent and child; resilience

- **Family/parents**—Healthy partner relationship; physical, emotional, and economic well-being; parent–child interactions

- **Community/neighborhood**—Adequate resources to meet community needs (e.g., safe playgrounds, libraries, access to healthy foods); networks for support and assistance; neighborhood violence

- **Society**—Family policies that provide support for families, lack of clarity on adequate parenting standards, concrete supports available to all families

14

Understanding the reasons for neglect that extend beyond parents and caregivers may lead child-welfare professionals to use strengths-based approaches and preventive strategies with parents who need support.

Consequences of Neglect

Although the initial impact may not be as obvious as physical or sexual abuse, the consequences of child neglect are just as serious. The effects of neglect are cumulative, and long-term research, such as that being performed by the Longitudinal Studies of Child Abuse and Neglect (LONGSCAN) funded by the Children's Bureau, helps child-welfare professionals better understand outcomes for children affected by neglect. Neglect can have a negative effect on children in the following areas:

- **Health and physical development**—Malnourishment, impaired brain development, delays in growth or a failure to thrive

- **Intellectual and cognitive development**—Poor academic performance, delayed or impaired language development

- **Emotional and psychological development**—Deficiencies in self-esteem, attachment, or trust

- **Social and behavioral development**—Interpersonal relationship problems, social withdrawal, poor impulse control.

The impacts in these areas are interrelated; problems in one developmental area may influence growth in another area. In addition, research has established a clear link between child maltreatment, including neglect, with health and well-being issues. The effects of neglect can vary, however, based on the following factors:

- The child's age

- The presence and strength of protective factors

- The frequency, duration, and severity of the neglect

- The relationship between the child and caregiver

Section 2.2

Chronic Child Neglect

This section includes text excerpted from "Chronic Child Neglect,"
Child Welfare Information Gateway, U.S. Department of Health and
Human Services (HHS), January 2013. Reviewed March 2019.

Chronic child neglect is one of the most daunting challenges to the well-being of children and families receiving child welfare services. The child welfare system is primarily geared to protect children who are in imminent danger or who experience egregious harm at the hands of their parents or caregivers. Chronic child neglect, however, which is less visible and often less sensational, is more pervasive and difficult to resolve.

This section discusses what we know about chronic neglect and then reviews ways to work with families experiencing chronic neglect, including critical elements of successful casework practice, examples of what agencies are doing, and ways agencies can integrate child welfare approaches to chronic neglect with prevention and early intervention efforts.

What Is Chronic Neglect?

While a universal definition of chronic neglect does not exist, there are several professionally agreed upon identifiers. Chronic neglect occurs when:

1. One or more needs basic to a child's healthy development are not met.

2. The neglect is perpetrated by a parent or caregiver.

3. The neglect happens on a recurring or enduring basis.

When these three identifiers result in cumulative harm or serious risk of harm to the child's safety, health, or well-being, a child can be said to be chronically neglected. Using this framework, "chronic child neglect" can be defined as a parent or caregiver's ongoing, serious pattern of deprivation of a child's basic physical, developmental, and/or emotional needs for healthy growth and development. Chronic neglect differs from incident-based neglect in terms of duration, frequency (e.g., number of reports), duration of need for services, and referrals for multiple types of maltreatment.

Scope of the Problem

For more than a decade, state reports to the National Child Abuse and Neglect Data System (NCANDS), a Children's Bureau initiative, have shown that the great majority of maltreatment reports in the United States involve neglect rather than physical or sexual abuse. The most recent child maltreatment reports show that children who experienced neglect made up approximately three-quarters of children who were identified as maltreatment victims. Additionally, cases involving neglect are more likely to recur than cases involving other maltreatment types and recur more quickly than abuse cases.

Characteristics of Families

Several parental stressors are associated with chronic neglect, including poverty, mental-health issues, and substance abuse. Of all forms of maltreatment, neglect has the strongest relationship to poverty. This relationship is not causal but contributory. Neglect is strongly associated with measures of socioeconomic disadvantage, which include welfare dependence, homelessness, low levels of education, and single-parent families, as well as limited income. It is often difficult to distinguish when neglect is a direct effect of family poverty and when it arises from lack of concern, insufficient knowledge of parenting, poor financial planning, mental incapacity, addiction, parental disabilities, medical conditions, or other factors. Families' lives at home are frequently characterized by a chaotic, unpredictable, and disorganized family life; low social cohesion and fewer positive interactions; fewer actual or perceived social supports and social isolation; a lack of life skills; limited nurturing; perceived or learned powerlessness; and exposure to violence and crime. The communities in which these families live are often typified by community poverty, high unemployment, inadequate housing, and high crime rates. In addition, these families are often victims of intergenerational issues. If parents do not engage in developmentally appropriate activities to encourage their children's physical, mental, and academic growth and promote their safety and well-being, their children are less likely to learn how to do those things when they are parents.

Effects on Children

Neglected children, relative to children impacted by other types of maltreatment, experience more severe cognitive and academic deficits, social withdrawal, and internalizing behaviors. Although single incidences of physical and sexual abuse may sometimes appear to be more extreme than neglect, the effects of chronic neglect, if not addressed, can have a considerable impact on the long-term health and well-being of children and youth. Child trauma expert Bruce Perry has indicated that the impact of child neglect is often similar to that of trauma. Permanent changes in the brain, including lack of neural connections and pathways, may permanently limit the child's ability to develop normally.

Children who have been the subject of chronic neglect exhibit problems with attachment, cognitive development, emotional self-regulation, social self-confidence, social competence, perseverance in problem-solving, and empathy and social conscience. They may experience language delay, as well as conduct disorders. The younger the child and more prevalent the neglect, the greater the cumulative harm and more pernicious the consequences for the child. The unremitting daily impact of these experiences on the child can be profound and exponential, diminishing a child's sense of safety, stability, and well-being. Given that neglect often co-occurs with other types of maltreatment, isolating the impacts of neglect alone is challenging. More research is needed in this area.

Effects on Society

In assessing the impact of chronic neglect on society, studies show a significant economic toll as resources are disproportionately dedicated to chronic neglect families to increase supports and enhance their capacity to parent their children. One study found that the costs associated with families who chronically neglect their children are seven times greater than the costs associated with families not experiencing chronic neglect in the child welfare system. Another study indicated that one-half of all child welfare expenditures are spent on chronic neglect cases, with one-fifth of all families responsible for one-half of the spending, averaging $13,000 per year per family over a five-year period. High-cost and long-term solutions can be considered if there are significant future benefits, especially cost-avoidance results. Cost-benefit and cost-effectiveness studies are essential to new programs aimed at chronic neglect families.

Chapter 3

Child Abuse Statistics

Chapter Contents

Section 3.1

Child Maltreatment Facts at a Glance

This section includes text excerpted from "Child Maltreatment 2017,"
Administration for Children and Families (ACF), U.S. Department of
Health and Human Services (HHS), 2017.

Number of Child Victims

In the National Child Abuse and Neglect Data System (NCANDS), a "victim" is defined as "a child for whom the state determined at least one maltreatment is substantiated or indicated." This includes a child who died of child abuse and neglect. Prior to federal fiscal year (FFY) 2015, children with alternative response victim dispositions were included in the victim count. To ensure analyses are comparable across years, the new victim definition was used for trend analyses for FFYs 2013 through 2017.

For FFY 2017, there are nationally 674,000 (rounded) victims of child abuse and neglect. This equates to a national rate of 9.1 victims per 1,000 children in the population. The FFY 2017 national number of victims is 2.7 percent higher than the FFY 2013 national (rounded) number of 656,000. The percent change is calculated using the national rounded number of victims for FFY 2013 and FFY 2017.

At the state level, the percent change of victims of abuse and neglect range from a 45 percent decrease to a 149.9 percent increase from FFY 2013 to 2017. The FFY 2017 state rates range from a high of 22.2 to a low of 1.7 per 1,000 children. Changes to legislation, child-welfare policy, and practice that may contribute to an increase or decrease in the number of victims are provided by state commentary. For example, one state changed its level of evidence to substantiate maltreatment from clear and convincing to preponderance. As the new level does not require as much evidence to substantiate as the previous level, one would expect to see an increase in the number of victims.

During FFY 2013 to 2017, the national rates remained relatively stable for victims who did not have a prior history of victimization (known as "first-time victims"). During the 5 years, the national rates fluctuated from a low of 6.5 to a high of 6.7 per 1,000 children in the population. States use the disposition date of prior substantiated or indicated maltreatment to determine whether the victim was a first-time victim.

Table 3.1. Exhibit 3–E Child Victimization Rates, 2013 to 2017

Year	Reporting States	Child Population of Reporting States	Victims from Reporting States	National Victimization Rate per 1,000 Children	Child Population of All 52 States	National Estimate/ Rounded Number of Victims
2013	52	74,378,641	656,359	8.8	74,378,641	656,000
2014	52	74,339,990	675,429	9.1	74,339,990	675,000
2015	52	74,360,792	683,221	9.2	74,360,792	683,000
2016	51	73,658,812	671,716	9.1	74,352,938	677,000
2017	52	74,312,174	673,830	9.1	74,312,174	674,000

The number of victims is a unique count. The national victimization rate is calculated by dividing the number of victims from reporting states by the child population of reporting states, and multiplying by 1,000. If fewer than 52 states report data in a given year, the national estimate/rounded number of victims is calculated by multiplying the national victimization rate by the child population of all 52 states, and dividing by 1,000. The result is rounded to the nearest 1,000. If 52 states report data in a given year, the number of wounded victims is calculated by taking the number of reported victims and rounding it to the nearest 1,000. Because of the rounding rule, the national estimate/rounded number could have fewer victims than the actual reported number of victims.

To better understand prior victimization, a new 3-year retrospective analysis uses the combination of the report date and unique child identifiers to determine the number and disposition type of victims' prior contact with child protective services (CPS). A prior CPS contact is defined as any investigation or assessment that results in a disposition prior to the current disposition. This analysis examines nonfatal victims in states' FFY 2017 submissions, with report dates of up to 3 years prior to the date of the most recent victim report. 5 percent of victims have prior victim contacts, and 13 percent have prior non-victim contacts. Some victims (1.8%) have both victim and non-victim prior contacts.

Child Victim Demographics

The youngest children are the most vulnerable to maltreatment. Nationally, states report that more than one-quarter (28.5%) of victims are younger than 3 years of age. The victimization rate is highest for children younger than 1 year of age at 25.3 per 1,000 children in the population of the same age. This is more than double the rate of victims who are 1 year of age (11.7 per 1,000 children). Victims who are 2 or 3 years of age have victimization rates of 11 and 10.4 victims per 1,000 children of those respective ages in the population. Readers may notice some states have lower rates across age groups than other states. The states with lower rates may assign low-risk cases to alternative response or have other state policies or programs in place for maltreatment allegations. In general, the rate of victimization decreases with the child's age.

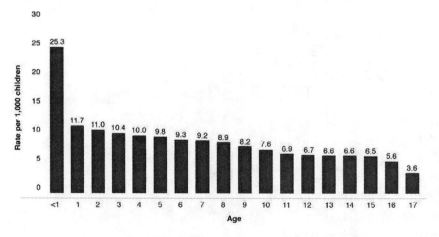

Figure 3.1. *Exhibit 3–G Victims by Age, 2017*

Table 3.2. Exhibit 3–F Nonfatal Victims by Prior CPS Contact, 2017

Number of Prior CPS Contacts	Victims	Victims with Prior Victim Contact	Victims with Prior Victim Contact Percentage	Victims with Prior Nonvictim Contact Percentage	Victims with Prior Victim and Nonvictim Contact	Victims with Prior Victim and Nonvictim Contact Percentage
1	—	29,782	4.5	10.4	—	—
2	—	2,888	0.4	2.0	7,856	1.2
3	—	377	0.1	0.4	2,810	0.4
>3	—	70	0	0.2	1,429	0.2
National	662,150	33,117	5	13.0	12,095	1.8

Based on data from 50 states. Percent is calculated against the number of total unique victims. Reports occurring on the same day as the prior report are excluded. Prior CPS contacts with a report date of up to 3 years prior to the date of the most recent victim report are counted. States are excluded from this analysis if victim child IDs are not unique across years.

The percentages of child victims are similar for both boys (48.6%) and girls (51.0%). The sex is unknown for 0.4 percent of victims. The FFY 2017 victimization rate for girls is 9.5 per 1,000 girls in the population, which is higher than boys at 8.6 per 1,000 boys in the population. Most victims are one of three races or ethnicities—White (44.6%), Hispanic (22.3%), or African American (20.7%). The racial distributions for all children in the population are 50.7 percent White, 13.7 percent African American, and 25.2 percent Hispanic. For FFY 2017, American Indian or Alaska Native children have the highest rate of victimization at 14.3 per 1,000 children in the population of the same race or ethnicity; and African American children have the second highest rate at 13.9 per 1,000 children. The 2017 table includes improved reporting compared with 2016 data in 3 states—Alaska, Massachusetts, and Michigan—by reducing the number of victims with unknown race.

Maltreatment Types
Individual Types (Unique Count of Child Victims and Duplicate Count of Maltreatment Types)

In this analysis, a victim who suffered more than one type of maltreatment is counted for each maltreatment type, but only once per type. This answers the question of how many different types of maltreatment victims suffered from, rather than how many occurrences of each type; for example:

- A victim with three reports of neglect—victim is counted once in neglect.

- A victim with one report of both neglect and physical abuse—victim is counted once in neglect and once in physical abuse.

The FFY 2017 data show, three-quarters (74.9%) of victims are neglected, 18.3 percent are physically abused, and 8.6 percent are sexually abused. In addition, 7.1 percent of victims experience other types of maltreatment as threatened abuse or neglect, drug/alcohol addiction, and lack of supervision. States may code any maltreatment as "other" if it does not fit in one of the NCANDS categories. A few states have specific policies about conducting investigations into specific maltreatment types.

Combination of Types (Unique Count of Child Victims and Unique Count of Maltreatment Types)

Polyvictimization in child welfare refers to children who experience multiple types of maltreatment. The FFY 2017 data show, 85.6 percent of victims suffered a single type of maltreatment, although they could suffer a single type multiple time. For example, 62.7 percent of victims are neglected only and did not suffer additional maltreatment types. The remaining victims (14.4%) experience a combination of maltreatment. A child is considered to have suffered a combination of maltreatment if:

- The child has two different types of maltreatment in a single report (e.g., neglect and physical abuse in the same report)

- The child suffers different maltreatment types in several reports (e.g., neglect in one report and physical abuse in a second report)

The most common combination is neglect and physical abuse (5.2%). The other common combinations include neglect and other/unknown at 3.7 percent, neglect and psychological maltreatment at 1.9 percent, and neglect and sexual abuse at 1.4 percent.

Section 3.2

Fatality

This section includes text excerpted from "Child Maltreatment 2017," Administration for Children and Families (ACF), U.S. Department of Health and Human Services (HHS), 2017.

The effects of child abuse and neglect are serious, and a child fatality is the most tragic consequence. National Child Abuse and Neglect Data System (NCANDS) collects case-level data in the Child File on child deaths from maltreatment. Additional counts of child fatalities, for which case-level data are not known, are reported in the Agency File.

Some child maltreatment deaths may not come to the attention of child protective services (CPS) agencies. Reasons for this include if there were no surviving siblings in the family or if the child had not (prior to her or his death) received child-welfare services. To improve the counts of child fatalities, states consult data sources outside of CPS for deaths attributed to child maltreatment. The Child and Family Services Improvement and Innovation Act (P.L. 112 to 34) lists the following additional data sources, which states must include a description of in their state plan or explain why they are not used to report child deaths due to maltreatment: state vital statistics departments, child death review teams, law-enforcement agencies, and offices of medical examiners or coroners. In addition to the sources mentioned in the law, some states also collect child fatality data from hospitals, health departments, juvenile justice departments, and prosecutor and attorney general offices. States that can provide these additional data do so as aggregate data via the Agency File. After the passage of P.L. 112 to 34, several states mentioned that they implemented new child death reviews or expanded the scope of existing reviews. Some states began investigating all unexplained infant deaths regardless of whether there was an allegation of maltreatment.

Number of Child Fatalities

For FFY 2017, a national estimate of 1,720 children died from abuse and neglect at a rate of 2.32 per 100,000 children in the population. The 2017 national estimate is an 11 percent increase from the 2013 national estimate of 1,550. Due to the relatively low frequency of child fatalities, the national rate and national estimate are sensitive to which states report data and changes in the child population estimates produced by the U.S. Census Bureau.

At the state level for FFY 2017, 50 states reported 1,688 fatalities. Of those states, 44 reported case-level data on 1,368 fatalities, and 44 reported aggregate data on 320 fatalities. Fatality rates by state range from 0 to 5.61 per 100,000 children in the population. The number of child fatalities in the Child File and Agency File fluctuated during the past 5 years.

The child fatality count in this report reflects the FFY in which the deaths are determined as due to maltreatment. The year in which a determination is made may be different from the year in which the child died. CPS agencies may need more time to determine that a child died due to maltreatment. The time needed to conclude if a child was a victim of maltreatment often does not coincide with the timeframe for concluding that the death was a result of maltreatment due to multiple agency involvement and multiple levels of review for child deaths.

Table 3.3. Exhibit 4–A Child Fatality Rates per 100,000 Children, 2013 to 2017

Year	Reporting States	Child Population of Reporting States	Child Fatalities from Reporting States	National Fatality Rate Per 100,000 Children	Child Population of all 52 States	National Estimate of Child Fatalities
2013	51	74,116,816	1,548	2.09	74,378,641	1,550
2014	51	74,081,066	1,585	2.14	74,339,990	1,590
2015	49	70,432,795	1,589	2.26	74,360,792	1,680
2016	49	72,028,582	1,699	2.36	74,352,938	1,750
2017	50	72,689,585	1,688	2.32	74,312,174	1,720

Data are from the Child File and Agency File. National fatality rates per 100,000 children are calculated by dividing the number of child fatalities by the population of reporting states and multiplying the result by 100,000. If fewer than 52 states reported data, the national estimate of child fatalities is calculated by multiplying the national fatality rate by the child population of all 52 states and dividing by 100,000. The estimate is rounded to the nearest 10. Because of the rounding rule, the national estimate could have more or fewer fatalities than the actual reported number of fatalities.

In FFY 2013, states began reporting the "maltreatment death date" to differentiate the year in which the death was reported to NCANDS in the Child File from the year in which the child died. As shown in the Child Maltreatment 2015 and 2016 reports, most (approximately 85%) reviews of child fatalities reach a determination about whether the death is due to maltreatment in 2 years or less.

Child Fatality Demographics

72 percent (71.8%) of all child fatalities are younger than 3 years of age. Nearly one-half (49.6%) of child fatalities are younger than 1 year of age and died at a rate of 21.92 per 100,000 children in the population of the same age. This is nearly 4 times the fatality rate for 1-year-old children (5.72 per 100,000 children in the population of the same age). The child fatality rates mostly decrease with age. As shown in exhibit 4–B, younger children are the most vulnerable to death as the result of child abuse and neglect.

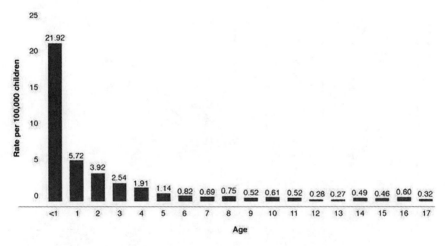

Figure 3.2. *Exhibit 4–B Child Fatality by Age, 2017*

Children <1-year-old died from abuse and neglect at nearly four times the rate of children who were 1-year-old.

Boys have a higher child fatality rate than girls; 2.68 per 100,000 boys in the population, compared with 2.02 per 100,000 girls in the population. 88 percent (88.5%) of child fatalities is one of three races: White (41.9%), African American (31.5%), and Hispanic (15.1%). Using the number of victims and the population data to create rates highlights some racial disparity. The rate of African American child fatalities (4.86 per 100,000 African American children) is 2.6 times greater than the rate of White children (1.84 per 100,000 White children) and 3.1 times greater than the rate of Hispanic children (1.59 per 100,000 Hispanic children).

Table 3.4. Exhibit 4–C Child Fatalities by Sex, 2017

Sex	Child Population	Child Fatalities	Child Fatalities Percent	Child Fatalities Rate per 100,000 Children
Boys	29,606,586	792	57.9	2.68
Girls	28,359,358	573	41.9	2
Unknown	—	5	0.2	N/A
National	57,965,944	1,368	100	—

Based on data from 44 states. Data are from the Child File. There are no population data for unknown sex and, therefore, no rates.

Table 3.5. Exhibit 4–D Child Fatalities by Race and Ethnicity, 2017

Race and Ethnicity	Child Population	Child Fatalities	Child Fatalities Percent	Child Fatalities Rate per 100,000 Children
Single Race	—	—	—	—
African American	8,556,624	416	31.5	4.86
American Indian or Alaska Native	486,121	15	1.1	3.09
Asian	2,282,011	14	1.1	0.61
Hispanic	12,512,722	199	15.1	1.59
Pacific Islander	89,418	4	0.3	4.47
Unknown	—	63	4.8	N/A
White	30,122,748	554	41.9	1.84
Multiple Race	—	—	—	—

Table 3.5. Continued

Race and Ethnicity	Child Population	Child Fatalities	Child Fatalities Percent	Child Fatalities Rate per 100,000 Children
Two or More Races	2,284,306	56	4.2	2.45
National	56,333,950	1321	100	—

Based on data from 42 states. Data are from the Child File. The multiple race category is defined as any combination of two or more race categories. Counts associated with specific racial groups (e.g., White) are exclusive and do not include Hispanic. States with more than 25.0 percent of victim race or ethnicity reported as unknown or missing are excluded from this analysis. This analysis includes only those states that reported both victim race and ethnicity.

Maltreatment Types

Of the children who died, 75.4 percent suffered neglect, and 41.6 percent suffered physical abuse either exclusively or in combination with another maltreatment type.

Table 3.6. Exhibit 4–E Maltreatment Types of Child Fatalities, 2017

Maltreatment Type	Child Fatalities	Maltreatment Types	Maltreatment Types Percent
Medical Neglect	—	101	7.4
Neglect	—	1,032	75.4
Other	—	223	16.3
Physical Abuse	—	569	41.6
Psychological Abuse	—	30	2.2
Sexual Abuse	—	8	0.6
Unknown	—	—	—
National	1,368	1,963	143.5

Based on data from 44 states. Data are from the Child File. A child may have suffered from more than one type of maltreatment, and therefore, the total number of reported maltreatments exceeds the number of fatalities, and the total percentage of reported maltreatment exceeds 100.0 percent. The percentages are calculated against the number of child fatalities in the reporting states.

Chapter 4

When Children Are Exposed to Violence

Violence and trauma can have serious and long-lasting consequences for children's physical and mental health, and the cost to families, communities, and the nation is staggering.

Too many children have been exposed to crime, abuse, and violence in their homes, schools, and communities. These experiences can lead to serious, long-term problems.

Early identification, intervention, and treatment are key. The federal government has a responsibility to act, but their efforts cannot succeed without local law enforcement, child and family services, community leaders, educators, coaches, and parents. Everyone plays a role in identifying, protecting, and treating children exposed to violence.

Facts about Children and Violence

A U.S. Department of Justice (DOJ) study showed that more than 60 percent of the children surveyed were exposed to violence in 2013, either directly or indirectly. Children's exposure to violence, whether as victims or witnesses, is often associated with long-term physical,

This chapter contains text excerpted from the following sources: Text in this chapter begins with excerpts from "Through Our Eyes: Children, Violence, and Trauma," Office for Victims of Crime (OVC), U.S. Department of Justice (DOJ), March 2014. Reviewed March 2019; Text under the heading "Facts about Children and Violence" is excerpted from "Facts about Children and Violence," U.S. Department of Justice (DOJ), April 11, 2017.

psychological, and emotional harm. Children exposed to violence are also at a higher risk of engaging in criminal behavior later in life and becoming part of a cycle of violence.

Some Findings from the Study

Children exposed to violence are more likely to abuse drugs and alcohol; suffer from depression, anxiety, and posttraumatic stress disorder (PTSD); fail or have difficulty in school, and become a delinquent and engage in criminal behavior.

60 percent of American children were exposed to violence, crime, or abuse in their homes, schools, and communities. Almost 40 percent of American children were direct victims of 2 or more violent acts, and 1 in 10 were victims of violence 5 or more times.

Children are more likely to be exposed to violence and crime than adults. Almost 1 in 10 American children saw 1 family member assault another family member, and more than 25 percent had been exposed to family violence during their life.

A child's exposure to one type of violence increases the likelihood that the child will be exposed to other types of violence multiple times.

Chapter 5

Child Exploitation

Chapter Contents

Section 5.1

An Overview of Child Exploitation

This section includes text excerpted from "Child Exploitation," U.S. Department of Justice (DOJ), January 19, 2017.

The advent of the Internet created a new tool for child-pornography collectors, traders, and manufacturers to sexually exploit children. Prior to the digital age, child pornographers relied on physical exchanges or the United States mail system to gain access to illegal material. The Internet provided an instant, somewhat anonymous, at-home vehicle for these individuals to meet one another, trade files, and access children to victimize.

What Is Child Pornography?

Under federal law, "child pornography" is defined as a visual depiction of any kind—including a drawing, cartoon, sculpture, painting, photograph, film, video, computer-generated image (CGI) or picture, whether made or produced by electronic, mechanical, or other means— of sexually explicit conduct. It is illegal to possess, distribute, or manufacture these images.

What Is Child Internet Enticement?

Online enticement—the use of the Internet to entice, invite, or persuade a child to meet for sexual acts or to help arrange a meeting—is a serious offense. Predators have used electronic mail (e-mail), instant messaging, bulletin boards, and chat areas to gain a child's confidence and then arrange a face-to-face meeting. This sometimes leads to the child traveling to meet the person she or he is chatting with or the person traveling to meet the child. Sometimes, the other person is an adult whose intent is to have sex with the child.

Is Your Child at Risk?

Many children who fall victim to Internet sex offenders spend large amounts of time online, particularly in chat rooms. They may go online after dinner and on weekends and would rather spend time online than hang out with peers from their school or neighborhood. Sex offenders often supply their potential victims with pornography as a means of opening sexual discussions and lowering the child's inhibitions.

Examples of Signs to Look Out For

1. Your child receives telephone calls from men or women you do not know or is making calls, sometimes long distance, to numbers you do not recognize.

2. Your child turns the computer monitor off or quickly changes the screen on the monitor when you come into the room.

3 Your child becomes withdrawn from the family.

4. Your child is using an online account belonging to someone else. (Even if you do not subscribe to an Internet service, your child may meet an offender while online at a friend's house or the library)

Parents and guardians are strongly encouraged to speak openly with their children about online dangers and monitor their online activities. There are several U.S. Department of Justice (DOJ)-sponsored resources on the Internet to help educate parents on the dangers their children face and to assist them in maintaining a safe home Internet environment.

What Is Being Done about This Problem?

Law-enforcement officials are tracking down an ever-increasing number of "predators" on the Internet. There are numerous local- and state-task forces that are combating Internet-related child exploitation. Through funding from the DOJ's Office of Juvenile Justice and Delinquency Prevention (OJJDP), 39 Internet Crimes Against Children (ICAC) task force units have been set up nationwide and focus on online child sexual exploitation. One of the most important tools for law enforcement and families was the development of the National Center for Missing and Exploited Children's (NCMEC) CyberTipline. (www.cybertipline.com) This online reporting mechanism has initiated numerous investigations and arrests of child predators.

NCMEC also has a Child Victim Identification Program (CVIP) which serves both as the national clearinghouse for child-pornography cases across the country and as the main point of contact to international agencies about child pornography victims.

In February 2006, the DOJ announced Project Safe Childhood (PSC), a department initiative aimed at preventing the abuse and exploitation of kids through the Internet. There are five main components of this program:

- To integrate federal, state, and local efforts to investigate and prosecute child-exploitation cases and to identify and rescue child victims

- To increase federal involvement in child pornography and enticement cases.

- The training of federal, state, and local law enforcement

- The participation of PSC partners in coordinated national initiatives

- To provide community awareness and educational programs

Section 5.2

Child Labor Trafficking

This section includes text excerpted from "Child Labor Trafficking," Office of Juvenile Justice and Delinquency Prevention (OJJDP), U.S. Department of Justice (DOJ), December 2016.

The Trafficking Victims Protection Act (TVPA) of 2000 defines "labor trafficking" as "the recruitment, harboring, transportation, provision, or obtaining of a person for labor or services through the use of force, fraud, or coercion for the purposes of subjection to involuntary servitude, peonage, debt bondage, or slavery." Child labor trafficking is the trafficking of individuals who are 18 years of age or younger. According to the TVPA definition, involuntary servitude (or forced labor) involves forcing someone to work by using physical and/or psychological tactics or by abusing the legal system. Involuntary servitude tends to be associated with occupations that take place in informal workplaces (e.g., domestic workers who work in private residences). Unfortunately, these types of workplaces are conducive to employee abuse because they are often isolated and less likely to be inspected by authorities. Another type of labor trafficking outlined in the TVPA is debt bondage, or bonded labor, which occurs when a trafficker demands labor as repayment for a loan or service; the value of the labor typically outweighs the loan/service.

As stated above, child labor trafficking requires the presence of force, fraud, and/or coercion. Force involves physically restraining or harming a victim; fraud intentionally deceives victims about certain aspects of their employment, such as job duties, work conditions, and payment. The coercion aspect of labor trafficking includes threats of serious psychological/physical harm to the victims or their loved ones, as well as real or threatened abuse of the legal system.

One important difference between child labor trafficking and child sex trafficking is that force, fraud, and/or coercion is present in child labor trafficking, whereas any minor involved in a commercial sex act, with or without the use of force, is considered a sex-trafficking victim. The different requirements for the two types of trafficking may be related to, in certain situations, the ability of children to work legally in the United States. Notably, child labor trafficking can, and often does, overlap with child sexual exploitation and abuse. In fact, victims may experience labor and sex trafficking simultaneously, such as being forced to engage in both prostitution and burglaries.

The force, fraud, or coercion requirement of labor trafficking is particularly important when distinguishing among legal child employment, child labor trafficking, child labor, and labor exploitation. Although employment laws vary by state and industry, children are typically allowed to work legally when they are between the ages of 14 and 16. If children are working legally but are denied basic legal rights (such as fair compensation), they are experiencing labor exploitation. In contrast, if minors under the legal working age are engaging in illegal work and/or work that is harmful to their health, development, or education, then this situation would constitute child labor. Child labor trafficking can have many of the same components as child labor and labor exploitation but is only considered labor trafficking if force, fraud, or coercion is present (e.g., forcing a child to work by threatening harm).

A common model that is used to determine if an individual is being labor trafficked is the "Actions Means-Purpose" (AMP) model. In the AMP model, "actions" include inducing, recruiting, harboring, transporting, providing, or obtaining an individual. The "means" component involves using force, fraud, and/or coercion. Finally, the "purpose" aspect is related to the reason an individual is being exploited, which, in the case of trafficking, is for labor or other services.

Scope of the Problem

There is no single estimate regarding rates of child labor trafficking in the United States, and estimates measuring occurrences of human trafficking in the United States and internationally vary substantially. There are many reasons for the lack of systematic, empirical data on victims of trafficking. First, the covert nature of trafficking makes it hard to study trafficking victims; traffickers tend to guard their victims closely and/or isolate them to their workplace. Trafficking victims may also not want to come forward for fear of violence or, if they are in the country illegally, deportation. In addition, inconsistent definitions and beliefs surrounding trafficking make it hard to measure; for example, a migrant, trafficked child may be labeled as an illegal immigrant rather than a trafficking victim. Some evidence suggests that law enforcement and social-service providers may not have the training to identify victims of child labor trafficking, which could limit the detection of victims. Despite these limitations, there is some available data that may provide insight into the scope of child labor trafficking.

Characteristics of Child Labor Trafficking Victims

Child labor trafficking victims have diverse sociodemographic backgrounds, and there is no standard typology; however, certain populations are more vulnerable to becoming victims.

Some research suggests that women and children are more likely to be victims of labor trafficking because of their "relative lack of power, social marginalization, and their overall status as compared to men." Other populations that are likely to experience labor trafficking are lesbian, gay, bisexual, transgender, questioning, intersex, and asexual (LGBTQIA) youth runaways; homeless youths; and child welfare populations. This aligns with research that trafficking perpetrators look for "youth with low self-esteem and minimal social support," characteristics that are often found among foster care youths, youths experiencing homelessness, and runaway youths. According to the Office for Victims of Crime (OVC), juveniles with emotional vulnerabilities, those who come from impoverished backgrounds, and those who have been abused are vulnerable to becoming victims of trafficking. Growing research also indicates that Native American children, who are more likely to have experienced trauma, are at risk of becoming trafficking victims. Finally, children who experience child labor violations or labor exploitation are at risk for labor trafficking.

Child labor trafficking victims can be found in legal industries, such as construction, and illegal industries, such as the arms trade. The most common industries in which child labor trafficking occurs are agriculture, domestic work, health and beauty, restaurants/small businesses, gang-involved drug sales and gun carrying, traveling sales crews (e.g., magazine sales), and peddling/begging rings. This can make identifying victims of labor trafficking difficult, especially if a child does not appear to be experiencing any type of physical force, psychological pressure, or other forms of coercion.

Other populations that comprise child labor trafficking victims are unaccompanied and/or undocumented migrant youths and children of foreigners. These youths may have come to the United States to escape poverty and/or violence in their home countries. Their desperation to support themselves and their families make them vulnerable to traffickers. Sometimes, smugglers (referred to as "snakeheads" and "coyotes") force children into debt bondage by requiring them to pay off an exorbitant smuggling debt. Traffickers may also manipulate these youths by threatening to have them deported. In 2015, the U.S. Department of Health and Human Services (HHS) assisted 124 child victims of trafficking through its Unaccompanied Refugee Minors (URM) Program. This involved connecting the victims with the same types of resources and services that are afforded to foster children, such as education and housing.

In a study of more than 142 migrant, trafficked children, about 70 percent were trafficked for sexual exploitation or for both sex and labor; roughly 24 percent were labor trafficked. Girls made up 80 percent of the sample and were more likely to experience sexual exploitation than boys. The youths in the sample ranged between 2 to 17 years of age, with 83 percent between the ages of 14 and 17. The sample varied greatly in socioeconomic background, ethnic/linguistic group, and the way they were trafficked (e.g., through strangers, family members). However, most of the youths in the study were from Mexico or Honduras and were trafficked by family members or friends.

Conclusion

Child labor trafficking is an often overlooked and misunderstood form of human trafficking. One of the main recommendations in the U.S. Department of State's Trafficking in Persons Report (2016) emphasizes "(increasing) efforts to identify child victims of labor trafficking." To achieve this goal, more training and education about child labor trafficking could be given to the public, law enforcement, and policymakers. Further, more resources could be put into developing and implementing evidence-based programs and treatments for victims of child labor trafficking. Finally, data collection on child labor trafficking would inform the scope of the phenomenon and assist in developing coordinated responses to prosecute traffickers and connect victims to services.

Section 5.3

Child Victims of Human Trafficking

This section includes text excerpted from "Human Trafficking,"
Administration for Children and Families (ACF), U.S. Department of
Health and Human Services (HHS), December 2016.

Human Trafficking is Modern-Day Slavery

It involves the exploitation of someone for the purpose of compelled labor or a commercial sex act through the use of force, fraud, or coercion. If a person younger than 18 of age is induced to engage in a sexual act for money or something else of value, it is a crime regardless of whether there is any force, fraud, or coercion. Victims can be anyone from around the world or right next door: women and men, adults and children, U.S. citizens and noncitizens. Some populations are at higher risk for human trafficking, including victims of other forms of violence, disconnected youth, and racial and ethnic minorities. Child victims of trafficking are often exploited for sexual purposes, including prostitution, pornography, and sex tourism. They are also exploited for forced labor, including domestic servitude, factory work, and farming.

Child victims of trafficking can be found in:

- Brothels, strip clubs

- Street prostitution, truck stops, online

- Illicit-drug trade (couriers)

- Farms, ranches, fisheries

- Domestic service, nannies

- Manufacturing, factories

- Construction, landscaping

- Restaurants, other food services

- Hotels, hospitality industry, tourism

- Sales crews, peddling, begging rings

Identifying Child Victims of Human Trafficking

Children who are victims of human trafficking may not disclose their trafficking situation or know that they are a victim of trafficking. It is crucial for health and human service providers, law enforcement, educators, and community members to assess potential safety risks, use trauma-informed practices, and create a safe and nonjudgmental space to identify trafficking indicators and assist a potential victim.

Human traffickers proactively target children and youth who have experienced other forms of abuse and violence, including those in the child welfare systems, runaway and homeless youth services, and unaccompanied minor programs. Migrant workers and domestic workers are also at higher risk due to increased social and physical isolation. By looking beneath the surface, picking up on the right clues, and asking the right questions, you may discover children who are being exploited.

- Children exploited for commercial sex may show evidence of untreated sexually transmitted diseases (STDs) or infections.

- Forced labor may expose children to physical abuse or dangerous work conditions. They may also develop back, vision, or respiratory problems.

- The psychological effects of exploitation include helplessness; shame; humiliation; depression; denial and disbelief; disorientation; or anxiety disorders including, posttraumatic stress disorder (PTSD).

- Children who are victims of trafficking can also be identified by environmental factors, including whether the child lives at the workplace or with an employer, lives with multiple people in a cramped space, or is not in school, attends school sporadically, or has a significant gap of schooling in the United States.

Communicating with Child Victims of Human Trafficking

When communicating with children who have been exploited, it is important to remember child victims may have experienced other forms of trauma and abuse prior to or during their trafficking situation. Children may have normalized violence, assume what has happened is their fault, react with hostility, and may not establish trust easily. They also may have been coached to answer your questions in a certain way. With the guidance of a trauma-informed child welfare expert, asking some of the following questions may help you determine indicators of human trafficking:

- Did you ever feel pressured to do something you did not want to do? Did anyone ever promise or give money or anything of value to you or someone else in exchange for touching or hurting you?

- Are you in school? Are you working? Can you leave if you want?

- Where do you live? Who else lives there? Are you scared to leave?

- Have you or someone you know been threatened?

Chapter 6

Sibling Abuse

The term "siblings" generally refers to biological brothers and sisters—children who share the same two parents—but in a broader sense, it may also refer to any children who are part of a family unit. These include half-siblings, who share one common parent, and step-siblings, who are not biologically related but become part of a family as a result of marriage or partnership between their parents. Studies have shown that the risk of sexual abuse is usually more common between step-siblings, but accurate statistics are difficult to compile about abuse between related individuals because of the powerful societal taboo against incest, which causes it to go underreported, due to embarrassment, fear, denial, or lack of understanding.

Defining Sibling Abuse

When a child is victimized by a sibling, it is termed sibling abuse. Physical aggression—pushing, shoving, or more serious acts of violence—as well as bullying or harassment, are examples of sibling abuse. Unless serious physical harm takes place, parents may ignore this behavior, believing it to be normal childhood activity. But sibling abuse can have severe consequences for survivors, often troubling them well into adulthood.

"Sibling Abuse," © 2016 Omnigraphics. Reviewed March 2019.

Classification of Sibling Abuse

Sibling abuse is a fairly broad term that can be classified into three types:

- Physical sibling abuse
- Emotional or psychological sibling abuse
- Sexual sibling abuse

Physical sibling abuse. This is a very common form of sibling abuse, as arguments can often lead to physical fighting, pinching, slapping, or hair pulling. These conflicts may become abusive in the course of time and may escalate into violence or serious injury. Weapons, if used, may even result in fatal consequences. What begins as sibling rivalry, if not checked, may end in tragedy within the family. One of the characteristic features of physical sibling abuse is that the perpetrator of the abuse is usually bigger and/or stronger than the victim, although this is not always the case. Physical sibling abuse is not gender-specific, and therefore, children of either sex may be the abusers.

Emotional/psychological sibling abuse. Physical sibling abuse is often quite evident, making it somewhat easier to take steps to protect the victim. However, emotional or psychological sibling abuse can be harder to detect. It is also very difficult to measure the impact of this form of sibling abuse. Quarrels between the adults in the family or acts of bullying at school can leave a deep impression upon the young mind. A child may also be emotionally abused by acts such as belittling, demeaning, frightening, humiliating, name-calling, or threatening. Survivors of such abuse may become emotionally closed off, withdrawing from social contact and preferring to be alone. They tend to underperform both at school and at home and become aggressive in other areas of their lives. Identifying emotional abuse early can help head off future problems.

Sexual sibling abuse. Many types of sexual contact or related activity between siblings can be termed as "sexual sibling abuse." This can include acts such as using sexually toned language, exposing genitals to another sibling, inappropriate touching, deliberate exposure to pornography, and sexual assaults or rape. Sexual sibling abuse can occur among full siblings, half-siblings, or step-siblings, although it is generally more common in the case of a half-sibling or step-sibling. The general belief is that boys tend to be the perpetrators, but there is also considerable evidence of girls being abusers.

Risk Factors for Sibling Abuse

There are several factors that may increase the likelihood of sibling abuse, and it is vital that parents understand the root cause behind such behavior. Some factors that researchers have identified include:

- Parents being absent from the home for long periods of time
- Lack of emotional attachment between parents and children
- Parents allowing sibling rivalry and fights to go unchecked
- Parents' inability to teach their children to deal with conflicts in a healthy manner
- Parents not intervening when children are involved in violent acts
- Parents creating a competitive environment by favoritism or frequently comparing siblings to each other
- Denial of the problem's existence, both by parents and children
- Overburdening children by giving responsibilities beyond their ability
- Exposure to violence from different environments, such as home, media, and school
- Parents failing to teach their children about sexuality and their personal safety
- Children who witness, or are victims of, sexual abuse
- Early access to pornography

Detecting Sibling Abuse

Sibling abuse may often be difficult to detect, especially when both parents are busy with their professional lives. Parents need to be alert to identify this behavior and take necessary action as early as possible. One symptom of sibling abuse is when one child is almost always the aggressor, while the other tends to be the victim. Other signs of sibling abuse include:

- A child avoiding his or her sibling
- Noticeable changes in behavior, eating habits, and sleep patterns
- Frequent nightmares

- A child staging abuse in a play or reveals it in a story
- A child acting out in an inappropriate sexual manner
- Increase in the intensity of animosity between the siblings

Safeguarding Children from Sibling Abuse

Some steps that parents can take to help safeguard children from sibling abuse include:

- Discourage rivalry between siblings.
- Establish rules that will bar children from indulging in emotional abuse of their siblings and stick to them, so that children realize their importance.
- Give responsibilities to children based on their abilities, rather than overburdening them with tasks for which they are unprepared.
- Talk to children on a regular basis to gain their trust, and encourage them to ask for help from parents when they need it.
- Learn the art of mediating conflicts.
- Teach children that any kind of unwanted physical contact is inappropriate and should be reported to an adult.
- Build a healthy environment for sharing and talking about any issues, especially sexual issues.
- Be aware of children's media preferences to identify inappropriate videos, games, music, etc.

Dealing with Sibling Abuse

Acts such as biting, hitting, or physical torture of a child by his or her sibling should not be taken lightly. Parents need to intervene and take necessary actions, including:

- Separate the siblings whenever they indulge in any kind of violence.
- When the situation is under control, discuss the behavior with all the members of the family, as well as the children involved.

- Listen patiently to understand the children's feelings.

- Restate what they say to clarify your understanding of the problem.

- Encourage the children to work together.

- Do not ignore, blame, or punish the child, but take a neutral stand and avoid favoritism.

- Be sure the children know the family rules, as well as the consequences of failing to follow them.

- Teach the children anger-management techniques.

- Follow up by observing future behavior carefully.

- Seek professional help if the parents feel that things are beyond their control.

Sibling Abuse and Its Impact on Adult Life

Events or incidents of sibling abuse that take place during childhood may have long-term psychological effects, but this impact may not be revealed until a later stage of life. Researchers have found that these effects may include:

- Alcohol and drug addiction

- Anxiety

- Depression

- Eating disorders

- Lack of trust

- Low self-esteem

Conclusion

Children who have been victims of sibling abuse tend to have feelings of insecurity and poor self-image well into adulthood. As much as physical abuse, emotional sibling abuse has a long-lasting impact. And the effects of this behavior do not only affect the victim; the abuser, too, has the potential to indulge in abusive relationships throughout her or his adulthood, making intervention critical for both individuals.

References

1. "Sibling Abuse Help Guide," LeavingAbuse, August 23, 2015.
2. Boyse RN, Kyla. "Sibling Abuse," University of Michigan Health System, November 2012.

Chapter 7

Bullying

Chapter Contents

Section 7.1

What Is Bullying?

This section includes text excerpted from "Bullying," *Eunice Kennedy Shriver* National Institute of Child Health and Human Development (NICHD), January 31, 2017.

Bullying is unwanted aggressive behavior by another person or group of people. In bullying, there is always an actual or perceived power imbalance, and the aggression is repeated multiple times or is highly likely to be repeated. Bullying also includes cyberbullying, a type of aggression that is carried out through electronic means, such as through the Internet, electronic mail (e-mail), or mobile devices. Because of cyberbullying, bullying can occur almost anywhere at any time.

Who Is Affected and How Many Are at Risk for Bullying?

People of all ages can be bullied. Bullying may take place at home, school, or work.

- A 2013 survey from the National Center for Education Statistics (NCES) found that bullying continues to affect many school-aged children; slightly more than 1 out of 5 students in middle and high school experienced traditional bullying at school during the 2012 to 2013 school year. 6 percent of students between the ages of 12 and 18 reported that they had been pushed, shoved, tripped, or spit on during the school year. Of these students, 22 percent reported being injured in the event.

- The 2013 survey found that, during the same school year, seven percent of students reported being cyberbullied.

- Data from the 2015 Youth Risk Behavior Surveillance System (YRBSS) from the Centers for Disease Control and Prevention (CDC) indicate that about 20 percent of U.S. students in grades 9 through 12 experienced bullying on school property in 2014.

What Are Common Signs of Being Bullied?

Some of the common signs of being bullying include:

- Depression, loneliness, or anxiety

- Low self-esteem

- Headaches, stomachaches, tiredness, or poor eating habits

- Missing school, disliking school, or having poorer school performance when compared to performance before being bullied

- Self-destructive behaviors, such as running away from home or inflicting harm on oneself

- Thinking about suicide or attempting to commit suicide

- Unexplained injuries

- Lost or destroyed clothing, books, electronics, or jewelry

- Difficulty sleeping or frequent nightmares

- Sudden loss of friends or avoidance of social situations

How Does Bullying Affect Health and Well-Being?

Bullying can affect physical and emotional health, both in short term and later in life. It can lead to physical injury, social problems, emotional problems, and even death. Those who are bullied are at increased risk for mental-health problems, headaches, and problems adjusting to school. Bullying also can cause long-term damage to one's self-esteem.

Children and adolescents who are bullies are at increased risk for substance use, academic problems, and violence to others later in life.

Those who are both bullies and victims of bullying suffer the most serious effects of bullying and are at greater risk for mental and behavioral problems than those who are only bullied or who are only bullies.

Research studies carried by *Eunice Kennedy Shriver* National Institute of Child Health and Human Development (NICHD) show that anyone involved with bullying—those who bully others, those who are bullied, and those who bully and are bullied—are at increased risk for depression.

The NICHD-funded research studies also found that unlike traditional forms of bullying, youth who are bullied electronically—such as through a computer or cell phone—are at higher risk for depression than the youth who bully them. Even more surprising, the same studies found that cyber victims were at higher risk for depression than were cyberbullies or bully-victims (i.e., those who both bully others and are bullied themselves), which was not found in any other form of bullying.

51

What Are Risk Factors for Being Bullied?

Those who are at risk of being bullied may have one or more risk factors:

- Are seen as different from their peers (e.g., overweight, underweight, wear their hair differently, wear different clothing or wear glasses, or come from a different race/ethnicity)

- Are seen as weak or not able to defend themselves

- Are depressed, anxious, or have low self-esteem

- Have few friends or are less popular

- Do not socialize well with others

- Suffer from an intellectual or developmental disability

What Can Be Done to Help Someone Who Is Being Bullied?

To help someone who is being bullied, support the person and address the bullying behavior. Other ways to help—including what to do if a person is in immediate danger—are listed below.
Support a child who is being bullied:

- You can listen to the child, and let her or him know you are available to talk or even help. A child who is being bullied may struggle to talk about it. Consider letting the child know that there are other people who can talk with him or her about bullying. In addition, you might consider referring the child to a school counselor, psychologist, or other mental-health specialists.

- Give the child advice about what she or he can do. You might want to include role-playing and acting out a bullying incident as you guide the child, so that the child knows what to do in a real situation.

- Follow up with the child to show that you are committed to helping put a stop to the bullying.

Address the bullying behavior:

- Make sure a child whom you suspect or know is bullying knows what the problem behavior is and why it is not acceptable.

- Show kids that bullying is taken seriously. If you know someone is being a bully to someone else, tell the bully that bullying will not be tolerated. It is important, however, to demonstrate good behavior when speaking with a bully so that you serve as a role model of good interpersonal behavior.

You can help someone who is being bullied in the following ways:

- Be a friend to the person who is being bullied, so they do not feel alone.

- Tell a trusted adult if you see someone being bullied.

- Help the person get away from the bullying without putting yourself at risk.

- Do not enable bullying by providing an audience.

- Set a good example by not bullying.

If you feel that you have taken all possible steps to prevent bullying and nothing has worked, or someone is in immediate danger, there are other ways for you to help.

Section 7.2

Warning Signs for Bullying

This section includes text excerpted from "Warning Signs for Bullying," StopBullying.gov, U.S. Department of Health and Human Services (HHS), February 7, 2018.

There are many warning signs that may indicate that someone is affected by bullying—either being bullied or bullying others. Recognizing the warning signs is an important first step in taking action against bullying. Not all children who are bullied or are bullying others ask for help.

It is important to talk with children who show signs of being bullied or bullying others. These warning signs can also point to other issues or problems, such as depression or substance abuse. Talking to the child can help identify the root of the problem.

Signs a Child Is Being Bullied

Look for changes in the child. However, be aware that not all children who are bullied exhibit warning signs.

Some signs that may point to a bullying problem are:

- Unexplainable injuries
- Lost or destroyed clothing, books, electronics, or jewelry
- Frequent headaches or stomach aches, feeling sick, or faking illness
- Changes in eating habits, such as suddenly skipping meals or binge eating. Kids may come home from school hungry because they did not eat lunch.
- Difficulty sleeping, or frequent nightmares
- Declining grades, loss of interest in schoolwork, or not wanting to go to school
- Sudden loss of friends or avoidance of social situations
- Feelings of helplessness or decreased self-esteem
- Self-destructive behaviors, such as running away from home, harming oneself, or talking about suicide

Signs a Child Is Bullying Others

Kids may be bullying others if they:

- Get into physical or verbal fights
- Have friends who bully others
- Are increasingly aggressive
- Get sent to the principal's office or to detention frequently
- Have unexplained extra money or new belongings
- Blame others for their problems
- Do not accept responsibility for their actions
- Are competitive and worry about their reputation or popularity

Why Don't Kids Ask for Help?

Statistics from the 2012 *Indicators of School Crime and Safety* shows that an adult was notified in less than half (40%) of bullying incidents. Kids do not tell adults for many reasons:

- Bullying can make a child feel helpless. Kids may want to handle it on their own to feel in control again. They may fear being seen as weak or a tattletale.

- Kids may fear a backlash from the kid who bullied them.

- Bullying can be a humiliating experience. Kids may not want adults to know what is being said about them, whether true or false. They may also fear that adults will judge them or punish them for being weak.

- Kids who are bullied may already feel socially isolated. They may feel like no one cares or could understand.

- Kids may fear being rejected by their peers. Friends can help protect kids from bullying, and kids can fear to lose this support.

Section 7.3

Effects of Bullying

This section includes text excerpted from "Effects of Bullying," StopBullying.gov, U.S. Department of Health and Human Services (HHS), September 12, 2017.

Bullying can affect everyone—those who are bullied, those who bully, and those who witness bullying. Bullying is linked to many negative outcomes, including impacts on mental health, substance use, and suicide. It is important to talk to kids to determine whether bullying—or something else—is a concern.

Kids Who Are Bullied

Kids who are bullied can experience negative physical, school, and mental-health issues. Kids who are bullied are more likely to experience:

- Depression and anxiety, increased feelings of sadness and loneliness, changes in sleep and eating patterns, and loss of interest in activities they used to enjoy. These issues may persist into adulthood.

- Health complaints
- Decreased academic achievement—grade point average (GPA) and standardized test scores—and school participation. They are more likely to miss, skip, or drop out of school.

A very small number of bullied children might retaliate through extremely violent measures. In 12 of 15 school-shooting cases in the 1990s, the shooters had a history of being bullied.

Kids Who Bully Others

Kids who bully others can also engage in violent and other risky behaviors into adulthood. Kids who bully are more likely to:

- Abuse alcohol and other drugs in adolescence and as adults
- Get into fights, vandalize property, and drop out of school
- Engage in early sexual activity
- Have criminal convictions and traffic citations as adults
- Be abusive toward their romantic partners, spouses, or children as adults

Bystanders

Kids who witness bullying are more likely to:

- Have increased use of tobacco, alcohol, or other drugs
- Have increased mental-health problems, including depression and anxiety
- Miss or skip school

The Relationship between Bullying and Suicide

Media reports often link bullying with suicide. However, most youth who are bullied do not have thoughts of suicide or engage in suicidal behaviors.

Although kids who are bullied are at risk of suicide, bullying alone is not the cause. Many issues contribute to suicide risk, including depression, problems at home, and trauma history. Additionally, specific groups have an increased risk of suicide, including American Indians, Alaskan Natives, Asian Americans, and lesbian, gay, bisexual, and transgender (LGBT) youth. This risk can be increased even more so when these kids are not supported by parents, peers, and schools. Bullying can make an unsupportive situation worse.

Section 7.4

Preventing and Responding to Bullying

This section includes text excerpted from "How to Prevent Bullying," StopBullying.gov, U.S. Department of Health and Human Services (HHS), September 8, 2017.

How to Prevent Bullying

Parents, school staff, and other caring adults have a role to play in preventing bullying. They can:

- **Help kids understand bullying.** Talk about what bullying is and how to stand up to it safely. Tell kids bullying is unacceptable. Make sure kids know how to get help.

- **Keep the lines of communication open.** Check in with kids often. Listen to them. Know their friends, ask about school, and understand their concerns.

- **Encourage kids to do what they love.** Special activities, interests, and hobbies can boost confidence, help kids make friends, and protect them from bullying behavior.

- **Model how to treat others with kindness and respect.**

Help Kids Understand Bullying

Kids who know what bullying is can better identify it. They can talk about bullying if it happens to them or others. Kids need to know ways to safely stand up to bullying and how to get help.

- Encourage kids to speak to a trusted adult if they are bullied or see others being bullied. The adult can give comfort, support, and advice, even if they cannot solve the problem directly. Encourage the child to report bullying if it happens.

- Talk about how to stand up to kids who bully. Give tips, such as using humor and saying "stop" directly and confidently. Talk about what to do if those actions do not work, such as walking away.

- Talk about strategies for staying safe, such as staying near adults or groups of other kids.

- Urge them to help kids who are bullied by showing kindness or getting help.

Keep the Lines of Communication Open

Research points out that children really do look to parents and caregivers for advice and help on tough decisions. Sometimes spending 15 minutes a day talking can reassure kids that they can talk to their parents if they have a problem. Start conversations about daily life and feelings with questions such as:

- What was one good thing that happened today? Any bad things?

- What is lunch time like at your school? Who do you sit with? What do you talk about?

- What is it like to ride the school bus?

- What are you good at? What would do you like best about yourself?

Talking about bullying directly is an important step in understanding how the issue might be affecting kids. There are no right or wrong answers to these questions, but it is important to encourage kids to answer them honestly. Assure kids that they are not alone in addressing any problems that arise. Start conversations about bullying with questions such as:

- What bullying mean to you?

- Describe what kids who bully are like. Why do you think people bully?

- Who are the adults you trust most when it comes to things like bullying?

- Have you ever felt scared to go to school because you were afraid of bullying? What ways have you tried to change it?

- What do you think parents can do to help stop bullying?

- Have you or your friends left other kids out on purpose? Do you think that was bullying? Why or why not?

- What do you usually do when you see bullying going on?

- Do you ever see kids at your school being bullied by other kids? How does it make you feel?

- Have you ever tried to help someone who is being bullied? What happened? What would you do if it happens again?

There are simple ways that parents and caregivers can keep up-to-date with kids' lives.

- Read class newsletters and school flyers. Talk about them at home.

- Check the school website.

- Go to school events.

- Greet the bus driver.

- Meet teachers and counselors at "Back to School" night or reach out via email.

- Share phone numbers with other kids' parents.

Encourage Kids to Do What They Love

Help kids take part in activities, interests, and hobbies they like. Kids can volunteer, play sports, sing in a chorus, or join a youth group or school club. These activities give kids a chance to have fun and meet others with the same interests. They can build confidence and friendships that help protect kids from bullying.

Model How to Treat Others with Kindness and Respect

Kids learn from adults' actions. By treating others with kindness and respect, adults show the kids in their lives that there is no place for bullying. Even if it seems like they are not paying attention, kids are watching how adults manage stress and conflict, as well as how they treat their friends, colleagues, and families.

Chapter 8

Long-Term Effects and Consequences of Child Abuse and Neglect

Chapter Contents

Section 8.1

Effects of Child Maltreatment on Brain Development

This section includes text excerpted from "Understanding the Effects of Maltreatment on Brain Development," Child Welfare Information Gateway, U.S. Department of Health and Human Services (HHS), April 2015. Reviewed March 2019.

Just as positive experiences can assist with healthy brain development, children's experiences with child maltreatment or other forms of toxic stress, such as domestic violence or disasters, can negatively affect brain development. This includes changes to the structure and chemical activity of the brain (e.g., decreased size or connectivity in some parts of the brain) and in the emotional and behavioral functioning of the child (e.g., oversensitivity to stressful situations). For example, healthy brain development includes situations in which babies' babbles, gestures, or cries bring reliable, appropriate reactions from their caregivers. These caregiver-child interactions—sometimes referred to as "serve and return"—strengthen babies' neuronal pathways regarding social interactions and how to get their needs met, both physically and emotionally. If children live in a chaotic or threatening world, one in which their caregivers respond with abuse or chronically provide no response, their brains may become hyperalert of danger or may not fully develop. These neuronal pathways that are developed and strengthened under negative conditions prepare children to cope in that negative environment, and their ability to respond to nurturing and kindness may be impaired.

The specific effects of maltreatment may depend on factors, such as the age of the child at the time of the maltreatment, whether the maltreatment was a one-time incident or chronic, the identity of the abuser (e.g., parent or other adult), whether the child had a dependable nurturing individual in her or his life, the type and severity of the maltreatment, the intervention, how long the maltreatment lasted, and other individual and environmental characteristics.

Effects of Maltreatment on Brain Structure and Activity

Toxic stress, including child maltreatment, can have a variety of negative effects on children's brains:

- **Hippocampus.** Adults who were maltreated may have reduced volume in the hippocampus, which is central to learning and memory. Toxic stress also can reduce the hippocampus's capacity to bring cortisol levels back to normal after a stressful event has occurred.

- **Corpus callosum.** Maltreated children and adolescents tend to have decreased volume in the corpus callosum, which is the largest white-matter structure in the brain and is responsible for interhemispheric communication and other processes (e.g., arousal, emotion, higher cognitive abilities).

- **Cerebellum.** Maltreated children and adolescents tend to have decreased volume in the cerebellum, which helps coordinate motor behavior and executive functioning.

- **Prefrontal cortex (PFC).** Some studies on adolescents and adults who were severely neglected as children indicate that they have a smaller prefrontal cortex, which is critical to behavior, cognition, and emotion regulation, but other studies show no differences. Physically abused children also may have reduced volume in the orbitofrontal cortex (OFC), a part of the prefrontal cortex that is central to emotion and social regulation.

- **Amygdala.** Although most studies have found that amygdala volume is not affected by maltreatment, abuse and neglect can cause overactivity in that area of the brain, which helps determine whether a stimulus is threatening and trigger emotional responses.

- **Cortisol levels.** Many maltreated children, both in institutional and family settings, and especially those who experienced severe neglect, tend to have lower-than-normal morning cortisol levels, coupled with flatter release levels throughout the day. (Typically, children have a sharp increase in cortisol in the morning, followed by a steady decrease throughout the day.) On the other hand, children in foster care who experienced severe emotional maltreatment had higher-than-normal morning cortisol levels. These results may be due to the body reacting differently to different stressors. Abnormal cortisol levels can have many negative effects. Lower cortisol levels can lead to decreased energy resources, which could affect learning and socialization; externalizing disorders; and increased vulnerability to autoimmune disorders. Higher cortisol levels could harm cognitive processes, subdue immune and inflammatory reactions, or heighten the risk for affective disorders.

- **Other.** Children who experienced severe neglect early in life while in institutional settings often have decreased electrical activity in their brains, decreased brain metabolism, and poorer connections between areas of the brain that are key to integrating complex information. These children also may continue to have abnormal patterns of adrenaline activity years after being adopted from institutional settings. Additionally, malnutrition, a form of neglect, can impair both brain development (e.g., slowing the growth of neurons, axons, and synapses) and function (e.g., neurotransmitter syntheses, the maintenance of brain tissue).

Some cases of physical abuse can cause immediate direct structural damage to a child's brain. For example, according to the National Center on Shaken Baby Syndrome (NCSBS), shaking a child can destroy brain tissue and tear blood vessels. In the short term, this can lead to seizures, loss of consciousness, or even death. In the long term, shaking can damage the fragile brain so that a child develops a range of sensory impairments, as well as cognitive, learning, and behavioral disabilities. Other types of head injuries caused by physical abuse can have similar effects.

Section 8.2

Long-Term Consequences of Child Maltreatment

This section contains text excerpted from the following sources:
Text in this chapter begins with excerpts from "Child Abuse and Neglect: Consequences," Centers for Disease Control and Prevention (CDC), April 10, 2018; Text beginning with the heading "Factors Affecting the Consequences of Child Abuse and Neglect" is excerpted from "Long-Term Consequences of Child Abuse and Neglect," Child Welfare Information Gateway, U.S. Department of Health and Human Services (HHS), July 2013. Reviewed March 2019.

Child abuse and neglect affect children's health now and later, and costs to our country are significant. Child abuse and neglect can lead to poor physical and mental health well into adulthood. The physical, psychological, behavioral, and economic consequences of child maltreatment are explained below.

Prevalence of Child Abuse

One in four children suffer abuse.

- An estimated 676,000 children were confirmed by child protective services (CPS) as being victims of abuse and neglect in 2016.

- At least one in four children have experienced child neglect or abuse (including physical, emotional, and sexual) at some point in their lives, and one in seven children experienced abuse or neglect in 2017.

Factors Affecting the Consequences of Child Abuse and Neglect

Individual outcomes vary widely and are affected by a combination of factors, including:

- The child's age and developmental status when the abuse or neglect occurred

- The type of maltreatment (physical abuse, neglect, sexual abuse, etc.)

- The frequency, duration, and severity of the maltreatment

- The relationship between the child and the perpetrator

Researchers also have begun to explore why, given similar conditions, some children experience long-term consequences of abuse and neglect while others emerge relatively unscathed. The ability to cope, and even thrive, following a negative experience is often referred to as "resilience." It is important to note that resilience is not an inherent trait in children but results from a mixture of both risk and protective factors that cause a child's positive or negative reaction to adverse experiences. A number of protective and promotive factors—individually, within a family, or within a community—may contribute to an abused or neglected child's resilience. These include positive attachment, self-esteem, intelligence, emotion regulation, humor, and independence.

Physical Consequences

The immediate physical effects of abuse or neglect can be relatively minor (bruises or cuts) or severe (broken bones, hemorrhage, or even death). In some cases, the physical effects are temporary; however, the pain and suffering they cause a child should not be discounted.

Child abuse and neglect can have a multitude of long-term effects on physical health. NSCAW researchers found that, at some point during the 3 years following a maltreatment investigation, 28 percent of children had a chronic health condition. Below are some outcomes other researchers have identified.

Abusive head trauma. Abusive head trauma, an inflicted injury to the head and its contents caused by shaking and blunt impact, is the most common cause of traumatic death for infants. The injuries may not be immediately noticeable and may include bleeding in the eye or brain and damage to the spinal cord and neck. Significant brain development takes place during infancy, and this important development is compromised in maltreated children. One in every four victims of shaken baby syndrome dies, and nearly all victims experience serious health consequences.

Impaired brain development. Child abuse and neglect have been shown to cause important regions of the brain to fail to form or grow properly, resulting in impaired development. These alterations in brain maturation have long-term consequences for cognitive, language,

66

and academic abilities and are connected with mental-health disorders. Disrupted neurodevelopment as a result of maltreatment can cause children to adopt a persistent fear state, as well as attributes that are normally helpful during threatening moments but counterproductive in the absence of threats, such as hypervigilance, anxiety, and behavior impulsivity.

Poor physical health. Several studies have shown a relationship between various forms of child maltreatment and poor health. Adults who experienced abuse or neglect during childhood are more likely to suffer from cardiovascular disease, lung and liver disease, hypertension, diabetes, asthma, and obesity. Specific physical health conditions are also connected to maltreatment type. One study showed that children who experienced neglect were at increased risk for diabetes and poorer lung functioning, while physical abuse was shown to increase the risk for diabetes and malnutrition. Additionally, child maltreatment has been shown to increase adolescent obesity. A longitudinal study found that children who experienced neglect had body mass indexes that grew at significantly faster rates compared to children who had not experienced neglect.

Psychological Consequences

The immediate emotional effects of abuse and neglect—isolation, fear, and an inability to trust—can translate into lifelong psychological consequences, including low self-esteem, depression, and relationship difficulties. Researchers have identified links between child abuse and neglect and the following:

Difficulties during infancy. Of children entering foster care in 2010, 16 percent were younger than 1 year of age. When infants and young children enter out-of-home care due to abuse or neglect, the trauma of a primary caregiver change negatively affects their attachments. Nearly half of infants in foster care who have experienced maltreatment exhibit some form of cognitive delay and have lower IQ scores, language difficulties, and neonatal challenges compared to children who have not been abused or neglected.

Poor mental and emotional health. Experiencing childhood trauma and adversity, such as physical or sexual abuse, is a risk factor for borderline personality disorder, depression, anxiety, and other psychiatric disorders. One study using ACE data found that roughly 54 percent of cases of depression and 58 percent of suicide

67

attempts in women were connected to adverse childhood experiences. Child maltreatment also negatively impacts the development of emotion regulation, which often persists into adolescence or adulthood.

Cognitive difficulties. NSCAW researchers found that children with substantiated reports of maltreatment were at risk for severe developmental and cognitive problems, including grade repetition. In its final report on the second NSCAW study (NSCAW II), more than 10 percent of school-aged children and youth showed some risk of cognitive problems or low academic achievement, 43 percent had emotional or behavioral problems, and 13 percent had both.

Social difficulties. Children who experience neglect are more likely to develop antisocial traits as they grow up. Parental neglect is associated with borderline personality disorders, attachment issues or affectionate behaviors with unknown/little-known people, inappropriate modeling of adult behavior, and aggression.

Behavioral Consequences

Not all victims of child abuse and neglect will experience behavioral consequences. However, behavioral problems appear to be more likely among this group. According to NSCAW, more than half of youth reported for maltreatment are at risk for an emotional or behavioral problem. Child abuse and neglect appear to make the following more likely:

Difficulties during adolescence. NSCAW data show that more than half of youth with reports of maltreatment are at risk of grade repetition, substance abuse, delinquency, truancy, or pregnancy. Other studies suggest that abused or neglected children are more likely to engage in sexual risk-taking as they reach adolescence, thereby increasing their chances of contracting a sexually transmitted disease (STD). Victims of child sexual abuse also are at a higher risk for rape in adulthood, and the rate of risk increases according to the severity of the child sexual abuse experience(s).

Juvenile delinquency and adult criminality. Several studies have documented the correlation between child abuse and future juvenile delinquency. Children who have experienced abuse are nine times more likely to become involved in criminal activities.

Economic Consequences

While child abuse and neglect usually occur within the family, the impact does not end there. Society as a whole pays a price for child abuse and neglect, in terms of both direct and indirect costs.

Direct costs. The lifetime cost of child maltreatment and related fatalities in 1 year totals $124 billion, according to a study funded by the Centers for Disease Control and Prevention (CDC). Child maltreatment is more costly on an annual basis than the two leading health concerns: stroke and type 2 diabetes. On the other hand, programs that prevent maltreatment have shown to be cost effective. The U.S. Triple P System Trial, funded by the CDC, has a benefit/cost ratio of $47 in benefits to society for every $1 in program costs.

Indirect costs. Indirect costs represent the long-term economic consequences to society because of child abuse and neglect. These include costs associated with increased use of our healthcare system, juvenile and adult criminal activity, mental illness, substance abuse, and domestic violence. Prevent Child Abuse America estimates that child abuse and neglect prevention strategies can save taxpayers $104 billion each year. According to the Schuyler Center for Analysis and Advocacy, every $1 spent on home visiting yields a $5.70 return on investment in New York, including reduced confirmed reports of abuse, reduced family enrollment in Temporary Assistance for Needy Families, decreased visits to emergency rooms, decreased arrest rates for mothers, and increased monthly earnings. One study found that all eight categories of adverse childhood experiences (ACEs) were associated with an increased likelihood of employment problems, financial problems, and absenteeism. The long-term costs—to the workforce and to society—are preventable.

Section 8.3

Child Abuse Leaves Epigenetic Marks

This section includes text excerpted from "Child Abuse Leaves
Epigenetic Marks," National Human Genome Research Institute
(NHGRI), July 3, 2013. Reviewed March 2019.

Child abuse is a serious national and global problem that cuts across economic, racial, and cultural lines. Each year, more than 1.25 million children are abused or neglected in the United States, with that number expanding to at least 40 million per year worldwide.

In addition to harming the immediate wellbeing of the child, maltreatment and extreme stress during childhood can impair early brain development and metabolic and immune system function, leading to chronic health problems. As a consequence, abused children are at increased risk for a wide range of physical health conditions, including obesity, heart disease, and cancer, as well as psychiatric conditions, such as depression, suicide, drug and alcohol abuse, high-risk behaviors, and violence.

They are also more susceptible to developing posttraumatic stress disorder (PTSD)—a severe and debilitating stress-related psychiatric disorder—after experiencing other types of trauma later in life.

Part of the explanation is that child abuse can leave marks, not only physically and emotionally, but also in the form of epigenetic marks on a child's genes. Although these epigenetic marks do not cause mutations in the deoxyribonucleic acid (DNA) itself, the chemical modifications—including DNA methylation—change gene expression by silencing (or activating) genes. This can alter fundamental biological processes and adversely affect health outcomes throughout life.

New research, published in the May 14, 2013 issue of the *Proceedings for the National Academy of Sciences* (NAS), shows that PTSD patients who were abused as children have different patterns of DNA methylation and gene expression compared to those who were not.

Researchers from the Max Planck Institute in Germany and Emory University in the United States investigated whether the timing of trauma, specifically childhood abuse early in life, had an effect on the underlying biology of PTSD at the genome-wide level. To address this question, the authors examined a subset of 169 participants from the Grady Trauma Project—a survey of more than 5,000 individuals in Atlanta with high lifetime exposure to multiple types of trauma, violence, and abuse.

Among the 169 participants in the study, most were African Americans in their late thirties and forties, and all had suffered from at least 2 types of trauma other than child abuse and 7 types of trauma on average. In spite of multiple trauma exposures, the majority (108 people) did not develop PTSD. Of the 61 that did, however, 32 reported a history of childhood abuse, and 29 did not.

To focus on the effect of childhood abuse in PTSD, the researchers examined genetic changes in peripheral blood cells from PTSD patients with and without previous exposure to childhood maltreatment. These were then compared to the trauma-exposed group that did not develop PTSD to rule out changes associated with trauma exposure alone.

Despite sharing a few common biological pathways, 98 percent of the changes in gene expression patterns in PTSD patients with childhood abuse did not overlap with those found in PTSD patients without childhood abuse. Interestingly, PTSD patients who experienced significant abuse as children exhibited more changes in genes associated with central nervous system (CNS) development and immune system regulation, whereas those without a history of childhood abuse displayed more changes in genes associated with cell death and growth rate regulation.

Furthermore, the researchers found that epigenetic marks associated with gene expression changes were up to 12-fold higher in PTSD patients with a history of childhood abuse. This suggests that although all patients with PTSD may show similar symptoms, abused children who subsequently develop PTSD may experience a systematically and biologically different form of the disorder when compared to those without childhood abuse.

"What this means is that we may need to rethink our classification of PTSD and the notion of providing the same treatment for all PTSD patients," said Dr. Divya Mehta, corresponding author at the Max Planck Institute of Psychiatry.

"At the biological level, these individuals may be very distinct, as we see with the epigenetics," Dr. Mehta explained. "As we move forward with more personalized medicine, we will need to delve a bit further into the environment and history of each individual to understand the biology of their PTSD and to determine the best treatment for their disorder."

Although it is unclear whether the epigenetic marks left by child abuse can be removed or the damage reversed, this discovery is important in the search for biomarkers with clinical indications that can be used to identify different forms of PTSD. This will help to direct more precise avenues for therapy and guide treatments tailored specifically to the biological process of individual patients.

By starting to distinguish subtypes of PTSD, this study highlights the multifactorial nature of psychiatric disorders triggered by a combination of environmental and genetic factors. As the next step, Dr. Mehta and her team planned to study whether the age at which abuse occurs or the type of abuse affects the biology of PTSD.

Since even small changes in DNA methylation signatures in child abuse can have long-term implications for fundamental biological processes and health, Dr. Mehta hopes their research will also increase public awareness and strengthen efforts to protect children from the consequences of childhood abuse and neglect.

Section 8.4

Pathways between Child Maltreatment and Adult Criminal Involvement

This section includes text excerpted from "Pathways between Child Maltreatment and Adult Criminal Involvement," National Institute of Justice (NIJ), U.S. Department of Justice (DOJ), October 12, 2017.

Child abuse and neglect have been shown to increase the risk of later forms of antisocial behavior, including violence perpetration and crime in adulthood. However, the processes through which child abuse leads to subsequent antisocial and criminal behavior are not well understood.

Findings from National Institute of Justice (NIJ)-funded research, conducted by Dr. Herrenkohl and colleagues, help to address this gap in knowledge by identifying factors that explain the link between child maltreatment and adulthood criminal behavior. Participants were drawn from the Lehigh Longitudinal Study, one of the longest running national studies examining the long-term effects of child abuse and neglect. Beginning in the 1970s, the study has tracked approximately 450 children from preschool to adulthood. Reports of child abuse from child protective services (CPS) records and parental reports of abusive parenting were collected when the children were 18 months to 6 years of age and linked to self-reported criminal involvement 3 decades later.

Antisocial behavior also was measured in the intervening years during middle childhood and adolescence.

Results showed that childhood abuse increased the risk of adulthood crime by promoting antisocial behavior during childhood and adolescence, followed by the formation of relationships with antisocial romantic partners and peers in adulthood.

The researchers also found gender differences in the pathways linking child abuse and adult crime. Although affiliations with antisocial peers in adulthood increased criminal involvement for both men and women with histories of childhood physical and emotional abuse, the role of adult romantic partners in the link between child abuse and adult crime varied between men and women.

Among men, a warm and caring romantic relationship in adulthood decreased criminal behavior by reducing men's affiliations with antisocial peers. This protective pathway was not, however, observed among women—a warm relationship in adulthood did not decrease their criminal behavior or affiliation with antisocial peers.

Among women, having an antisocial romantic partner was linked to affiliations with antisocial peers, which in turn increased criminal involvement. For men, having an antisocial partner was associated with less partner warmth, which in turn predicted an affiliation with antisocial peers, itself a proximal predictor of adult crime. Relationships with antisocial peers and romantic partners in adulthood may increase criminal involvement by normalizing crime and reinforcing coping skills that promote criminal behavior among both men and women.

Additional findings from a subset of participants with histories of childhood physical and emotional abuse further showed that female participants were more likely to exhibit internalizing problems, such as depression, social withdrawal, and anxiety, during middle childhood, which in turn increased the risk of adult crime. In contrast, male participants were more likely to exhibit externalizing behavioral problems, such as aggression, hostility, and delinquency, during middle childhood, which subsequently led to adult criminal behavior.

The researchers also found evidence of a "cycle of violence" among individuals with child maltreatment histories. This pattern of behavior occurs when victims of childhood violence perpetrate violence toward their peers or partners later in the life cycle. In Herrenkohl and colleagues' research, individuals with substantiated child maltreatment histories were more likely to perpetrate sexual and physical intimate partner violence in adulthood when compared to their non-maltreated peers. The research did not examine the processes through which child maltreatment leads to violence perpetration in adulthood.

Overall, Herrenkohl and colleagues' findings suggest that interventions aimed at reducing the negative consequences of child abuse on adult criminal behavior should be tailored to the developmental timing of the antisocial behavior. In particular, antisocial behavior that begins during childhood and adolescence should be targeted directly to disrupt the persistence of antisocial behavior into adulthood, with an emphasis on reducing internalizing problems for female adolescents. In contrast, interventions with adults should focus on relationships with antisocial peers and romantic partners to reduce the normalization of criminal behavior. Tailoring intervention efforts to address different factors in the pathways linking child abuse and adult crime may more effectively promote desistance from antisocial behavior associated with childhood abuse.

Part Two

Physical and Sexual Abuse of Children

Chapter 9

Physical Abuse of Children

Chapter Contents

Section 9.1

Recognizing Signs of Abuse and Neglect

This section includes text excerpted from "What Is Child Abuse and Neglect? Recognizing the Signs and Symptoms," Child Welfare Information Gateway, U.S. Department of Health and Human Services (HHS), July 2013. Reviewed March 2019.

In addition to working to prevent a child from experiencing abuse or neglect, it is important to recognize high-risk situations and the signs and symptoms of maltreatment. If you do suspect a child is being harmed, reporting your suspicions may protect her or him and get help for the family. Any concerned person can report suspicions of child abuse or neglect. Reporting your concerns is not making an accusation; rather, it is a request for an investigation and assessment to determine if help is needed.

Some people (typically certain types of professionals, such as teachers or physicians) are required by state law to make a report of child maltreatment under specific circumstances—these are called "mandatory reporters." Some states require all adults to report suspicions of child abuse or neglect.

Signs of Child Abuse

The following signs can be noticed in a child that may be or may have faced abuse:

- Shows sudden changes in behavior or school performance

- Has not received help for physical or medical problems brought to the parents' attention

- Has learning problems (or difficulty concentrating) that cannot be attributed to specific physical or psychological causes

- Is always watchful, as though preparing for something bad to happen

- Lacks adult supervision

- Is overly compliant, passive, or withdrawn

- Comes to school or other activities early, stays late, and does not want to go home

- Is reluctant to be around a particular person

- Discloses maltreatment

The parent:

- Denies the existence of—or blames the child for—the child's problems in school or at home

- Asks teachers or other caregivers to use harsh physical discipline if the child misbehaves

- Sees the child as entirely bad, worthless, or burdensome

- Demands a level of physical or academic performance the child cannot achieve

- Looks primarily to the child for care, attention, and satisfaction of the parent's emotional needs

- Shows little concern for the child

The parent and the child:

- Rarely touch or look at each other

- Consider their relationship entirely negative

- State that they do not like each other

The above list may not be all the signs of abuse or neglect. It is important to pay attention to other behaviors that may seem unusual or concerning.

Signs of Physical Abuse

Consider the possibility of physical abuse when the child:

- Has unexplained burns, bites, bruises, broken bones, or black eyes

- Has fading bruises or other marks noticeable after an absence from school

- Seems frightened of the parents and protests or cries when it is time to go home

- Shrinks at the approach of adults

- Reports injury by a parent or another adult caregiver

- Abuses animals or pets

Consider the possibility of physical abuse when the parent or other adult caregivers:

- Offers conflicting, unconvincing, or no explanation for the child's injury, or provides an explanation that is not consistent with the injury
- Describes the child as "evil" or in some other negative way
- Uses harsh physical discipline with the child
- Has a history of abuse as a child
- Has a history of abusing animals or pets

Signs of Neglect

Consider the possibility of neglect when the child:

- Is frequently absent from school
- Begs or steals food or money
- Lacks needed medical or dental care, immunizations, or glasses
- Is consistently dirty and has severe body odor
- Lacks sufficient clothing for the weather
- Abuses alcohol or other drugs
- States that there is no one at home to provide care for them

Consider the possibility of neglect when the parent or other adult caregivers:

- Appears to be indifferent to the child
- Seems apathetic or depressed
- Behaves irrationally or in a bizarre manner
- Is abusing alcohol or other drugs

Signs of Sexual Abuse

Consider the possibility of sexual abuse when the child:

- Has difficulty walking or sitting
- Suddenly refuses to change for gym or to participate in physical activities

- Reports nightmares or bedwetting
- Experiences a sudden change in appetite
- Demonstrates bizarre, sophisticated, or unusual sexual knowledge or behavior
- Becomes pregnant or contracts a venereal disease, particularly if under the age of 14
- Runs away
- Reports sexual abuse by a parent or another adult caregiver
- Attaches very quickly to strangers or new adults in their environment

Consider the possibility of sexual abuse when the parent or other adult caregivers:

- Is unduly protective of the child or severely limits the child's contact with other children, especially of the opposite sex
- Is secretive and isolated
- Is jealous or controlling with family members

Signs of Emotional Maltreatment

Consider the possibility of emotional maltreatment when the child:

- Shows extremes in behavior, such as being overly compliant or demanding behavior, extreme passivity, or aggression
- Is either inappropriately adult (parenting other children, for example) or inappropriately infantile (frequently rocking or head-banging, for example)
- Is delayed in physical or emotional development
- Has attempted suicide
- Reports a lack of attachment to the parent

Consider the possibility of emotional maltreatment when the parent or other adult caregivers:

- Constantly blames, belittles, or berates the child
- Is unconcerned about the child and refuses to consider offers of help for the child's problems
- Overtly rejects the child

Section 9.2

Helping First Responders Identify Child Abuse

This section includes text excerpted from "The Role of First Responders in Child Maltreatment Cases: Disaster and Nondisaster Situations," Child Welfare Information Gateway, U.S. Department of Health and Human Services (HHS), 2010. Reviewed March 2019.

There are four commonly recognized forms of child maltreatment—physical abuse, neglect, psychological abuse, and sexual abuse. The definitions of these types of child maltreatment may vary depending on the state or the locality in which the first responder works. First responders should become familiar with the definitions that apply in their jurisdictions. Additionally, the signs of child maltreatment listed in this section do not indicate absolutely that child maltreatment has occurred. They are meant to act as general guidelines for identifying the possibility of each type of maltreatment. Actual child maltreatment, as well as the perpetrator's identity, can be determined only after a thorough response and investigation.

Physical Abuse

The physical abuse of children includes any nonaccidental physical injury caused by the child's caretaker. Physical abuse can vary greatly in frequency and severity. It may include injuries sustained from burning, beating, kicking, or punching. Although the injury is not an accident, it is not necessarily the intent of the child's caretaker to injure the child. Physical abuse may result from the punishment that is inappropriate to the child's age, developmental level, or condition. Additionally, it may be caused by a parent's recurrent lapses in self-control that are brought on by immaturity, stress, or the use of alcohol or illicit drugs. Caretakers may physically abuse children during discipline or as a way to "teach the child a lesson."

Behavioral Clues That May Indicate Possible Child Maltreatment

Children who possibly are maltreated may:

- Be aggressive, oppositional, or defiant
- Cower or demonstrate a fear of adults

- Act out, displaying aggressive or disruptive behavior

- Be destructive to self or others

- Come to school too early or not want to leave school, indicating a possible fear of being at home

- Show fearlessness or extreme risk-taking

- Be described as "accident prone"

- Cheat, steal, or lie (may be related to too high expectations at home)

- Be a low achiever

- Be unable to form good peer relationships

- Wear clothing that covers the body and may be inappropriate in warmer months, such as wearing a turtleneck sweater in the summer (Be aware that this may possibly be a cultural issue instead.)

- Show regressive or less mature behavior

- Dislike or shrink away from physical contact (e.g., may not tolerate physical praise, such as a pat on the back)

Signs of possible physical abuse include:

- Fractures unexpectedly discovered in the course of an otherwise routine medical examination (e.g., discovering a broken rib while listening to the child's heartbeat)

- Injuries that are inconsistent with, or out of proportion to, the history provided by the caretaker or with the child's age or developmental stage (e.g., a three-month-old burning herself by crawling on top of the stove)

- Multiple fractures, often symmetrical (e.g., in both arms or legs), or fractures at different stages of healing

- Fractures in children who are not able to walk

- Skeletal trauma (e.g., fractures) combined with other types of injuries, such as burns

- Subdural hematomas, which are hemorrhages between the brain and its outer lining that are caused by ruptured blood vessels

- Burns on the buttocks, around the anogenital region, on the backs of the hands, or on both hands, as well as those that are severe. Some injuries that may have been caused by physical abuse have distinct marks.

Some injuries, however, may not be visible without a complete medical examination. For instance, injuries caused by abuse directed to the abdomen or to the head often are undetected because many of the injuries are internal.

The first response in child physical abuse cases is handled predominately by social service agencies (SSA), such as child protective services (CPS). Many jurisdictions across the country have interagency agreements and protocols that define when a joint investigation by law enforcement and CPS will be conducted. Some have put guidelines in place for law enforcement to respond to all physical abuse cases involving young children, as well as to all cases of serious physical abuse. Serious physical abuse cases generally are defined as those requiring medical treatment or hospitalization. A response by law enforcement is also often required in cases involving any blows to the face or the head or the use of a particular instrument (e.g., clubs, bats, sticks, chains), which can indicate an attempt to do serious harm.

Distinguishing Physical Abuse from Unintentional Injury

Children may receive bruises during the course of play or while being active. The areas that are bruised most commonly during normal play include the leading or bony edges of the body, such as knees, elbows, forearms, or eyebrows. The soft tissue areas, such as cheeks, buttocks, and thighs, are not normally injured during play. Additionally, bruises received during the normal course of childhood activity rarely are indistinct shapes, such as a hand, a belt buckle, or adult teeth marks. Bruises in soft tissue areas or indistinct shapes may be indicative of physical abuse.

Section 9.3

Making and Screening Reports of Child Abuse and Neglect

This section includes text excerpted from "Making and Screening Reports of Child Abuse and Neglect," Child Welfare Information Gateway, U.S. Department of Health and Human Services (HHS), January 2017.

All 50 states, the District of Columbia, American Samoa, Guam, the Northern Mariana Islands, Puerto Rico, and the U.S. Virgin Islands have laws and policies that specify procedures for making and responding to reports of suspected child abuse or neglect. These laws require certain professionals, known as "mandated reporters," to make an immediate report when they suspect or know of abusive or neglectful situations. State laws and policies also specify the required content of reports, criteria for screening reports, investigation procedures, timeframes for completing investigations, and classification of investigative findings. Many states also have special procedures for handling child fatalities and substance-exposed children.

Content of Reports

Oral reports can be made to child protective services (CPS), a local law enforcement agency, or a statewide child abuse hotline. In 18 states, American Samoa, Guam, and Puerto Rico, a mandated reporter is required to submit a written report after she or he has made an oral report. In 9 states, the District of Columbia, and the Virgin Islands, a written report is required only when requested by the department or agency that received the initial report. Most states specify in statute the types of information that should be included in a report of suspected abuse or neglect. The reporter will be asked to provide as much information about the child's situation as she or he can, including the names and addresses of the child and the child's parents or other persons responsible for the child's care, the child's age, conditions in the child's home environment, the nature and extent of the child's injuries, and information about other children in the same environment.

Reporting Suspicious Deaths

Approximately 34 states, American Samoa, Guam, the Northern Mariana Islands, and Puerto Rico provide for specific reporting procedures to be followed when the reporter suspects that child abuse or neglect may have caused the death of a child. Typically, the statutes instruct a mandatory reporter to report a suspicious child death to a medical examiner or coroner. For states that do not have specific reporting procedures for suspicious child deaths, standard child abuse reporting procedures apply.

Reporting Substance-Exposed Infants

Mothers who use drugs or alcohol during their pregnancy may give birth to infants who show signs or symptoms of drug exposure. The federal Child Abuse Prevention and Treatment Act (CAPTA) requires states to have policies and procedures to address the needs of substance-exposed infants. Approximately 24 states and the District of Columbia have specific reporting procedures for cases of suspected substance-exposed infants. In general, these statutes make drug exposure or a positive drug test alone the basis for reporting child abuse or neglect. Standard reporting procedures apply in those states that statutorily define "infant drug exposure" as child abuse and neglect but have no specific reporting procedures for substance-exposed infants.

Agency Receiving the Reports

In all jurisdictions, the initial report may be made to either CPS or a law enforcement agency. Laws in 34 states, the District of Columbia, Guam, and Puerto Rico require state agencies to maintain centralized telephone lines 24 hours a day, 7 days a week, for the acceptance of child maltreatment reports. In practice, most states have statewide, toll-free numbers for accepting reports of maltreatment. In some states, reports may be made via the Internet.

In four states, a report involving an Indian child residing on tribal lands can be made directly to a tribal authority or be referred to the tribe for investigation by the state agency. In three states, the state agency may assist in an investigation only when the tribe requests assistance. For Indian children not residing on tribal lands, protective agencies in four states may respond to a report, but the child's tribe must be notified that a report has been received. In six states, the appropriate military authorities must be notified when a report is received that concerns a child whose parent or guardian is a member of the armed forces. In these cases, CPS and military authorities may share information and coordinate their investigations of the reports. In Florida and Idaho, a report is referred to military authorities when the children named in the report reside on a federal military base. In those cases, the military authorities have the sole responsibility to investigate the reports.

Initial Screening Decisions

The laws and policies in all jurisdictions specify procedures for the initial response required by the agencies receiving the reports. The ultimate purpose of the reporting system is to ensure the child's safety and well-being. In most states, the agency that receives a report of suspected child abuse or neglect will first screen the report to determine whether it meets the criteria for acceptance. For acceptance, the report must concern actions that meet the statutory definition of child abuse or neglect in that state. Typically, this will involve situations of harm or threatened harm to a child committed by a parent, guardian, or other person responsible for the child's care. Reports that do not meet the statutory criteria are screened out. Reports that meet the criteria are screened in and referred to the state CPS agency for response.

The approaches used to screen reports vary from state to state, but nearly all states utilize a type of safety assessment to determine which reports require immediate responses. Approximately 37 states and the District of Columbia categorize reports based on the level of risk of harm to the child and assign different response times. 21 states and the District of Columbia use differential response systems in which any case identified as presenting a high risk of harm is assigned to be investigated, and any case where the risk of harm is low is assigned to receive an assessment of the family's strengths and need for intervention services to reduce the risk of future harm to the child.

Agency Conducting the Assessment/Investigation

Investigations may be conducted by the CPS agency, a law enforcement agency, or cooperatively by both agencies. To better coordinate the investigative process, five states and the District of Columbia use multidisciplinary teams. These teams typically include representatives from CPS, law enforcement, prosecutors' offices, and health and mental-health services who work to reduce trauma to child victims by avoiding the necessity of multiple interviews.

In approximately 20 states and the Virgin Islands, cases that involve physical or sexual abuse or possible criminal conduct may be investigated by a law enforcement agency. In 13 states, reports are referred to law enforcement agencies when the alleged perpetrator is a person other than the parent or other caregivers. Most states also require cross-reporting among professional entities. Typically, reports are shared among social services agencies, law enforcement agencies, and prosecutors' offices. In states that have differential response systems, in which cases identified as presenting a low risk of harm to the child are assigned to family assessment, those assessments are conducted by CPS or other social services agencies.

Assessment/Investigation Procedures

The primary purpose of an investigation is the protection of the alleged child victim. The focus is on determining the nature, extent, and cause of the abuse or neglect and identifying the person responsible for the maltreatment. Elements of an investigation may include the following:

- A check of agency records to determine prior involvement of the family with CPS

- A visit to the child's home

- An interview or observation of the child victim

- Interviews or observation of other children living in the child's home

- Risk and safety assessments

- Evaluation of the home environment

- Interviews of the child's parents, caregivers, or other adults residing in the child's home

- Checks of criminal records and central registry records for all adults residing in the home

- Medical and mental-health evaluations

In states that offer a differential response track, an assessment of the family is conducted when the initial referral does not allege a serious safety or immediate risk of harm to the child. The assessment consists of many of the same elements as an investigation, but the focus is more on engaging the family to identify strengths and service needs and referring the family to community services that will reduce the risk of harm and improve family well-being. Acceptance of the services by the family is voluntary, and no finding of abuse or neglect is made. A case that has been assigned to the differential response track may be referred for a CPS investigation if, at any time during a family assessment, the department determines that there is a reason to believe that substantial child abuse or neglect or a serious threat to the child's safety exists. A report that has been referred for an investigation may be reassigned for family assessment and services at any time if the department determines there is a lower risk to the child.

Timeframes for Completing Investigations

All states require CPS to initiate an investigation in a timely manner, generally within 72 hours. In addition, most states require investigations to be initiated immediately, in as little as 2 hours and no longer than 24 hours, when there is reasonable cause to believe that a child is in imminent danger. In 28 states, the District of Columbia, Guam, and the Northern Mariana Islands, laws also specify a timeframe for completing the investigation or assessment, generally between 30 and 60 days.

Classification of Reports

During the course of an investigation, a determination must be made as to whether child abuse or neglect has occurred and the identity of the person responsible for the maltreatment. Many states specify a system for classifying these findings. Generally, reports are "substantiated" when the investigation reveals that maltreatment did, in fact, occur. Other terms for "substantiated" include "founded," "indicated," or "confirmed." In 21 states, the investigation must provide a "preponderance of evidence" before a report can be substantiated; that is, the evidence must show that it is more likely than not that the maltreatment occurred. 9 states and the District of Columbia require credible or substantial evidence for substantiation; 6 states will substantiate a report when there is probable or reasonable cause to believe that abuse or neglect has occurred. When the results of the investigation are unable to confirm the occurrence of abuse or neglect, a report may be classified as "unsubstantiated." Other terms for "unsubstantiated" can include "unfounded," "not indicated," or "unconfirmed."

Chapter 10

Abusive Head Trauma

What Is Abusive Head Trauma?

Abusive head trauma (AHT), which includes shaken baby syndrome (SBS), is a preventable and severe form of physical child abuse that results from an injury to the child's brain. AHT is most common in children under the age of five, with children under one year of age at most risk. It is caused by violent shaking and/or with blunt impact. The resulting injury can cause bleeding around the brain or on the inside back layer of the eyes.

Nearly all victims of AHT suffer serious, long-term health consequences such as vision problems, developmental delays, physical disabilities, and hearing loss. At least one of every four babies who experience AHT dies from this form of child abuse.

AHT often happens when a parent or caregiver becomes angry or frustrated because of a child's crying. The caregiver then shakes the child and/or hits or slams the child's head into something in an effort to stop the crying.

Crying—including long bouts of inconsolable crying—is normal behavior in infants. Shaking, throwing, hitting, or hurting a baby is never the right response to crying.

This chapter includes text excerpted from "Preventing Abusive Head Trauma in Children," Centers for Disease Control and Prevention (CDC), April 10, 2018.

Did you know that:

- AHT is a leading cause of physical child abuse deaths in children under five years of age in the United States.

- AHT accounts for approximately one-third of all child maltreatment deaths.

- The most common trigger for AHT is inconsolable crying.

- Babies less than one year of age are at the greatest risk of injury from AHT

How Can Abusive Head Trauma Be Prevented?

Anyone can play a key role in preventing AHT by understanding the dangers of violently shaking or hitting a baby's head into something, knowing the risk factors and the triggers for such abuse, and finding ways to support parents and caregivers in their community. The Centers for Disease Control and Prevention's (CDC) *Technical Package for Preventing Child Abuse and Neglect* identifies a number of strategies to help states and communities prioritize prevention activities based on the best available evidence.

If you are a parent or caregiver:

- Understand that infant crying is worse in the first few months of life, but it will get better as the child grows.

- Try calming a crying baby by rocking them gently, offering a pacifier, singing or talking softly, taking a walk with a stroller, or going for a drive in the car.

- If the baby does not stop crying, check for signs of illness and call the doctor if you suspect the child is sick.

- If you are getting upset or losing control, focus on calming yourself down. Put the baby in a safe place and walk away to calm down, checking on the baby every five to ten minutes.

- Call a friend, relative, neighbor, or parent helpline for support.

- Never leave your baby with a person who is easily irritated or has a temper or history of violence.

If you are a friend, family member, or observer of a parent or caregiver:

- Be aware of new parents in your family and community who may need help or support.

- Offer to give a parent or caregiver a break when needed.

- Let the parent know that dealing with a crying baby can be very frustrating, but infant crying is normal and it will get better.

- Encourage parents and caregivers to take a calming break if needed while the baby is safe in the crib.

- Be sensitive and supportive in situations when parents are dealing with a crying baby.

- Be supportive of work policies (e.g., paid family leave) that make it easier for working parents to stay with their infants during the period of increased infant crying (i.e., between 4 to 20 weeks of age).

Chapter 11

Munchausen Syndrome by Proxy

Munchausen syndrome by proxy (MSBP) is a form of child abuse that describes children whose parents or caregivers invent illness stories and substantiate the stories by fabricating false physical signs.

The World Health Organization (WHO) defines "child abuse" as "intentionally or unintentionally performed attitudes, resulting in actual or potential harm to the child's health and psychosocial development." Child abuse is a complex phenomenon, and unfortunately, it can be seen all over the world.

Munchausen syndrome was first described in 1951 by Asher in a group of patients who invented illness stories and made doctors perform unnecessary surgical procedures. MSBP is a specific form of child abuse first described by Meadow in 1977. It describes the situations in which the parents or the caregivers, almost always the mother, invent illness stories about their children and substantiate the stories by fabricating physical signs. Usually, families or caregivers bring the child to the hospital with symptoms that cannot be explained easily via physiologic ways, and these symptoms occur only when the child is with the parents. MSBP can be easily missed, and it is also possible to harm the child while trying to treat the symptoms. A belief that the

---

This chapter includes text excerpted from "A Serial Munchausen Syndrome by Proxy," U.S. National Library of Medicine (NLM), September 2017.

parents or caregivers do not harm the children deliberately makes the evaluation of MSBP difficult.

MSBP is now termed as a "factitious disorder imposed on another individual" in the *Diagnostic and Statistical Manual of Mental Disorders, 5th edition*.

Families can fabricate almost all diseases; they can visit the hospital with several symptoms, including any form of bleeding (hematuria, hematochezia, and hematemesis), seizures, depression, apnea, diarrhea, vomiting, fever, and rash.

Diagnosing MSBP needs a very careful approach, and there are some specific features. There are certain typical signs, such as persistent symptoms that occur only when the perpetrator is with the victim, inconsistency of the symptoms and the history of the illness, inconsistency of the treatment, a calm perpetrator who accepts all painful medical tests for the child and family history of a sudden death of a child, and history of a similar illness in the family.

Unlike other forms of abuse, psychodynamics of MSBP are constructed to draw attention to the interests of parents instead of giving harm. It has been reported that the majority of the perpetrators had chronic somatoform disorders or personality disorders and often lacked other mental or physical illnesses.

MSBP is a form of child abuse with a high risk of repetition that might have severe results. Diagnosing MSBP is difficult, and failure to diagnose MSBP might result in the death of the child. Presence of continuous and repetitive symptoms, an inconsistency of clinical findings, history of the illness, symptoms occurring when the child is with the caregiver (usually the mother), and similar illness stories for the other children of the family should be the warning signs for MSBP cases. MSBP cases need a careful and multidisciplinary team approach for diagnosing and preparing a treatment plan. Physicians should be very careful in managing these types of cases and make a legal notice. These cases should be followed up in rooms with camera surveillance systems in the hospital. Safety of the victim is also important, and hence, while trying to obtain the evidence, the child should be protected. Follow-up of the patients and perpetrators is also important to prevent future cases of abuse.

Chapter 12

Shaken Baby Syndrome

What Is Shaken Baby Syndrome?

Shaken baby syndrome (SBS) is a severe form of physical child abuse. SBS may be caused from vigorously shaking an infant by the shoulders, arms, or legs. The "whiplash" effect can cause intracranial (within the brain) or intraocular (within the eyes) bleeding. Often there is no obvious external head trauma. Still, children with SBS may display some outward signs, such as:

- Change in sleeping pattern or inability to be awakened
- Confused, restless, or agitated state
- Convulsions or seizures
- Loss of energy or motivation
- Slurred speech
- Uncontrollable crying
- Inability to be consoled
- Inability to nurse or eat

This chapter contains text excerpted from the following sources: Text beginning with the heading "What Is Shaken Baby Syndrome?" is excerpted from "Shaken Baby Syndrome," Centers for Disease Control and Prevention (CDC), September 15, 2017; Text beginning with the heading "Treatment for Shaken Baby Syndrome" is excerpted from "Shaken Baby Syndrome Information Page," National Institute of Neurological Disorders and Stroke (NINDS), July 2, 2018.

SBS can result in death, mental retardation or developmental delays, paralysis, severe motor dysfunction, spasticity, blindness, and seizures.

Who Is at Risk for Shaken Baby Syndrome?

Small children are especially vulnerable to this type of abuse. Their heads are large in comparison to their bodies, and their neck muscles are weak. Children under 1 year of age are at highest risk, but SBS has been reported in children up to 5 years of age. Shaking often occurs in response to a baby crying or having a toilet-training accident. The perpetrator tends to be male and is primarily the biological father or the mother's boyfriend or partner. Caregivers are responsible for about 9 to 21 percent of cases. The explanation typically provided by the caregiver—"I was playing with the baby"—does not begin to account for the severity of trauma. Many times there is also a history of child abuse.

Can Shaken Baby Syndrome Be Prevented?

SBS is completely preventable. However, it is not known whether educational efforts will effectively prevent this type of abuse. Home-visitation programs are shown to prevent child abuse in general. Because the child's father or the mother's partner often causes SBS, they should be included in home-visitation programs. Home visits bring community resources to families in their homes. Health professionals provide information, healthcare, psychological support, and other services that can help people to be more effective parents and caregivers.

Note:

- Shaking a baby can cause death or permanent brain damage. It can result in lifelong disability.

- Healthy strategies for dealing with a crying baby include: finding the reason for the crying; checking for signs of illness or discomfort, such as diaper rash, teething, tight clothing; feeding or burping; soothing the baby by rubbing its back; gently rocking; offering a pacifier; singing or talking; taking a walk using a stroller or a drive in a properly-secured car seat; or calling the doctor if sickness is suspected.

- All babies cry. Caregivers often feel overwhelmed by a crying baby. Calling a friend, relative, or neighbor for support or assistance lets the caregiver take a break from the situation. If immediate support is not available, the caregiver could place the baby in a crib (making sure the baby is safe), close the door, and check on the baby every five minutes.

Treatment for Shaken Baby Syndrome

Emergency treatment for a baby who has been shaken usually includes life-sustaining measures such as respiratory support and surgery to stop internal bleeding and bleeding in the brain. Doctors may use brain scans, such as magnetic resonance imaging (MRI) and computed tomography (CT), to make a more definite diagnosis.

Prognosis for Shaken Baby Syndrome

In comparison with accidental traumatic brain injury (TBI) in infants, shaken baby injuries have a much worse prognosis. Damage to the retina of the eye can cause blindness. The majority of infants who survive severe shaking will have some form of neurological or mental disability, such as cerebral palsy (CP) or cognitive impairment, which may not be fully apparent before six years of age. Children with SBS may require lifelong medical care.

Chapter 13

Sexual Abuse of Children

What Is Child Sexual Abuse?

Child sexual abuse includes a wide range of sexual behaviors that take place between a child and an older child or adult. These sexual behaviors are intended to erotically arouse the older person, generally without consideration for the reactions or choices of the child and without consideration for the effects of the behavior upon the child.

Behaviors that are sexually abusive often involve bodily contact, such as sexual kissing; touching; fondling of genitals; and oral, anal, or vaginal intercourse. However, behaviors may be sexually abusive even if they do not involve contact, such as in the case of genital exposure ("flashing"), forcing children to watch pornography, verbal pressure for sex, and sexual exploitation for purposes of prostitution or pornography.

Researchers estimate that, in the United States, about 1 out of 6 boys and 1 out of 4 girls are sexually abused before the age of 18.

Who Are the Perpetrators of Child Sexual Abuse?

Legal definitions of what constitutes child sexual abuse usually require that the perpetrator be older than the victim. For example, in

This chapter includes text excerpted from "Child Sexual Abuse," National Center for Posttraumatic Stress Disorder (NCPTSD), U.S. Department of Veterans Affairs (VA), September 24, 2018.

some states perpetrators must be at least 5 years older than their victims for the behavior to be considered child sexual abuse. Most often, sexual abusers know the child they abuse but are not relatives. In fact, about 60 percent of perpetrators are nonrelative acquaintances, such as a friend of the family, babysitter, or neighbor. About 30 percent of those who sexually abuse children are relatives of the child, such as fathers, uncles, or cousins. Strangers are perpetrators in only about 10 percent of child sexual abuse cases. Men are perpetrators in most cases, regardless of whether the victim is a boy or a girl. However, women are perpetrators in about 14 percent of cases reported against boys and about 6 percent of cases reported against girls. Child pornographers and other perpetrators who are strangers also make contact with children using the Internet.

What Are the Effects of Childhood Sexual Abuse?

It is not always easy to tell whether a child has been sexually abused. Because sexual abuse often occurs in private, and because it often does not result in physical evidence, child sexual abuse can be difficult to detect.

Some child sexual abuse survivors may show symptoms of post-traumatic stress disorder (PTSD), including agitated behavior, frightening dreams, and repetitive play in which aspects of the abuse are expressed. They might exhibit other fears and anxieties or lose developmental skills and begin bed-wetting or thumb-sucking. They may show inappropriate sexual behavior or seductiveness or have difficulty maintaining appropriate boundaries with others. As a result of abuse, children, especially boys, might "act out" with behavior problems, such as cruelty to others and running away. Other children "act in" by becoming depressed or by withdrawing from friends or family. Older children or adolescents might try to injure themselves or attempt suicide.

Sexual abuse can be very confusing for children. A child who is used or manipulated by a trusted adult might learn that the only way for them to be attended to or loved is for them to give something of themselves or give up their dignity. Some children believe the abuse is their fault or that the perpetrator chose them because they must have wanted it or because there is something wrong with them. If the abuser was of the same sex, children (and parents) might question their sexual orientation and wonder if they are gay.

Almost every child sexual abuse victim describes the abuse as negative. Most children know it is wrong and experience fear, shock, anger, and disgust. However, a small portion of children might not realize it is wrong, especially if they are very young or have cognitive delays. In addition, some victims might enjoy the attention, closeness, and physical contact, especially if these needs are not met by a primary caregiver. Together, these reactions make the events very difficult and confusing for children.

If childhood sexual abuse is not effectively treated, long-term symptoms may persist into adulthood. These may include:

- PTSD and/or anxiety

- Depression and thoughts of suicide

- Sexual anxiety and disorders, including promiscuity

- Difficulty maintaining appropriate boundaries with others, including enmeshed or avoidant relationships

- Poor body image and low self-esteem

- The use of unhealthy behaviors, such as alcohol abuse, drug abuse, self-mutilation, or bingeing and purging, to help mask painful emotions related to the abuse

What Can Caregivers Do to Help Keep Children Safe?

Talk to children about the difference between safe touching and unsafe touching. Tell the child that if someone tries to touch his or her body in their private areas or do things that make the child feel unsafe, she or he should say "no" to the person and tell you or a trusted adult about it right away. Let children know that their bodies are private and that they have the right to forbid others to touch their bodies in an unsafe way. Let them know that respect does not always mean doing what adults or those with authority tell them to do. Do not tell them to do everything the babysitter, family member, or group leader tells them to do. Alert children that perpetrators may use the Internet, and monitor children's access to online websites. Most importantly, provide a safe, caring environment so children feel able to talk openly about sexual abuse.

What Can Professionals Do If They Suspect Abuse?

Most states have mandatory reporting laws that require professionals to report suspected child abuse to authorities. Professionals should not only provide crisis counseling to the child, but also help the non-offending caregiver attend sensitively to their child in a way that is helpful to her or his recovery. Also, many cities have child advocacy centers where a child and her or his family can receive crisis intervention; be interviewed in a sensitive, comfortable environment; make the report to legal authorities; and be directed to a multidisciplinary team skilled in child sexual abuse.

Chapter 14

Incest

One of the least discussed issues related to child abuse is incest. The victims of incest often don't want to talk about it, because of the powerful societal taboo attached to the act. According to the U.S. Bureau of Justice Statistics (BJS), about 44 percent of sexual-assault victims are under the age of 18. The data also show that many perpetrators are known to the victims, and one-third are members of the victims' own families. And although it is commonly believed that only men initiate incest, women can also be the perpetrators of such abuse. But since this takes place at a much lower rate than incest by men, and since so many of such cases are not reported, it often goes unnoticed.

Considering the gravity of the issue, it is vital to understand what incest is and what can be done about it. This chapter aims to define incest, identify the causes of incest, elucidate the reasons behind the difficulty in sharing information about sexual abuse by a family member, and suggest ways to find help and support for the victim.

What Is Incest?

Incest is defined as sexual contact, including intercourse, between close relatives. In most cultures incest is considered immoral, and in virtually all parts of the United States and many other countries it is also illegal. An adult engaging in incest with a child, however, is considered child abuse under the law, and while legislation pertaining

---

"Incest," © 2016 Omnigraphics. May 2016. Reviewed March 2019.

to sexual assault varies, incest with a minor is illegal in all U.S. jurisdictions. The trauma experienced by a young victim of incest can be severe, and the incident can have a serious impact upon the life of the survivor.

Although incest can take place between consenting adults, when it occurs between adults and children some common forms include:

- Incest between a parent and a child

- Incest between an older and younger sibling

- Incest between another older relative (for example, an uncle or aunt) and a child

Signs and Symptoms of Abuse

To identify whether a child has been a victim of incest, both physical and psychological symptoms must be considered. The physical symptoms include vaginal or rectal pain, vaginal discharge, bleeding, painful urination, bed-wetting, and constipation. The psychological signs include self-harm, nightmares, eating disorders, sleep disorders, aggressive behavior, withdrawal from social interactions, posttraumatic stress disorder (PTSD), lack of concentration, poor performance at school, depression, phobias, and precocious sexual behavior.

Characteristics of Incest Offenders

Learning to identify offenders is very important in order to protect children from becoming victims of incest. There are certain characteristics, conditions, and behaviors that are often evident in abusive incest situations. Some examples include:

- Adolescent perpetrators often seek victims who are quite young. They tend to abuse them for a considerably long period of time. And they may behave more violently than adult perpetrators.

- The absence or unavailability of parents may present the opportunity for incest by siblings or other relatives.

- Dominant or abusive siblings often tend to use incest as a way of expressing their power over the other(s).

Incest is not always between an adult and a child. Studies have revealed that sibling incest is the most prevalent form of incest.

Difficulty in Sharing Information on Sexual Abuse with a Family Member

The very thought of sexual abuse can be disturbing, and talking about it can often be very traumatic. It can become even more difficult to share such incidents if the survivor and the perpetrator are part of the same family.

Some struggles that a victim might face while sharing such information with another family member include:

- Concern about the abuser's future

- Response or reaction by the family towards the incident, perpetrator, and also the survivor

- Negligence or downplaying the issue by the family

- Being told that such things are normal in most families

- Inability of the family to recognize the incest as a type of abuse

- The victim being unaware of available help or difficulty in finding a trustworthy person

- Fear of being harassed by the perpetrator

Helping the Victims of Incest

Victims of incest may feel hopeless and, thus, can be hesitant to seek help. If you observe any symptoms of this type of abuse, some ways to help include:

- **Have a talk**. By talking to a child who has experienced abuse, you can provide them with comfort and try to ease their pain.

- **Show faith**. When a victim of abuse reveals their traumatic experience, lend a patient ear. Assure them that you are absolutely serious about what they are saying, and let them know that you are on their side. Then seek the assistance of child protective services (CPS).

- **Child protective services**. Reporting to CPS is an option whether the victim is a minor or a vulnerable adult (that is, one who is susceptible to harm due to mental illness, age, or other factors). Contacting the U.S. Department of Health and Human Services (HHS) or the police are other options available to help get assistance for the victim.

References

1. "Incest," Rape, Abuse & Incest National Network (RAINN), July 2, 2015.

2. Willacy, Hayley, Dr. "Incest," Patient, February 21, 2013.

Chapter 15

Extraterritorial Sexual Exploitation of Children

The extraterritorial sexual exploitation of children is the act of traveling to a foreign country and engaging in sexual activity with a child in that country. Federal law prohibits an American citizen or resident to travel to a foreign country with the intent to engage in any form of sexual conduct with a minor (defined as persons under 18 years of age). It is also illegal to help organize or assist another person to travel for these purposes. This crime is a form of human trafficking, also referred to as "child sex tourism." Convicted offenders face fines and up to 30 years of imprisonment

Extraterritorial Sexual Exploitation of Children: The Growing Problem

The relative ease of international travel in modern-day society has led to the growth of a dark, more clandestine phenomenon—the extraterritorial sexual exploitation of children. The various modes of international travel provide easier means and more opportunities for individuals to travel abroad and engage in sexual activity with children.

This chapter includes text excerpted from "Extraterritorial Sexual Exploitation of Children," Child Welfare Information Gateway, U.S. Department of Health and Human Services (HHS), July 2013. Reviewed March 2019.

In addition, technological advances have revolutionized the travel industry. The Internet allows individuals to quickly and easily exchange information about how and where to find child victims in foreign locations. Violators are also finding it easier to organize and navigate travel to foreign countries for these purposes online. Moreover, the utilization of the Internet may promote or encourage others to become involved in this form of child sexual exploitation.

American Offenders

Each year, Americans are convicted of committing this crime against children. While some offenders are pedophiles who preferentially seek out children for sexual relationships, others are situational abusers. These individuals do not consistently seek out children as sexual partners, but do occasionally engage in sexual acts with children when the opportunity presents itself. Children from developing countries are seen as easy targets by American perpetrators because they are often disadvantaged by unstable or unfavorable economic, social, or political conditions, or their home country lacks effective law enforcement against this crime. However, incidents of the extraterritorial sexual exploitation of children involving American perpetrators are reported and occur all over the world, including less-developed areas in southeast Asia, Central and South America, to more developed areas in Europe.

Some perpetrators rationalize their sexual encounters with children with the idea that they are helping the children financially better themselves and their families. Other perpetrators are drawn towards this crime because they enjoy the anonymity that comes with being in a foreign land. Racism, gender discrimination, and cultural differences are among other justifications. However, the reason for travel makes no difference under the law; any American citizen or resident who engages in sexual conduct with a minor in a foreign land is subject to federal prosecution.

Child Exploitation and Obscenity Section Role

Child Exploitation and Obscenity Section Role (CEOS) attorneys work with the High Technology Investigative Unit (HTIU), the Federal Bureau of Investigation (FBI), Immigration and Customs Enforcement (ICE)/Homeland Security Investigations (HSI), and the United States Attorney's Offices around the country, as well as foreign governments and law enforcement personnel to investigate and prosecute cases arising under federal statutes prohibiting the extraterritorial sexual exploitation of children.

CEOS is dedicated to developing strategies and long-lasting relationships with foreign governments, law enforcement agencies, and prosecutors to more efficiently and effectively prosecute Americans that sexually exploit children in foreign countries. The enforcement of these laws abroad is part of the United States' effort to eradicate the sexual exploitation of children. Offenders prosecuted in the United States often face more appropriate penalties than if they were prosecuted in the country where the sexual abuse occurred.

In addition, CEOS attorneys travel all over the country to conduct trainings for investigators, law enforcement personnel and others involved in an effort to investigate and prosecute this crime. Moreover, CEOS designs, implements, and supports law enforcement strategies, legislative proposals, and policy initiatives relating to federal laws on the extraterritorial sexual exploitation of children.

Chapter 16

Teen Dating Abuse

Unhealthy relationships can start early and last a lifetime. Teens often think some behaviors, such as teasing and name-calling, are a normal part of a relationship. However, these behaviors can become abusive and develop into more serious forms of violence.

Figure 16.1. *Teen Dating Violence: How Big the Problem Is* (Source: "Preventing Teen Dating Violence," Centers for Disease Control and Prevention (CDC).)

What Is Teen Dating Violence?

Teen dating violence is defined as the physical, sexual, psychological, or emotional aggression within a dating relationship, including stalking. It can occur in person or electronically and might occur

---

This chapter includes text excerpted from "Teen Dating Violence," Centers for Disease Control and Prevention (CDC), January 31, 2019.

between a current or former dating partner. Several different words are used to describe teen dating violence. Below are just a few:

- Relationship abuse
- Intimate partner violence (IPV)
- Relationship violence
- Dating abuse
- Domestic abuse
- Domestic violence

Teen dating violence is widespread with serious long- and short-term effects. Many teens do not report it because they are afraid to tell friends and family.

What Are the Consequences of Teen Dating Violence?

As teens develop emotionally, they are heavily influenced by experiences in their relationships. Healthy relationship behaviors can have a positive effect on a teen's emotional development. Unhealthy, abusive, or violent relationships can have short- and long-term negative effects on a developing teen. Youth who experience dating violence are more likely to:

- Experience symptoms of depression and anxiety
- Engage in unhealthy behaviors, such as using tobacco, drugs, and alcohol
- Exhibit antisocial behaviors
- Think about suicide

Additionally, youth who are victims of dating violence in high school are at higher risk for victimization during college.

Why Does Teen Dating Violence Happen?

Teens receive messages about how to behave in relationships from peers, adults, and the media. All too often, these examples suggest that violence in a relationship is normal, but violence is never acceptable.

Violence is related to certain risk factors. The risk of having unhealthy relationships increases for teens who:

- Believe that dating violence is acceptable
- Are depressed, anxious, or have other symptoms of trauma
- Display aggression towards peers or display other aggressive behaviors
- Use drugs or illegal substances
- Engage in early sexual activity and have multiple sexual partners
- Have a friend involved in teen dating violence
- Have conflicts with a partner
- Witness or experience violence in the home

Communicating with your partner; managing uncomfortable emotions, such as anger and jealousy; and treating others with respect are a few ways to keep relationships healthy and nonviolent. Dating violence can be prevented when teens, families, organizations, and communities work together to implement effective prevention strategies.

Chapter 17

Statutory Rape

Chapter Contents

Section 17.1

What Is Statutory Rape?

This section includes text excerpted from "Statutory Rape
Known to Law Enforcement," National Criminal Justice
Reference Service (NCJRS), August 2005. Reviewed March 2019.

Statutory rape is a general term used to describe an offense that
takes place when an individual (regardless of age) has consensual
sexual relations with an individual that is not old enough to legally
consent to the behavior. Stated another way, statutory rape is sexual
relations between individuals that would be legal if not for their ages.
In accordance with the Federal Bureau of Investigation (FBI) definition, statutory rape is described as nonforcible sexual intercourse with
a person who is younger than the statutory age of consent.

How Is Statutory Rape Different from Forcible Rapes?

Statutory rapes and forcible rapes differ in that a substantial proportion (about two-thirds) of forcible rapes involve the use of a weapon
(e.g., firearm, fist), and in one-fifth of forcible rapes, law enforcement
reported that the victim was physically injured. Weapon use and bodily
injury were not attributes of statutory rapes.

Are There Laws That Prohibit Sex with a Minor?

Each state has laws that prohibit sex with a minor. The offender
may be an adult or a juvenile. The age of consent varies from state
to state as well as the label of and the punishment for the crime. In
addition to individual ages, some state laws define statutory rape by
the age difference between the minor and the older individual or if
the older individual is a person of authority, such as an athletic coach
or teacher.

Section 17.2

State Laws on Statutory Rape

This section includes text excerpted from "Statutory Rape:
A Guide to State Laws and Reporting Requirements," Office of
the Assistant Secretary for Planning and Evaluation (ASPE),
December 15, 2004. Reviewed March 2019.

It has been noted that few states use the term "statutory rape" in their codes. Instead, criminal codes specify the legality of specific sexual acts. The applicable laws are often embedded in the section of the code dealing with other sexual offenses (e.g., sexual assault, forcible rape). This section summarizes some key provisions of state statutory rape laws.

Statutory Rape—Criminal Offenses

Sexual Intercourse with Minors

States' statutory rape offenses detail the age at which an individual can legally consent to sexual activity. This section focuses on laws addressing sexual intercourse and defines some key terms and phrases.

- **Age of consent** is the age at which an individual can legally consent to sexual intercourse under any circumstances.

- **Minimum age of victim** is the age an individual must reach before legally consenting to sexual intercourse.

- **Age differential**. If the victim is above the minimum age and below the age of consent, the age differential is the maximum difference in age between the victim and the defendant where an individual can legally consent to sexual intercourse.

- **Minimum age of defendant in order to prosecute** is the age below which an individual cannot be prosecuted for engaging in sexual activities with minors.

A common misperception about statutory rape is that state codes define a single age at which an individual can legally consent to sex. Only 12 states have a single age of consent, below which an individual cannot consent to sexual intercourse under any circumstances, and above which it is legal to engage in sexual intercourse with another

119

person above the age of consent. For example, in Massachusetts, the age of consent is 16 years of age.

In the remaining 39 states, other factors come into play: age differentials, the minimum age of the victim, and the minimum age of the defendant. Each is described below.

Minimum age requirement. In 27 states that do not have a single age of consent, statutes specify the age below which an individual cannot legally engage in sexual intercourse regardless of the age of the defendant. The minimum age requirements in these states range from 10 to 16 years of age. The legality of sexual intercourse with an individual who is above the minimum age requirement and below the age of consent is dependent on the difference in ages between the two parties and/or the age of the defendant.

- In New Jersey, the age of consent is 16 years of age, but individuals who are at least 13 years of age can legally engage in sexual activities if the defendant is less than 4 years older than the victim.

Age differential. In 27 states, the legality of engaging in sexual intercourse with minors is, at least in some circumstances, based on the difference in age between the two parties. In 12 of these states, the legality is based solely on the difference between the ages of the two parties. For example:

- In the District of Columbia, it is illegal to engage in sexual intercourse with someone who is under the age of consent (16 years of age) if the defendant is 4 or more years older than the victim.

Although it is less common, the age differentials in some states vary depending on the age of the victim.

- In Washington, sexual intercourse with someone who is at least 14 years of age and less than 16 years of age is illegal if the defendant is 4 or more years older than the victim. The age differential decreases in cases where the victim is less than 14 years of age (3 years), further decreasing if the victim is less than 12 years of age (2 years).

Minimum age of defendant in order to prosecute. 16 states set age thresholds for defendants, below which individuals cannot be prosecuted for engaging in sexual intercourse with minors.

- In Nevada, the age of consent is 16 years of age; however, sexual intercourse with someone who is under 16 years of age is illegal only if the defendant is at least 18 years of age (the age at which the defendant can be prosecuted).

States that set a minimum age of the defendant also tend to have minimum age requirements for the victim. Often, the age of the defendant is only relevant if the victim is above the minimum age requirement.

- In Ohio, sexual intercourse with someone under 13 years of age is illegal regardless of the age of the defendant. However, if the victim is above this minimum age requirement (13 years of age) and below the age of consent (16 years of age), it is only illegal to engage in sexual intercourse with that individual if the defendant is at least 18 years of age.

Some states define minimum age thresholds for defendants and age differentials.

- In North Carolina, the age of consent is 16 years of age. Sexual intercourse with someone who is under the age of consent is only illegal if the defendant is:

  - At least 4 years older than the victim

  - At least 12 years of age (the age at which the defendant can be prosecuted)

Part Three

Child Neglect and Emotional Abuse

Chapter 18

Child Neglect

The first step in helping abused or neglected children is learning to recognize the signs of child abuse and neglect. The presence of a single sign does not mean that child maltreatment is occurring in a family, but a closer look at the situation may be warranted when these signs appear repeatedly or in combination.

How Federal Laws Define Child Neglect

Federal legislation lays the groundwork for state laws on child maltreatment by identifying a minimum set of acts or behaviors that define child abuse and neglect. The federal Child Abuse Prevention and Treatment Act (CAPTA), (42 U.S.C.A. §5106g), as amended and reauthorized by the CAPTA Reauthorization Act of 2010, defines neglect as, at the minimum:

"Any recent act or failure to act on the part of a parent or caretaker which results in death, serious physical or emotional harm, sexual abuse or exploitation; or an act or failure to act which presents an imminent risk of serious harm."

Most federal and state child protection laws primarily refer to cases of harm to a child caused by parents or other caregivers; they generally do not include harm caused by other people, such as acquaintances or

---

This chapter includes text excerpted from "What Is Child Abuse and Neglect? Recognizing the Signs and Symptoms," Child Welfare Information Gateway, U.S. Department of Health and Human Services (HHS), July 2013. Reviewed March 2019.

strangers. Some state laws also include a child's witnessing of domestic violence as a form of neglect.

Types of Child Neglect

Neglect is the failure of a parent, guardian, or other caregivers to provide for a child's basic needs. Neglect may be:

- **Physical** (e.g., failure to provide necessary food or shelter, or a lack of appropriate supervision)

- **Medical** (e.g., failure to provide necessary medical or mental-health treatment)

- **Educational** (e.g., failure to educate a child or attend to special education needs)

- **Emotional** (e.g., inattention to a child's emotional needs, failure to provide psychological care, or permitting the child to use alcohol or other drugs)

What Leads to Child Neglect

Sometimes cultural values, the standards of care in the community, and poverty may contribute to maltreatment, indicating that the family is in need of information or assistance. When a family fails to use information and resources, and the child's health or safety is at risk, then child welfare intervention may be required. In addition, many states provide an exception to the definition of neglect for parents who choose not to seek medical care for their children due to religious beliefs.

What Can Child Neglect Lead To

Child neglect can have lifelong implications for victims, including on their well-being. While the physical wounds heal, there are several long-term consequences of experiencing the trauma of abuse or neglect. A child or youth's ability to cope and even thrive after trauma is called "resilience," and with help, many of these children can work through and overcome their past experiences. Children who are maltreated often are at risk of experiencing cognitive delays and emotional difficulties, among other issues. Childhood trauma also negatively affects the nervous system and immune system development, putting children who have been maltreated at a higher risk for health problems as adults.

Chapter 19

Neglect of Children's Healthcare

Defining Neglected Health

Neglect of children's health is difficult to define in a precise way because this type of neglect can take many forms. Many different factors are considered when identifying neglect, including actual harm, the potential for harm, short- and long-term consequences, physical and mental consequences, and availability of medical care. Healthcare neglect also covers the full spectrum of a child's condition, including physical, dental, and mental health.

One simple definition states that healthcare neglect occurs when a child's basic needs are not met, and those unmet needs present a substantial or life-threatening risk to the child. Under this definition, the determination of substantial risk is somewhat subjective and depends upon the opinion of an authority figure such as a healthcare provider or social worker. Another definition of child health neglect goes a step further and includes the probability that meeting the child's needs would result in a greatly improved quality of life (QOL) and/or possibly saving the child's life. There is also a legal definition of neglect which requires evidence that parents failed to seek medical attention for their child.

"Neglect of Children's Healthcare," © 2016 Omnigraphics. Reviewed March 2019.

Child healthcare neglect is also defined by severity. For example, lack of medical care for a bump or bruise might not be seen as neglect, but failed to seek medical attention for a broken bone would be seen as neglect. The frequency of potentially neglectful episodes is considered when defining child health neglect. Repeated or persistent absence of medical attention, when needed, is much more likely to be cited as neglect than a missed appointment or two.

Harm Caused by Neglect of Medical Health

Children can experience harm due to healthcare neglect in a variety of ways. Physical, mental, and behavioral problems can all arise from neglected healthcare, and children may suffer from problems in more than one area. Babies and toddlers without adequate healthcare can develop a low-weight condition known as "failure to thrive." Lack of adequate healthcare in toddlers and young children can cause brain disorders, learning disabilities, and other developmental delays. Children can suffer from emotional problems, such as depression and anxiety. In the absence of professional medical care, older children may turn to self-medicating behaviors for untreated physical or mental conditions. Self-medication often includes substance abuse, drug use, overeating, smoking, or other high-risk activities. These attempts to self-medicate can result in new health problems including cancer, addiction, or sexually transmitted diseases (STDs).

Factors Determining Neglected Health

Just as there is no single definition of child health neglect, there is also no single cause. Health neglect in children is often the result of a combination of issues at home, in the community, and in society at large. Poverty is a major contributing factor to healthcare neglect in children, as is the environment in which a child lives. Children are much more likely to experience healthcare neglect if they live in families affected by drug or alcohol abuse, chronic unemployment, eviction or homelessness, criminal activity, chronic or serious illness, domestic violence, or social isolation. The untreated physical and mental illnesses of caregivers can also be a factor in child healthcare neglect.

The intellectual ability of caregivers often plays a role in child healthcare neglect. In order for children to receive adequate healthcare, caregivers must be able to identify and understand the child's problem, respond appropriately to the problem, and implement recommended treatment. Other factors include a lack of understanding of the recommended treatment, perceived or actual adverse side effects of treatment, and the cost of treatment. Sometimes the child is also directly or indirectly responsible for her or his own healthcare neglect, such as in cases of older children refusing to comply with recommended treatment.

Incidence/Prevalence

Because healthcare neglect is difficult to define, it is difficult to measure the true extent of child healthcare neglect. It is generally understood that neglect of children's dental care is widespread, and it is also known that millions of children in the United States live without access to adequate healthcare and health insurance coverage.

Manifestations of Neglected Healthcare

Child healthcare neglect manifests in several ways. The most common are not seeking medical attention when necessary, not following the recommended treatment, missed appointments, and unfilled prescriptions for medication. Some healthcare neglect occurs when caregivers are aware of the need for treatment, but refuse treatment based on religious beliefs. In these cases, lack of medical care is often not labeled as neglect. 30 U.S. states have religious exemptions from child abuse statutes where medical care is concerned.

Neglected healthcare can also manifest as environmental hazards. Examples include exposure to toxic materials, such as lead paint in the home; exposure to dangerous objects, such as unsecured weapons; exposure to domestic violence; failure to use a car seat or seat belt; failure to use a bicycle helmet; and prenatal drug or alcohol abuse by pregnant women.

Principles for Assessing Neglected Healthcare

When assessing child healthcare neglect, the primary consideration is whether a child's basic needs are being met. The severity of the case is another important consideration and is evaluated according to actual or possible harm and the degree of harm involved. The frequency of incidents is examined to identify a pattern of neglect.

Assessments often include interviews or conversations with the affected child. In these cases, interviewers may attempt to understand the situation by asking children questions such as "Who helps you when you are sick?" or "What happens if you don't feel good?"

The interviewer evaluates the child's responses to determine if the child's needs are being met. Consideration is also given to the type of possible neglect (physical, mental, etc.) and the frequency of incidents. Interviews may be conducted with caregivers as well, focusing on topics, such as whether child protective services (CPS) has been involved in the past, the presence or absence of support systems and other resources for caregivers, and possible interventions.

Once all relevant information has been gathered, an assessment decision can be made. Recommendations for future actions are developed, and caregivers usually receive guidance and/or counseling to prevent further neglect of the child's health. Sometimes caregivers must first address and treat their own health problems in order to provide adequate care for the child. Depending on the issues involved, caregivers may be provided with information about child nutrition, developmental milestones, and the importance of closely monitoring the child's progress and noting any changes in the child's condition. Caregivers may also receive help in identifying informal support systems within the family, church, community, or other groups.

The CPS may be involved in more serious interventions, and caregivers may be referred to social services provided by the government (e.g., food stamps, Medicaid, etc.). Child healthcare neglect often requires a long-term plan to prevent future lapses. Ongoing follow-up, support, progress reviews, and monitoring may be required.

References

1. Dubowitz, Howard. "Neglect of Children's Health Care," The APSAC Handbook on Child Maltreatment, 3rd ed. Edited by John E.B. Myers. Thousand Oaks, CA: Sage Publications, 2011.

2. "Long-Term Consequences of Child Abuse and Neglect," Child Welfare Information Gateway, U.S. Department of Health and Human Services (HHS), July 2013.

3. "Medical Neglect," *Child Welfare Manual.* May 3, 2005.

Chapter 20

Educational Neglect and Truancy

Defining Educational Neglect

Educational neglect occurs when a child frequently misses school because of the direct or indirect actions of caregivers. This type of neglect includes failure to enroll children in school or to implement an adequate homeschooling program if allowed by law, and failure to ensure that children attend school as required by law. In many cases of excessive absence from school, educational neglect is considered to occur only when the caregiver refuses to work with the school in attempt to improve the child's attendance.

Characteristics of Educational Neglect

Educational neglect takes many forms, and each case varies according to individual circumstances. Educational neglect situations typically include more than one characteristic. When caregivers do not regard school attendance as important, children may not be prepared to attend school each day (e.g., child is not fed and dressed in time for school). Young children are often dependent upon the caregiver to ensure regular school attendance, and caregivers may fail to accomplish

"Educational Neglect and Truancy," © 2016 Omnigraphics. Reviewed March 2019.

this. Once an attendance problem is identified by the school, caregivers are typically contacted to participate in an intervention plan that will encourage children to attend school regularly. Educational neglect occurs when caregivers ignore attempts by the school to discuss and address the child's attendance problem and/or refuse to encourage or facilitate the child's school attendance. Caregivers may also fail to comply with special education or remedial instruction programs for the child when the child is not succeeding in school.

Children are at risk of educational neglect when they experience a chaotic or disorganized homelife. Some children suffer from the family's lack of sufficient financial resources and are responsible for caring for other children while the caregiver is at work. In many cases of educational neglect, other indicators of child abuse or neglect are also present.

Different Types of Educational Neglect

There are several different types of educational neglect. Caregivers may fail to enroll children in school or establish a homeschooling program where permitted by law. Educational neglect occurs when this failure to enroll causes the child to miss at least one month of school without valid reasons. Caregivers may also fail to seek adequate education for children with special needs, or fail to comply with recommendations for special education. If the child has been diagnosed with a learning disability, educational neglect intersects with healthcare neglect.

School Truancy

Truancy is another type of educational neglect. A truant is generally defined as a child between the ages of 6 and 17 who is often absent from school without valid reasons. In addition to missing whole days of school, truancy can also apply to frequently arriving late or skipping classes. A distinction is often made between educational neglect and truancy. If a child misses school as a result of their own choices, that is generally considered truancy and not educational neglect.

Permitted truancy means that caregivers have been informed of the child's excessive absences and do nothing to resolve the problem. Habitual truancy applies to children between the ages of 12 and 17 who fail to comply with intervention plans developed and agreed upon by the school and caregivers, and who continues to miss school without valid reasons. Chronic truancy refers to children between the ages of

12 and 17 who receive a court order to attend school and continue to miss school without valid reasons.

Effects of School Truancy

School truancy affects children in many ways. Early effects include required participation in school-based intervention programs and increased monitoring by schools. If these programs are not successful, children may be referred to a government- or school-sponsored program, in which a social worker or other caseworker attempts to resolve the truancy problem. Court intervention may be required, in which children and their parents must appear before a judge or other court officials. At this stage, the court can set requirements for school attendance, often with strict consequences for noncompliance. A legal charge of truancy is a serious offense that can result in the child being removed from the home and placed under the jurisdiction of the court. Sometimes, the court will order the family or caregiver to pay for the cost of intervention services for the child.

Longer-term effects of school truancy can also be quite serious. Missing many days of school usually results in poor performance when the child does attend classes. Children can then become discouraged and drop out of school entirely. Quitting school has been shown to greatly limit future career opportunities, while increasing the probability of engaging in criminal activity. Children who leave school are more likely to use alcohol and other drugs. Parents and caregivers also suffer the consequences of school truancy through lost income or work time to attend meetings, court hearings, counseling sessions, or other intervention services.

Factors Responsible for School Truancy

There are many different factors that contribute to truancy. Some of the most common are issues associated with a troubled home life. This includes any problem that causes disruption at home, such as domestic violence, substance abuse, marital problems and divorce, a family that moves around a lot, or caregivers whose work schedules leave children frequently unsupervised. Medical issues with mental health or chronic illness of children or caregivers can also contribute to truancy. Children with learning disabilities sometimes find school too frustrating and discouraging, and choose not to attend for these reasons. A family history of school dropouts can lead to caregivers who do not value education.

133

Other potential causes of truancy are based on economic factors. Poverty may require caregivers to work multiple jobs, and older children may also be required to work to help support the family. A lack of transportation and/or affordable care for younger children also contribute to school truancy. The environment at school can also be a factor. Large schools, large class sizes, the behavior of other students, the attitudes of teachers and school administrators, and a lack of individual attention can all result in truancy. Another issue in some schools is the lack of consequences for truancy, or inconsistent truancy policies.

References

1. "Educational Neglect," *Child Welfare Manual*. August 28, 2009.

2. "Educational Neglect and School Truancy: What Parents and Children Need to Know," Youth Assistance of Oakland County. n.d.

3. "Educational Neglect Statutes," Coalition for Responsible Home Education, 2015.

Chapter 21

Emotional Abuse of Children

Chapter Contents

Section 21.1

Understanding Emotional Abuse of Children

This section includes text excerpted from "Helping Students with Emotional Abuse: A Critical Area of Competence for School Counselors," Education Resources Information Center (ERIC), U.S. Department of Education (ED), June 18, 2013. Reviewed March 2019.

What Is Childhood Emotional Abuse?

Childhood maltreatment refers to acts of commission or omission by an adult, that endanger the physical or psychological well-being of a child and violate social sanctions regarding proper parenting. Theorists and many state statutes categorized childhood maltreatment into four basic types: physical abuse, sexual abuse, emotional abuse, and neglect. The three types of abuse (i.e., physical, sexual, and emotional abuse) are generally understood to include acts of commission, or active forms of maltreatment, which endanger the well-being of a child, while neglect includes acts of omission, or passive forms of maltreatment, which endanger the well-being of a child. In this section, we address the distinguishing characteristics of emotional abuse as well as cultural considerations pertinent to its identification.

Childhood emotional abuse is arguably the most challenging form of abuse to classify and define. Unlike physical abuse and sexual abuse, which include various forms of physical contact between a child and older person, emotional abuse is essentially a noncontact form of maltreatment. That is, emotional abuse does not involve physical contact between the abuser and child. Hence, markers of emotional abuse are less tangible when compared to other types of abuse.

Moreover, researchers grouped diverse behaviors under the construct of childhood emotional abuse—a practice which presents additional challenges in defining and differentiating emotional abuse. For example, Garbarino defined "childhood emotional abuse" as "a child's experience of being rejected (i.e., denied a sense of positive self-regard and worth), isolated (i.e., removed from relationships with others), terrorized (i.e., intimidated or frightened with threats of harm), ignored (i.e., denied responsiveness from others), or corrupted (i.e., encouraged to engage in deviant behavior) by an older person."

More recently, definitions of childhood emotional abuse emphasized hostile verbal communications, which attack a child's sense of psychological or physical well-being. Examples of hostile verbal communications include an adult's behavior of ridiculing a child's physical appearance or threatening the safety of a child. Emotional abuse may also include nonverbal, noncontact behaviors. Examples of nonverbal forms of childhood emotional abuse include isolating a child from relationships and solitary confinement of a child for extended periods of time.

Emotional Abuse as a Pattern of Behavior

There is consensus that childhood emotional abuse refers to a pattern of behaviors over time, rather than a single, isolated incident. As argued by various authors, many parents make the mistake of verbally demeaning or attacking their children at one time or another. In general, then, childhood emotional abuse pertains to parent-child relationships where noncontact forms of aggression (e.g., verbal assaults) become repetitive. Emotional abuse is not just a single event, but a systematic diminishment of the victim. It is the continuous behavior by the abuser that reduces a child's self-concept to the point where the child feels unworthy. Thus, school counselors are generally recommended to consider patterns of interaction over time when conceptualizing a case of suspected childhood emotional abuse. It should be noted, however, that emotional abuse may be understood as a single event in extreme situations. An example of extreme emotional abuse is the solitary confinement of a child in a closet for days. In such cases, the school counselor may not need to await the repetition of behaviors before reporting to a child protective services (CPS) agency.

Cultural Considerations in Defining Emotional Abuse

In further specifying the nature of childhood emotional abuse, consideration has been given to cultural standards of parenting conduct. Any definition of childhood emotional abuse—as is the case with other forms of abuse—involves cultural assumptions about appropriate parenting and human development. The influence of these assumptions, however, is a complex issue. On the one hand, several authors have noted that there is substantive agreement across cultures regarding the propriety of basic parental behaviors (e.g., providing a safe environment, responding to the child's emotional and physical needs, and refraining from having sexual intercourse with the child). In support of this view, researchers observed similarities across cultural groups in definitions and experiences of child abuse. Likewise, Slep, co-author of *Child Emotional Aggression and Abuse: Definitions and Prevalence*, cited an international agreement on child rights by member states of the United Nation (UN) as evidence of cross-cultural overlap in assumptions about proper parenting and child abuse.

On the other hand, numerous authors argued that assumptions about parenting might differ by cultural group, thereby yielding dissimilar conceptions of childhood abuse across groups. Gough, in his article, *Child Abuse in Japan*, for example, recorded the views of Japanese individuals, who perceived cruelty in Westerners' practice of leaving infants by themselves at night to sleep. Relatedly, recruited participants from different cultural groups in Singapore (N = 401; 78.3% Chinese, 14.5% Malay, 5.5% Indian, 1.7% other) and found widespread disagreement on whether verbal threats of abandonment, name-calling, and constant criticisms constituted abuse. Furthermore, it is possible that the same parental behavior can have different outcomes for children in different cultures. Along this line, Deater-Deckard, Dodge, Bates, and Pettit, in their research article, *Physical Discipline among African American and European American Mothers: Links to Children's Externalizing Behaviors*, found that a harsh parental discipline style (consisting of physically and verbally aggressive acts) was associated with adverse outcomes for children in some cultural groups but not others. In view of such cultural variations, concluded that emotionally abusive behaviors must be considered within the context of cultural norms of parenting conduct.

Childhood emotional abuse is defined as a pattern of hostile verbal or nonverbal behaviors, apart from physical contact, which is directed toward a child by an adult, endangers the child's psychological and/or physical well-being, and violates cultural norms of parenting conduct. Within the cultural context of the United States, commonly recognized forms of emotional abuse include the repeated humiliation, derogation, and intimidation of children by adults. As Wekerle, in his research article, *Emotionally Maltreated: The Undercurrent of Impairment?* argued that parents are ultimately accountable to laws and definitions of abuse in their current place of residence, even if these definitions vary from cultural traditions of their country of origin. Moreover, school counselors are legally protected from liability when making a report as long as the report was pursuant to state law.

Section 21.2

The Nature and Consequences of Emotional Abuse

This section includes text excerpted from "Helping Students
with Emotional Abuse: A Critical Area of Competence for School
Counselors," Education Resources Information Center (ERIC), U.S.
Department of Education (ED), June 18, 2013. Reviewed March 2019.

Childhood Emotional Abuse and Adverse Outcomes

It could be argued that the distress caused by emotional abuse is
betrayed by the very existence of oft-repeated adages, which implore
us to believe that "words will never hurt me." In fact, emotional abuse
may be especially damaging to children.

In some studies, researchers found that emotional abuse is more
strongly related than physical or sexual abuse to psychological difficulties, such as self-injurious behaviors, bipolar disorder, emotional
dysregulation, eating disorders, depression and anxiety, and personality disorders.

The preferential relationship between emotional abuse and adverse
outcomes is perhaps most consistently seen in research on pessimistic
explanatory style. Pessimistic explanatory style—a cognitive predictor
of depression—refers to an individual's tendency to construe the causes
of negative events as stable in duration (rather than temporary), global
in their influence over multiple domains of life functioning (rather than
impacting only a select few domains), and located within, or internal
to, the person.

In several studies, researchers found that emotional abuse, but not
sexual or physical abuse, was related to pessimistic explanatory style.
In view of such findings, school counselors must remain sensitive to
the seriousness of this form of abuse, its potential impact on children,
and the necessity for well-informed intervention efforts.

Chapter 22

Technology and Abuse

Chapter Contents

Section 22.1

What Is Cyberbullying?

This section includes text excerpted from "What Is
Cyberbullying," StopBullying.gov, U.S. Department of
Health and Human Services (HHS), July 26, 2018.

Cyberbullying is bullying that takes place over digital devices,
such as cell phones, computers, and tablets. Cyberbullying can occur
through SMS (short message service), texting, and apps, or online on
social media, forums, or gaming where people can view, participate in,
or share content. Cyberbullying includes sending, posting, or sharing
negative, harmful, false, or mean content about someone else. It can
include sharing personal or private information about someone else
causing embarrassment or humiliation. Some cyberbullying crosses
the line into unlawful or criminal behavior.

The most common places where cyberbullying occurs are:

- Social media, such as Facebook, Instagram, Snapchat, and Twitter

- SMS, also known as a "text message sent through devices"

- Instant message (via devices, email provider services, apps, and
  social media messaging features)

- E-mail

Cyberbullying: Special Concerns

With the prevalence of social media and digital forums, comments,
photos, posts, and content shared by individuals can often be viewed by
strangers, as well as by acquaintances. The content an individual shares
online—both their personal content, as well as any negative, mean, or
hurtful content—creates a kind of permanent public record of their views,
activities, and behavior. This public record can be thought of as an online
reputation, which may be accessible to schools, employers, colleges, clubs,
and others who may be researching an individual now or in the future.
Cyberbullying can harm the online reputations of everyone involved—not
just the person being bullied, but those doing the bullying or participating
in it. Cyberbullying has unique concerns in that it can be:

- **Persistent.** Digital devices offer an ability to immediately and
  continuously communicate 24 hours a day, so it can be difficult
  for children experiencing cyberbullying to find relief.

- **Permanent.** Most information communicated electronically is permanent and public, if not reported and removed. A negative online reputation, including for those who bully, can impact college admissions, employment, and other areas of life.

- **Hard to notice.** Because teachers and parents may not overhear or see cyberbullying taking place, it is harder to recognize.

Laws and Sanctions to Control Cyberbullying

Although all states have laws requiring schools to respond to bullying, many states do not include cyberbullying under these laws or specify the role schools should play in responding to bullying that takes place outside of school. Schools may take action either as required by law or with local or school policies that allow them to discipline or take other action. Some states also have provisions to address bullying if it affects school performance.

Cyberbullying Tactics

It is important to understand how children are cyberbullied, so it can be easily recognized and action can be taken. Some of the most common cyberbullying tactics include:

- Posting comments or rumors about someone online that are mean, hurtful, or embarrassing

- Threatening to hurt someone or telling them to kill themselves

- Posting a mean or hurtful picture or video

- Pretending to be someone else online in order to solicit or post personal or false information about someone else

- Posting mean or hateful names, comments, or content about any race, religion, ethnicity, or other personal characteristics online

- Creating a mean or hurtful webpage about someone

- Doxing, an abbreviated form of the word documents, is a form of online harassment used to exact revenge and to threaten and destroy the privacy of individuals by making their personal information public, including addresses; social security; credit card, and phone numbers; links to social media accounts; and other private data.

Viral Tactics: Examples

Because cyberbullying can happen in different ways, examples based on real-life experiences can provide a deeper understanding of the tactics typically used. Along with other risk factors, bullying can increase the risk for suicide-related behaviors. Furthermore, cyberbullying can be relentless, increasing the likelihood of anxiety and depression. Some states have chosen to prosecute young people who bully for criminal harassment, including encouraging someone to commit suicide. Some forms of cyberbullying are forms of harassment that cross the line into criminal activity, and some tactics occur in dating relationships and can turn into interpersonal violence.

The stories below are examples of different cyberbullying tactics that could happen. In reality, with the right interventions, cyberbullying can be addressed positively to lessen the harm and negative outcomes that could result. When not addressed, cyberbullying can have long-term mental-health effects. Cyberbullying and bullying can negatively impact the lives of all who are involved.

Sharing of Nude Photo

A teenage girl sent a nude photo of herself to her boyfriend while they were dating. After they broke up, he shared the photo with others, who then called her hurtful, derogatory names via text and social media.

Lies and False Accusations

A group of students got into trouble at school for being drunk, and accused a girl who knew nothing about it of reporting them to school officials. They began texting her day and night, and posted hateful, derogatory messages on social media. Other students saw their messages and joined in harassing the girl. She was bullied constantly via text, and in person at school. She eventually shut down her social media accounts and changed her phone number. Still, bullying at school continued.

Bullied for Being Economically Challenged

Students posted mean, negative comments on another classmates' social media account, commenting on his clothes and sneakers, which were not the more expensive name brands most of them were wearing. They ridiculed him, calling him "poor" and continued bullying in school. The boy missed many days of school trying to avoid the harassment and embarrassment.

False Identity Profile, Sometimes Referred to as a "Sockpuppet"

A girl's classmate created a fake social media account in a boy's name, and began an online relationship with her. Though she had not met him in person, the girl divulged her personal information; about herself, and her family, to the boy. The classmate who created the fake account then shared the personal information with other children, who used it to bully, shame, and harass the girl.

Encouraging Self-Harm or Suicide

A young boy with a physical disability and scars on his face was harassed on social media and via text by other students. They called him derogatory names and told him he would be better off dead. They wrote "why don't you die?" on his school locker and encouraged him to take his own life.

Bullied for Being Gay

A teenage boy who was openly gay began receiving death threats via phone, text, and social media for being gay. Students created an antigay social media group and harassed him, posting hateful messages about him.

Jealousy Bullying

A teenage girl was harassed by other girls in her class for dating a very popular boy. The girls sent her hateful messages via text and social media and wrote derogatory messages on her school locker.

Doxing over Online Gaming

A teenage boy posted comments on a public gaming forum, expressing his dislike of certain game features and tactics. Another user disagreed with him in the forum, then searched for the boy's information online and posted his address, email address, and social media links in another comment. The boy then received multiple emails and messages from strangers threatening to come to his home and assault him and to block him from games.

Prevent Cyberbullying
Be Aware of What Your Kids Are Doing Online

A child may be involved in cyberbullying in several ways. A child can be bullied, bully others, or witness bullying. Parents, teachers, and other adults may not be aware of all the digital media and apps that a child is using. The more digital platforms that a child uses, the more opportunities there are for being exposed to potential cyberbullying.

Warning Signs a Child Is Being Cyberbullied or Is Cyberbullying Others

Many of the warning signs that cyberbullying is occurring happen around a child's use of their device. Some of the warning signs that a child may be involved in cyberbullying are:

- Noticeable increases or decreases in device use, including texting

- A child exhibits emotional responses (laughter, anger, upset) to what is happening on their device.

- A child hides their screen or device when others are near, and avoids discussing about what they are doing on their device.

- Social media accounts are shut down or new ones appear.

- A child starts to avoid social situations, even those that were enjoyed in the past.

- A child becomes withdrawn or depressed, or loses interest in people and activities.

What to Do When Cyberbullying Happens

If you notice warning signs that a child may be involved in cyberbullying, take steps to investigate that child's digital behavior. Cyberbullying is a form of bullying, and adults should take the same approach to address it: support the child being bullied, address the bullying behavior of a participant, and show children that cyberbullying is taken seriously. Because cyberbullying happens online, responding to it requires different approaches. If you think that a child is involved in cyberbullying, there are several things you can do.

- **Notice**. Recognize if there has been a change in mood or behavior, and explore what the cause might be. Try to determine if these changes happen around a child's use of their digital devices.

- **Talk.** Ask questions to learn what is happening, how it started, and who is involved.

- **Document.** Keep a record of what is happening and where. Take screenshots of harmful posts or content if possible. Most laws and policies note that bullying is a repeated behavior, so records help to document it.

- **Report.** Most social media platforms and schools have clear policies and reporting processes. If a classmate is cyberbullying, report it to the school authorities. You can also contact app or social media platforms to report offensive content and have it removed. If a child has received physical threats, or if a potential crime or illegal behavior is occurring, report it to the police.

- **Support.** Peers, mentors, and trusted adults can sometimes intervene publicly to positively influence a situation where negative or harmful content is posted about a child. Public intervention can include posting positive comments about the person targeted with bullying to try to shift the conversation in a positive direction. It can also help to reach out to the bully and the target of the bullying to express your concern. If possible, try to determine if more professional support is needed for those involved, such as speaking with a guidance counselor or mental-health professional.

Kids on Social Media and Gaming
Social Media Apps and Sites Commonly Used by Children and Teens

Digital media and apps allow children to communicate and express their creativity, connect with peers, and share their feelings. However, these mediums can also be an avenue through which cyberbullying occurs. There are many types of apps and sites available for free that give users the ability to search for people and share or post information about them anonymously.

Parents may not be aware of the apps that their children use regularly or may not be aware of the risks involved in using them. There are many ways that cyberbullying can be hidden in apps and sites, such as texts, videos, and web calls, that disappear or do not appear on the device's call or text message logs.

Many apps also make it easy for users to access, view, or participate in adult or harmful content. Privacy and location settings may make

147

them more vulnerable to stalking, cyberbullying, exposure to adult content, or other dangers.

Some current popular social media venues and apps include:

- **Askfm:** A social networking site that allows users to ask other people questions, often anonymously.

- **Chatroulette:** There are over 20 different chat roulette sites that allow users to instantly connect via webcam and video chat. Sites typically pair the users randomly and instantly.

- **Discord:** A voice-over-IP (VOIP) app that allows users to video chat with others private message, and join, create, or participate in public and private chat rooms. This app is often used by players to chat with each other while playing videogames.

- **Facebook and Facebook Live:** The most commonly used social media site that is accessible on many different media platforms.

- **Instagram:** A photo and video sharing networking site that connects users through other social networking sites (e.g., Facebook).

- **Kik:** A messaging app that allows users of all ages to contact others anonymously.

- **Line:** A messaging app that allows users to make free phone calls, leave voice messages, and text. Users can delete texts or chats from recipient's phone using a timer.

- **Reddit:** A site that stores social news, rates and evaluates web content, and discussion threads.

- **Sarahah:** An anonymous messaging app that allows users to send anonymous messages to people they may know.

- **Snapchat:** A photo messaging app that allows for sharing pictures and short videos that are intended to be erased shortly after delivery.

- **Telegram:** A messaging app that allows users to share photos, videos, and files; make calls, and delete texts or chats from recipient's phone using a timer.

- **TikTok:** Users can post their own videos and view videos posted by others.

- **Tumblr:** A social networking site that allows posting of short blogs and media.

- **Twitter:** A microblogging site that allows users to send, read, and reply to "tweets" or short messages.

- **WeChat:** An app that allows users to chat with friends and search for people nearby and around the globe.

- **WhatsApp:** A private messaging app that allows users to text, send photos, videos, and location information to their contacts.

- **YouTube:** A video sharing platform that allows users to post and share videos.

Social media has many benefits that must be balanced with the risks it presents. Risks to be aware of include:

- Screening for harmful content on websites and apps varies widely

- Content posted can be incorrect, harmful, or hurtful (e.g., why are you so dumb?)

- Can be used to share harmful or adult content

- Privacy controls over who can view or access posted material vary across apps, and many users are not aware of how to use them effectively

- Apps that allow for real-time user videos "live streaming" can been used to show bullying, violence, suicide, and harmful acts as they are happening

- Some apps that include location information can be used to get personal information such as someone's age, current location, or where someone lives

- Apps that support telephone calls do not show up on a call log, so parents may not know who their children are talking to

Cyberbullying and Online Gaming

Playing video games is a popular activity, with 72 percent of teens gaming online. Many video games—whether they are console, web, or computer-based—allow users to play with friends they know in person and others they have met only online. While gaming can have positive benefits, such as making new friends, socializing, and learning how to strategize and problem solve, it is also another place where cyber-bullying occurs.

149

Anonymity of players and the use of avatars allow users to create alter-egos or fictional versions of themselves, which is part of the fun of gaming. But it also allows users to harass, bully, and sometimes gang up on other players, sending or posting negative or hurtful messages and using the game as a tool of harassment. If someone is not performing well, other children may curse or make negative remarks that turn into bullying, or they might exclude the person from playing together.

Because players are anonymous, they cannot necessarily be held accountable for their behavior, and their harassment can cause some players to leave games. Some anonymous users use games as a means to harass strangers or to get their personal information, such as user name and passwords.

There are things adults can do to prevent cyberbullying of children who are gaming:

- Play the game or observe when the gaming happens to understand how it works and what a child is exposed to in the game.

- Check in periodically with your child about who is online and playing the game with them.

- Teach your children about safe online behavior, including not clicking on the links from strangers, not sharing personal information, not participating in bullying behavior of other players, and what to do if they observe or experience bullying.

- Establish rules about how much time a child can spend playing video games.

Digital Awareness for Parents

The digital world is constantly evolving with new social media platforms, apps, and devices, and children and teens are often the first to use them. Some negative things that may occur include cyberbullying, sexting, posting hateful messages or content, and participating in negative group conversations. If your child posts harmful or negative content online, it may not only harm other children; it can affect their online reputation, which can have negative implications for their employment or college admission.

While you may not be able to monitor all of your child's activities, there are things you can do to prevent cyberbullying and protect your child from harmful digital behavior, such as:

- Monitor a teen's social media sites, apps, and browsing history, if you have concerns that cyberbullying may be occurring.

- Review or reset your child's phone location and privacy settings.

- Follow or friend your teen on social media sites or have another trusted adult do so.

- Stay up-to-date on the latest apps, social media platforms, and digital slang used by children and teens.

- Know your child's usernames and passwords for email and social media accounts.

- Establish rules about appropriate digital behavior, content, and apps.

Digital Monitoring Apps and Software for Parents

Parents who want to protect their children from cyberbullying, harmful digital behavior, and exposure to adult content can use parental control and monitoring software to help them set up systems that are less invasive to their children.

There are free software options and apps available to help parents restrict content, block domains, or view their children's online activities, including social media, without looking at their child's device every day. Most of the free software options provide some features for free, but charge for more robust insight.

A parent should consider a child's age, device use, and digital behavior when selecting software—what is suitable to restrict for a ten-year old may not be useful for a teenager.

Establishing Rules: Tips for Parents
Talk to Your Child about Appropriate Digital Behavior and Content

Parents create trust with children by initiating open, honest discussions. These dialogues are an opportunity to communicate values and expectations about your family's appropriate digital behavior, including viewing or sharing content, and apps they can and cannot use.

Check in frequently with your children about their digital experiences to address any potential risk of cyberbullying and harm. Be clear that your intention is to look out for their wellbeing, and that you want to have an open dialogue. Listen to their concerns and express your perspective.

To minimize the risk of cyberbullying or harm from digital behavior, parents can:

- Set clear expectations about digital behavior and online reputation.

- Educate about the harmful effects of cyberbullying, posting hateful speech or comments, sexting, and sharing naked photos of themselves or others (including potential legal issues).

- Be clear about what content can be viewed or shared.

- Identify which apps are appropriate for your child's use and which are not.

- Establish rules about the amount of time that a child can spend online or on their devices.

- Model positive, respectful digital behavior on your own devices and accounts.

Talk to Your Child about Being a Bystander to Cyberbullying

Having conversations with children about cyberbullying and digital behavior is not a one-time event—it is an ongoing dialogue. Begin talking about these issues before children delve into the world of texting, social media, online gaming, and chat rooms. Help them reflect on real and potential cyberbullying situations, and provide ongoing opportunities to practice ways to respond. Doing so can support the transition from being passive bystanders to being allies who serve as powerful role models for others. The Substance Abuse and Mental Health Services Administration's (SAMHSA) free Knowbullying app for parents, teachers, and educators provides conversation starters, tips and other tools you can use to help prevent bullying.

If you think your child is witnessing cyberbullying, there are things that you can encourage them to do and not do, such as:

- **Do not participate.** Encourage children not to "like," share, or comment on information that has been posted about someone, and do not forward a hurtful text to others. Not participating may limit the potential damage of the messages—to others and to themselves.

- **Do not retaliate or respond negatively.** If a child feels that they must respond, encourage a calm, clear, and constructive response. Angry and aggressive reactions can make a bad situation worse. Encourage children (and adults!) to step away from the device so they do not resort to blaming, shaming, or retaliation. This provides time to get calm and centered so they can create a response that makes it clear that others' digital behaviors are hurtful and unacceptable.

- **Respond privately to the person who created the hurtful message.** If they feel safe doing so, it may be helpful to follow up with the person who created or shared the hurtful message privately, either online, in a phone call, or in person. Doing so can make it clear they do not support the negative actions. It also provides an opportunity to authentically share concerns about the behavior and what might be behind it.

- **Follow up with the person who was targeted.** By reaching out, a child can send a powerful message that they care about the person and they do not support the negative behaviors. If needed, this connection can also provide an opportunity to assist the person in finding help related to the cyberbullying situation.

Establishing Rules: Tips for Teachers
Warning Signs a Child Is Being Cyberbullied or Is Cyberbullying

A child may be involved in cyberbullying in several ways. A child can be bullied, bully others, or witness bullying. Parents, teachers, and other adults may not be aware of all the social media platforms and apps that a child is using. The more digital platforms that a child uses, the more opportunities there are for being exposed to potential cyberbullying.

Many of the warning signs that cyberbullying is occurring happen around a child's use of their device. Since children spend a lot of time on their devices, increases or decreases in use may be less noticeable. It is important to pay attention when a child exhibits sudden changes in digital and social behavior. Some of the warning signs that a child may be involved in cyberbullying are:

- Noticeable, rapid increases or decreases in device use, including texting

- A child exhibits emotional responses (laughter, anger, upset) to what is happening on their device

153

- A child hides their screen or device when others are near, and avoids discussing about what they are doing on their device.

- Social media accounts are shut down or new ones appear

- A child starts to avoid social situations, even those that were enjoyed in the past

- A child becomes withdrawn or depressed, or loses interest in people and activities

Preventing and Addressing Cyberbullying

Teachers, school administrators, camp, community, and faith-based staff are in unique positions to use their skills and roles to create safe environments with positive social norms. They are also in positions where they may notice children's behavior changes in group settings, such as when a group or cluster of children focuses on another child, or other signs that cyberbullying may be occurring. There are things that you can do in the classroom or other group settings to address or prevent cyberbullying.

- If you think a child is being cyberbullied, speak to them privately to ask about it. They may also have proof on their digital devices.

- If you believe a child is being cyberbullied, speak to a parent about it. Serve as a facilitator between the child, parent, and the school if necessary.

- To understand children's digital behavior and how it relates to cyberbullying, increase your digital awareness.

- Develop activities that encourage self-reflection, asking children to identify and express what they think and feel, and to consider the thoughts and feelings of others. Help children develop emotional intelligence so that they can learn self-awareness and self-regulation skills and learn how to have empathy for others.

- Role model, reinforce, and reward positive behavior towards others.

- Encourage peer involvement in prevention strategies.

Report Cyberbullying

When cyberbullying happens, it is important to document and report the behavior so it can be addressed.

Steps to Take Immediately

- Do not respond to and do not forward cyberbullying messages.

- Keep evidence of cyberbullying. Record the dates, times, and descriptions of instances when cyberbullying has occurred. Save and print screenshots, emails, and text messages. Use this evidence to report cyberbullying to web and cell phone service providers.

- Block the person who is cyberbullying.

Report Cyberbullying to Online Service Providers

Cyberbullying often violates the terms of service established by social media sites and Internet service providers.

- Review their terms and conditions or rights and responsibilities sections. These describe content that is or is not appropriate.

- Visit social media safety centers to learn how to block users and change settings to control who can contact you.

- Report cyberbullying to the social media site, so they can take action against users abusing the terms of service.

Report Cyberbullying to Law Enforcement

When cyberbullying involves these activities it is considered a crime and should be reported to law enforcement:

- Threats of violence

- Child pornography or sending sexually explicit messages or photos

- Taking a photo or video of someone in a place where she or he would expect privacy

- Stalking and hate crimes

Some states consider other forms of cyberbullying criminal. Consult your state's laws and law enforcement for additional guidance.

Report Cyberbullying to Schools

- Cyberbullying can create a disruptive environment at school and is often related to in-person bullying. The school can use the information to help inform prevention and response strategies.

- In many states, schools are required to address cyberbullying in their anti-bullying policy. Some state laws also cover off-campus behavior that creates a hostile school environment.

Section 22.2

Child Pornography

This section includes text excerpted from "Child Pornography," U.S. Department of Justice (DOJ), July 25, 2017.

Child pornography is a form of child sexual exploitation. Federal law defines child pornography as any visual depiction of sexually explicit conduct involving a minor (persons less than 18 years of age). Images of child pornography are also referred to as "child sexual abuse images."

Federal law prohibits the production, distribution, importation, reception, or possession of any image of child pornography. A violation of federal child pornography laws is a serious crime, and convicted offenders face fines and severe statutory penalties.

Child Pornography Today

Because the term "child pornography" is used in federal statutes, it is also commonly used by lawmakers, prosecutors, investigators, and the public to describe this form of sexual exploitation of children. However, this term fails to describe the true horror that is faced by countless children every year. The production of child pornography creates a permanent record of a child's sexual abuse. When these images are placed on the Internet and disseminated online, the victimization of the children continues in perpetuity. Experts and victims agree that victims depicted in child pornography often suffer a lifetime of revictimization by knowing that the images of their sexual abuse are on the Internet forever. The children exploited in these images must live with the permanency, longevity, and circulation of such a record of their sexual victimization. This often creates lasting psychological damage to the child, including disruptions in sexual development, self-image, and developing trusting relationships with others in the future.

The expansion of the Internet and advanced digital technology lies parallel to the explosion of the child pornography market. Child pornography images are readily available through virtually every Internet technology, including social networking websites, file-sharing sites, photo-sharing sites, gaming devices, and even mobile apps. Child pornography offenders can also connect on Internet forums and networks to share their interests, desires, and experiences abusing children, in addition to selling, sharing, and trading images.

These online communities have promoted communication and collaboration between child pornography offenders, thereby fostering a larger relationship premised on a shared sexual interest in children. This has the effect of eroding the shame that typically would accompany this behavior, as well as desensitizing those involved to the physical and psychological damage caused to the child victims. For this reason, online communities attract and encourage new individuals to join them in the sexual exploitation of children.

The methods many offenders use to evade law enforcement detection have also become increasingly sophisticated. Purveyors of child pornography continue to use various encryption techniques and anonymous networks on "The Dark Internet," attempting to hide their amassed collections of illicit child abuse images. Several sophisticated online criminal organizations have even written security manuals to ensure that their members follow preferred security protocols and encryption techniques in an attempt to evade law enforcement and facilitate the sexual abuse of children.

Unfortunately, no area of the United States or country in the world is immune from individuals who seek to sexually exploit children through child pornography. The continuous production and distribution of child pornography increases the demand for new and more egregious images, perpetuating the continued molestation of child victims, as well as the abuse of new children.

Victims of Child Pornography

It is important to distinguish child pornography from the more conventional understanding of the term pornography. Child pornography is a form of child sexual exploitation, and each image graphically memorializes the sexual abuse of that child. Each child involved in the production of an image is a victim of sexual abuse.

While some child sexual abuse images depict children in great distress and the sexual abuse is self-evident, other images may depict children that appear complacent. However, just because a child appears complacent does not mean that sexual abuse did not occur. In most child pornography cases, the abuse is not a one-time event, but rather ongoing victimization that progresses over months or years. It is common for producers of child pornography to groom victims, or cultivate a relationship with a child and gradually sexualize the contact over time. The grooming process fosters a false sense of trust and authority over a child in order to desensitize or break down a child's resistance to sexual abuse. Therefore, even if a child appears complacent in a particular image, it is important to remember that the abuse may have started years before that image was created.

Furthermore, victims of child pornography suffer not just from the sexual abuse inflicted upon them to produce child pornography, but also from knowing that their images can be traded and viewed by others worldwide. Once an image is on the Internet, it is irretrievable and can continue to circulate forever. The permanent record of a child´s sexual abuse can alter her or his live forever. Many victims of child pornography suffer from feelings of helplessness, fear, humiliation, and lack of control, given that their images are available for others to view in perpetuity.

Unfortunately, emerging trends reveal an increase in the number of images depicting sadistic and violent child sexual abuse, and an increase in the number of images depicting very young children, including toddlers and infants.

Section 22.3

Online Sexual Exploitation of Children

This section includes text excerpted from "Online Sexual Exploitation of Children: An Alarming Trend," U.S. Department of State (DOS), June 27, 2017.

New technologies are facilitating the online sexual exploitation of children, including the live streaming of sexual abuse of children using web cameras or cellphones, often for profit. Mobile devices also provide new and evolving means by which offenders sexually abuse children as apps are being used to target, recruit, and coerce children to engage in sexual activity. Experts believe tens of thousands of children globally are sexually exploited online, and the number appears to be growing. The victims may be boys or girls, ranging from very young children to adolescents, and hailing from all ethnic and socio-economic backgrounds.

The process often begins when an offender gains access to a potential child victim and, through psychological manipulation and coercion, grooms the child for sexual exploitation. The offender then connects via the Internet with a paying client who often specifically requests a child. The child is further victimized through commercial sexual exploitation and abuse and the live streaming of commercial sex acts. Perpetrators can pay to direct the sexual abuse of children from anywhere in the world, while the abuse takes place in private homes, Internet cafes, or "cyber dens" in or near the child's community. Disturbingly, closed and highly protected online communities dedicated to the sexual abuse of children have proliferated. Children have been reported to be victims of this crime in Colombia, India, Mexico, the Philippines, Thailand, and the United States. Many countries, including Australia, Britain, Canada, the Netherlands, the Philippines, and the United States, have prosecuted perpetrators—both paying clients and offenders who facilitate the exploitation of the child.

In the Philippines, where many are impoverished and nearly half of the population is connected to the Internet, numerous individuals in poor communities reportedly earn income from this type of child exploitation. Online sessions can be conducted at a low cost using a cellphone or a computer with a webcam. Connections to prospective clients are made easily; clients remain anonymous and make payments by wire transfer. Children, often naked, have been exploited on camera—including by family members or neighbors—and coerced into exhibiting themselves and performing sex acts for the viewing of individuals watching online. In many cases, family members justify facilitating the online sexual exploitation by asserting that it is not harmful to the child, especially in cases where there is no direct physical contact with the child. This lack of understanding of the detrimental psychological, developmental, and physical impact of this crime on children, the complicity of relatives, and the easy flow of money have contributed to the practice becoming more prevalent.

Another growing threat to children is sextortion, which is a form of online sexual exploitation of children where offenders hack, coerce, deceive or otherwise obtain incriminating photos or information from a child and then threaten exposure if that child does not perform sex acts via web cameras.

The online sexual exploitation of children presents new challenges for law enforcement, prosecutors, judges, and victim service providers. Law enforcement and prosecutors in most countries have little training or experience in detecting this crime, conducting online investigations, obtaining evidence from Internet service providers, and presenting relevant evidence in court. Enhanced mechanisms of encryption by the offenders, such as networks of technologies and platforms that obfuscate traditional IP addresses, have also delayed or complicated investigations. In addition, difficulties in obtaining the cooperation of family members and others who facilitate the crime is a widespread challenge in these cases, as is the lack of specialized trauma-informed care and services for the child victims, especially boys.

Despite such challenges, governments, international organizations, and NGOs are working together to address the online sexual exploitation of children. Successful detection and prosecution of perpetrators requires advanced cybercrime investigative skills, criminal laws and procedures that secure cyber evidence and allow for prosecution of crimes committed online, specialized training for prosecutors and judges, cross-border law enforcement cooperation, and specialized care for child victims. The low financial cost of this criminal enterprise (an Internet connection and a mobile device or computer-linked webcam), coupled with its low-risk nature (as seen by the relatively small number of convictions globally) and high profitability are driving the rapid growth of online sexual exploitation of children. To reverse this trend, governments must rally significant political will and resources to hold perpetrators accountable, provide comprehensive services to child victims, and prevent the crime from occurring.

Chapter 23

International Parental Kidnapping

Federal law prohibits a parent from removing a child from the United States or retaining a child in another country with the intent to obstruct another parents' custodial rights. This crime is known as "international parental kidnapping" (IPK). For example, consider that a married couple had a son together in the United States. During a marital dispute, the father moves with his son to another country in order to keep him away from the mother, and he has no intent of returning. In this situation, the father has committed IPK, which is considered as a federal crime. Convicted offenders of this crime can face up to three years of imprisonment.

Child Victims of International Parental Kidnapping

Every year, situations of IPK are reported in the United States. It is common for the removal of a child to occur during a heated or emotional marital dispute, in the early stages of separation or divorce, or in the waiting period for a court custody order or agreement. IPKs of U.S. children have been reported in countries all over the world, including Australia, Brazil, Canada, Colombia, Germany, India, Japan, Mexico, the Philippines, and the United Kingdom.

This chapter includes text excerpted from "International Parental Kidnapping," U.S. Department of Justice (DOJ), June 3, 2015. Reviewed March 2019.

Child victims of IPK are often taken from a familiar environment and suddenly isolated from their community, family, and friends. They may miss months or even years of schooling. The child may be moved to multiple locations in order to stay hidden or out of reach of the parent remaining in the United States. In some cases, the child's name, date of birth, and physical appearance are altered or concealed to hide their identity.

In addition, the tense and unfavorable situation between the parents may be emotionally troubling to a child. Kidnapped children are at high risk for long-term psychological problems including anxiety, eating disorders, nightmares, mood swings, sleep disturbances, and aggressive behavior. As adults, child victims of IPK may struggle with identity, relationships, and family issues.

Legal Hurdles and the Return of a Kidnapped Child to the United States

Under federal law, prosecutors may investigate and prosecute the parent who kidnapped the child, however, prosecutors generally have no control over the custodial decisions affecting the child or whether foreign authorities will order the return of the child.

The return of kidnapped children is often settled through negotiation. The U.S. Department of State (DOS) handles the coordination of efforts with foreign officials and law enforcement agencies to effectuate the return of children to the United States. In some circumstances, the return may be governed by the Hague Convention on the Civil Aspects of International Parental Child Abduction (1980). This Convention was established to facilitate the return of children abducted to foreign countries. However, it only applies if both countries involved in the IPK situation are signatories to the Convention. The United States is a signatory state.

Adhering to the provisions of the Convention, when applicable, and working with the U.S. Department of State are the best methods to legally and safely return a kidnapped child to the United States. In acts of desperation, some parents will attempt to use extra-judicial forms of recovery, such as personally traveling to the foreign country to recover their child. Although it may seem easier and faster to use extra-judicial methods, they often violate U.S. federal laws and the laws of the foreign country involved, and may potentially exacerbate the situation. For example, the parent who kidnapped the child may have sought assistance from a foreign court or obtained a foreign custody order. In such circumstances, the other parent's direct removal of a child from the foreign jurisdiction, without the assistance of the U.S. Department of State (DOS), could result in her or his arrest or even imprisonment in that foreign country. Furthermore, any unlawful attempt to recover a child may adversely impact a petition for return under the Hague Convention.

Child Exploitation and Obscenity Section's Role

The Child Exploitation and Obscenity Section (CEOS) provides advice and litigation support to the U.S. Attorneys' Offices throughout the country regarding IPK prosecutions. While CEOS does not have the authority to intervene in the return of children, they work directly with the DOS and the National Center for Missing and Exploited Children (NCMEC) to monitor active IPK cases and provide legal assistance.

In addition, CEOS conducts training for federal prosecutors and law enforcement personnel on federal IPK law and its interplay with the Hague Convention.

Child Custody and Visitation Matters

With the exception of international parental kidnapping, child custody and visitation matters are handled by local and state authorities, not by the federal government. The matters are governed by the relevant state family court system and human services agency. Therefore, child custody or visitation issues should be reported to state or local law enforcement authorities or a state judicial officer.

Chapter 24

Childhood Maltreatment among Children with Disabilities

Disability and Maltreatment: Facts

Children with disabilities may be at higher risk for abuse or neglect than children without disabilities. There are steps that parents can take to protect children with disabilities from abuse or neglect.

- Parents can more easily become stressed with the demands placed on them by parenting a child with a disability.

- Kids with behavior problems, such as attention deficit/ hyperactivity disorder (ADHD) or other conduct problems, may be more likely to experience physical abuse because parents can become frustrated by the child's difficult behavior and respond harshly.

- Kids who are less able to do things independently rely more on adults for their care. These children may be more likely to be sexually abused or neglected by adults.

This chapter includes text excerpted from "Childhood Maltreatment among Children with Disabilities," Centers for Disease Control and Prevention (CDC), June 22, 2018.

- Abusers may take advantage of kids who have problems with speaking or hearing, or those who do not understand social situations very well. These children may be more likely to experience sexual abuse.

What Can You Do?
Be Informed

Parents can prevent abuse and neglect of children by:

- Knowing the signs of possible abuse, such as:
  - Sudden changes in, or unusual behavior
  - Cuts and bruises
  - Broken bones (not due to a medical condition)
  - Burns
  - Complaints about painful genitals
- Knowing the signs of possible neglect, such as:
  - Constant hunger or thirst (not due to a medical condition)
  - Dirty hair or skin
  - Chronic diaper rash (not due to a medical condition)
- Knowing where your child is and what she or he is doing when they are not at home.
- Getting to know the people who take care of your child. Only leave your child with someone you know and who can take care of your child in a place where your child will be safe from harm and danger.
- Knowing that your child's school must treat your child with dignity. Your child should not be punished by being mistreated, restrained, or secluded.
- Taking steps to make sure your house is a safe place for your child so she or he will not get injured.
- Talking to your child about behavior and situations that are safe and not safe.
- Identifying and reminding your child of safe adults that he or she can turn to. Role-playing and practicing how to find a safe adult can help young children learn where to go.

If you think your child has been abused or neglected you can:

- Talk to your child's doctor about your concerns

- Take your child to a hospital or doctor's office to be examined

- Call the police (dial 911 on your phone)

- Call the Childhelp National Child Abuse Hotline: 800-422-4453

Take Care of Yourself

Being a parent is the hardest job you will ever have. It is easy to become overwhelmed, especially if you have a child who has a disability or other special healthcare needs.

Here are some things to remember when parenting gets stressful or difficult:

- Be realistic about what your child can and cannot do.

- If you are frustrated, give yourself a time-out to calm down and refocus.

- Ask people who you trust to help you.

- Focus on the positive.

- Make time for yourself.

- Talk to a healthcare professional, such as your doctor or therapist, if you do not know how to handle your child's behavior.

Chapter 25

Parental Drug Use as Child Abuse

Abuse of drugs or alcohol by parents and other caregivers can have negative effects on the health, safety, and well-being of children. Approximately 47 states, the District of Columbia, Guam, and the U.S Virgin Islands have laws within their child protection statutes that address the issue of substance abuse by parents. Two areas of concern are the harm caused by prenatal drug exposure and the harm caused to children of any age by exposure to illegal drug activity in their homes or environment.

Prenatal Drug Exposure

The Child Abuse Prevention and Treatment Act (CAPTA) requires states to have policies and procedures in place to notify child protective services (CPS) agencies of substance-exposed newborns (SENs) and to establish a plan of safe care for newborns identified as being affected by illegal-substance abuse or having withdrawal symptoms resulting from prenatal drug exposure. Several states currently address this requirement in their statutes. Approximately 19 states and the District of Columbia have specific reporting procedures for

---

This chapter includes text excerpted from "Parental Drug Use as Child Abuse," Child Welfare Information Gateway, U.S. Department of Health and Human Services (HHS), April 2015. Reviewed March 2019.

infants who show evidence at birth of having been exposed to drugs, alcohol, or other controlled substances; 14 states and the District of Columbia include this type of exposure in their definitions of child abuse or neglect.

Some states specify in their statutes the response the CPS agency must make to reports of SENs. Maine requires the state agency to develop a plan of safe care for the infant. California, Maryland, Minnesota, Missouri, Nevada, Pennsylvania, and the District of Columbia require the agency to complete an assessment of needs for the infant and for the infant's family and to make a referral to appropriate services. Illinois and Minnesota require mandated reporters to report when they suspect that pregnant women are substance abusers so that the women can be referred for treatment.

Children Exposed to Illegal Drug Activity

There is increasing concern about the negative effects on children when parents or other members of their household abuse alcohol or drugs or engage in other illegal drug-related activity, such as the manufacture of methamphetamines in home-based laboratories. Many states have responded to this problem by expanding the civil definition of child abuse or neglect to include this concern. Specific circumstances that are considered child abuse or neglect in some states include:

- Manufacturing a controlled substance in the presence of a child or on premises occupied by a child

- Exposing a child to, or allowing a child to be present where, chemicals or equipment for the manufacture of controlled substances are used or stored

- Selling, distributing, or giving drugs or alcohol to a child

- Using a controlled substance that impairs the caregiver's ability to adequately care for the child

- Exposing a child to the criminal sale or distribution of drugs

Approximately 34 states and the U.S. Virgin Islands address in their criminal statutes the issue of exposing children to illegal drug activity.

For example, in 20 states, the manufacture or possession of methamphetamine in the presence of a child is a felony, while in 10 states, the manufacture or possession of any controlled substance in the presence of a child is considered a felony. 9 states have enacted enhanced penalties for any conviction for the manufacture of methamphetamine when a child was on the premises where the crime occurred.

Exposing children to the manufacture, possession, or distribution of illegal drugs is considered child endangerment in 11 states. The exposure of a child to drugs or drug paraphernalia is a crime in 8 states and the Virgin Islands. In North Carolina and Wyoming, selling or giving an illegal drug to a child by any person is a felony.

Part Four

Adult Survivors of
Child Abuse

Chapter 26

Adverse Childhood Experiences

Adverse childhood experiences (ACEs) are stressful or traumatic events, including abuse and neglect. They may also include household dysfunction, such as witnessing domestic violence or growing up with family members who have substance-use disorders (SUD). ACEs are strongly related to the development and prevalence of a wide range of health problems throughout a person's lifespan, including those associated with substance misuse.

ACEs include:

- Physical abuse

- Sexual abuse

- Emotional abuse

- Physical neglect

- Emotional neglect

- Intimate partner violence (IPV)

- Mother treated violently

- Substance misuse within the household

This chapter includes text excerpted from "Adverse Childhood Experiences," Substance Abuse and Mental Health Services Administration (SAMHSA), July 9, 2018.

- Household mental illness
- Parental separation or divorce
- Incarcerated household member

ACEs are a good example of the types of complex issues that the prevention workforce often faces. The negative effects of ACEs are felt throughout the nation and can affect people of all backgrounds. Successfully addressing their impact requires:

- Assessing prevention needs and gathering data
- Effective and sustainable prevention approaches guided by applying the Strategic Prevention Framework (SPF), a guide to prevent substance use
- Prevention efforts aligned with the widespread occurrence of ACEs
- Building relationships with appropriate community partners through strong collaboration

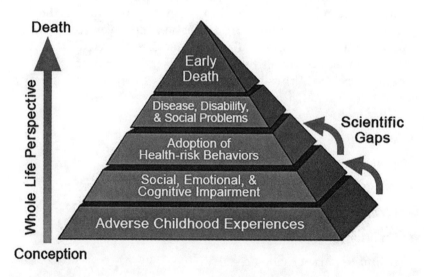

Figure 26.1. *Adverse Childhood Experiences Pyramid*

Many studies have examined the relationship between ACEs and a variety of known risk factors for disease, disability, and early mortality. The Division of Violence Prevention (DVP) at the Centers for Disease Control and Prevention (CDC), in partnership with Kaiser

Permanente, conducted a landmark ACE study from 1995 to 1997 with more than 17,000 participants. The study found that:

- **ACEs are common.** For example, 28 percent of study participants reported physical abuse, and 21 percent reported sexual abuse. Many also reported experiencing a divorce or parental separation or having a parent with a mental and/or SUD.

- **ACEs cluster.** Almost 40 percent of the Kaiser sample reported 2 or more ACEs, and 12.5 percent experienced 4 or more. Because ACEs cluster, many subsequent studies now look at the cumulative effects of ACEs rather than the individual effects of each.

- **ACEs have a dose-response relationship with many health problems.** As researchers followed participants over time, they discovered that a person's cumulative ACEs score has a strong, graded relationship to numerous health, social, and behavioral problems throughout their lifespan, including SUDs. Furthermore, many problems related to ACEs tend to be comorbid or co-occurring.

Adverse Childhood Experiences and Prevention Efforts

Preventing ACEs and engaging in early identification of people who have experienced them could have a significant impact on a range of critical health problems. You can strengthen your substance misuse prevention efforts by:

- Informing local decision-making by collecting state- and county-level ACEs data

- Increasing awareness of ACEs among state- and community-level substance misuse prevention professionals, emphasizing the relevance of ACEs to behavioral health disciplines

- Including ACEs among the primary risks and protective factors when engaging in prevention planning efforts

- Selecting and implementing programs, policies, and strategies designed to address ACEs, including efforts focusing on reducing intergenerational transmission of ACEs

- Using ACEs research and local ACEs data to identify groups of people who may be at higher risk for substance use disorders and to conduct targeted prevention

Adverse Childhood Experiences Research and Behavioral Health

Research has demonstrated a strong relationship between ACEs, SUDs, and behavioral problems. When children are exposed to chronic stressful events, their neurodevelopment can be disrupted. As a result, the child's cognitive functioning or ability to cope with negative or disruptive emotions may be impaired. Over time, and often during adolescence, the child may adopt negative coping mechanisms, such as substance use or self-harm. Eventually, these unhealthy coping mechanisms can contribute to disease, disability, and social problems, as well as premature mortality.

Adverse Childhood Experiences and Substance Use

- **Early initiation of alcohol use**. Efforts to prevent underage drinking may not be effective unless ACEs are addressed as a contributing factor. Underage drinking prevention programs may not work as intended unless they help youth recognize and cope with stressors of abuse, household dysfunction, and other adverse experiences.

- **Higher risk of mental and SUDs as an older adult (50 years of age or older).** ACEs, such as childhood abuse (physical, sexual, and psychological) and parental substance abuse, are associated with a higher risk of developing a SUD.

- **Continued tobacco use during adulthood.** Prevalence ratios for smoking increased as ACEs scores increased, according to a 2011 study on ACEs and smoking status.

- **Prescription drug use.** For every additional ACE score, the rate of the number of prescription drugs used increased by 62 percent, according to a 2017 study of ACEs and adolescent prescription drug use.

- **Lifetime illicit-drug use, drug dependency, and self-reported addiction.** Each ACE increased the likelihood of early initiation into illicit-drug use by two to four-fold, according to a 2003 study on childhood abuse, neglect, and household dysfunction and the risk of illicit-drug use.

Adverse Childhood Experiences and Behavioral Problems

- **Suicide attempts.** ACEs in any category increased the risk of attempted suicide by 2- to 5-fold throughout a person's lifespan, according to a 2001 study. According to 2017 article, individuals who reported 6 or more ACEs had 24.36 times increased odds of attempting suicide.

- **Lifetime depressive episodes.** Exposure to ACEs may increase the risk of experiencing depressive disorders well into adulthood—sometimes decades after ACEs occur.

- **Sleep disturbances in adults**. People with a history of ACEs have a higher likelihood of experiencing self-reported sleep disorders, according to a 2015 systematic review of research studies on ACEs and sleep disturbances in adults.

- **High-risk sexual behaviors.** Women with ACEs have reported risky sexual behaviors, including early intercourse, having had 30 or more sexual partners, and perceiving themselves to be at risk for human immunodeficiency virus (HIV)/acquired immunodeficiency syndrome (AIDS). Sexual minorities who experience ACEs also demonstrate earlier sexual debut, according to a 2015 study.

- **Fetal mortality.** Fetal deaths attributed to adolescent pregnancy may result from underlying ACEs rather than adolescent pregnancy, according to a 2004 study of the association between ACEs and adolescent pregnancy.

- **Pregnancy outcomes.** Each additional ACE a mother experienced during early childhood is associated with decreased birth weight and gestational age of her infant at birth, according to a 2016 study on the association between ACEs and pregnancy outcomes.

- **Negative physical health outcomes.** Experiencing adverse childhood family experiences may increase the risk of long-term physical health problems (e.g., diabetes, heart attack) in adults.

- **Poor dental health.** Children who have experienced at least one ACE are more likely to have poor dental health.

179

Chapter 27

Early Life Stress and Adult Chronic Fatigue Syndrome

It is a well-established fact that experiences during early life shape the development of the brain, particularly during sensitive periods. Adverse experiences can 'program' the development of certain brain regions that are involved in the regulation and integration of hormonal, autonomic, and immune responses to challenges later in life. Such challenges may encompass infections, physical stresses or emotional challenges.

Approximately 14 percent of children in the United States are subjected to some form of maltreatment, and in 2007, over 3 million reports of childhood abuse and neglect were investigated. "Childhood trauma," defined as abuse, neglect, or loss, is a stressor that affects the physical and mental well-being of humans from infancy throughout the lifespan. In various animal and human studies, childhood trauma has been associated with low resting cortisol levels, altered stress response, increased inflammatory markers, and cognitive impairment.

Childhood abuse has been connected to a wide range of disorders—such as depression, anxiety disorders, and substance-abuse problems—as

This chapter contains text excerpted from the following sources: Text in this chapter begins with excerpts from "Chronic Fatigue Syndrome (CFS)," Centers for Disease Control and Prevention (CDC), November 5, 2014. Reviewed March 2019; Text under the heading "Helping Your Child Manage Chronic Fatigue Syndrome (CFS)" is excerpted from "ME/CFS in Children: Fact Sheet for Parents/Guardians," Centers for Disease Control and Prevention (CDC), July 12, 2018.

well as more classic medical diseases, such as cardiovascular disease. Of note, markedly elevated levels of pain and fatigue have been reported in studies of survivors of childhood abuse.

Chronic fatigue syndrome (CFS) is a debilitating illness that can sometimes occur in response to a stressor or a challenge. For example, there have been reports of people developing CFS after being in a serious car accident. Other examples of challenges are increased rates of CFS in Gulf War veterans and triggered relapses of CFS in persons affected by Hurricane Andrew.

Upon stress exposure, our central nervous system will activate hormone and immune responses that help the body to maintain balance during stress. There is evidence that childhood maltreatment may alter the way how the body's regulatory systems respond to stress. Early adversity may thus increase a person's risk to develop adult CFS, particularly in response to challenges. Therefore, childhood trauma may be an important risk factor for adult CFS. Research has shown that when adults with CFS and without CFS were asked about childhood trauma, those with CFS self-reported higher levels of childhood maltreatment. In particular, for women, emotional and sexual abuse during childhood was associated with a greater risk of developing CFS later in life.

Of note, a risk factor is not "the cause" of a disorder; it increases the relative risk, but is not present in all cases. The cause of CFS is still unknown, but childhood trauma might be a factor that contributes to adult CFS risk in a subset of people. While these findings are important and have the potential to help many people, it is important to realize that not all persons with adult CFS experienced maltreatment as a child. Childhood maltreatment is just one risk factor for CFS and does not explain how other people with CFS (who did not experience such trauma) developed the illness.

The results from this research are important because healthcare providers can help people with a history of childhood maltreatment. For some people that have both a past of childhood maltreatment and CFS, talk therapy may be beneficial. While more research is needed on CFS and childhood maltreatment, patients are encouraged to talk to their healthcare provider about their physical and mental-health history.

Helping Your Child Manage Chronic Fatigue Syndrome

CFS is a complex illness that can be challenging for parents and children. The following are some tips to help you in dealing with this illness, whether it affects you or your child.

Be an Advocate for Your Child

Take an active role in managing your child's illness and encourage him or her to do the same. This can allow you to make the best possible choices for his or her health.

- Learn as much as you can about CFS and how it affects your child.

- Talk with your child's healthcare provider about your questions and concerns.

- Speak with school staff, such as teachers, guidance counselors, and school nurses, about concerns you have with your child in school.

- Work closely with teachers, counselors, and other school staff to develop an action plan and find resources to help your child succeed in school.

- Educate others involved in your child's life about CFS, such as school staff, other family members, and your child's peers. When people know more about this illness, they may be better able to help and accommodate your child. This is particularly important at your child's school.

Be Familiar with School Resources

CFS can affect a child or adolescent's experience at school. Fatigue, pain, and concentration or memory problems can make it hard for a child to complete homework assignments. It may also be difficult for them to participate in the classroom or attend school on a regular basis. With some planning, teachers and parents can help a child or adolescent with CFS to have a successful school experience.

Evaluation is an important part of identifying the needs of a student with CFS. It can guide the development of programs to help them succeed in school. It is important to know that:

- Receiving a CFS diagnosis will not immediately qualify a child for services. A child will need to be further evaluated and identified as needing services at school.

- Evaluations will need to be conducted by a team from the school. This team will assess the student through in-class observations, tests, interviews, and conversations with teachers and parents.

- Parents will need to give consent before a student undergoes an evaluation.

Additional services could include an Individualized Education Plan (IEP) or a 504 Plan. A 504 plan lists your child's disability and how the school can help. An IEP is a legal document that tells the school what it must do to help meet your child's needs. These programs are developed with help from administrators, teachers, and parents.

Participate in Family and Social Activities

Having a chance to socialize is just as important for your child as having a chance to succeed in school. With limited social involvement inside and outside of school, students with CFS may feel isolated from their friends and peers. It can be challenging for families to be involved in social events or family activities. However, these activities are essential for the well-being of the child and family. Some families may find it helpful to connect with support groups to talk with other families who have a child with CFS.

Children with CFS may not be able to attend classes on a regular basis or stay for a full school day. Therefore, it is important to talk to your child's school about opportunities for your child to interact with peers. For example, the school could allow your child to participate in after-school activities or attend lunch periods.

Chapter 28

Effects of Domestic Violence on Children

Many children exposed to violence in the home are also victims of physical abuse. Children who witness domestic violence or are victims of abuse themselves are at serious risk for long-term physical and mental-health problems. Children who witness violence between parents may also be at greater risk of being violent in their future relationships. If you are a parent who is experiencing abuse, it can be difficult to know how to protect your child.

What Are the Short-Term Effects of Domestic Violence or Abuse on Children?

Children may feel fearful and anxious in homes where one parent is abused. They may always be on guard, wondering when the next violent event will happen. This can cause them to react in different ways, depending on their age:

- **Children in preschool.** Young children who witness intimate partner violence may start doing things they used to do when they were younger, such as bed-wetting, thumb-sucking, increased crying, and whining. They may also develop difficulty

---

This chapter includes text excerpted from "Effects of Domestic Violence on Children," Office on Women's Health (OWH), U.S. Department of Health and Human Services (HHS), January 30, 2019.

falling or staying asleep; show signs of terror, such as stuttering or hiding; and show signs of severe separation anxiety.

- **School-aged children.** Children in this age range may feel guilty about the abuse, and blame themselves for it. Domestic violence and abuse hurt children's self-esteem. They may not participate in school activities or get good grades, have fewer friends than their peers, and get into trouble more often. They also may have a lot of headaches and stomachaches.

- **Teens.** Teens who witness abuse may act out in negative ways, such as fighting with family members or skipping school. They may also engage in risky behaviors, such as having unprotected sex and using alcohol or drugs. They may have low self-esteem and have trouble making friends. They may start fights or bully others and are more likely to get in trouble with the law. This type of behavior is more common in teen boys who are abused in childhood than in teen girls. Girls are more likely than boys to be withdrawn and to experience depression.

What Are the Long-Term Effects of Domestic Violence or Abuse on Children?

More than 15 million children in the United States live in homes in which domestic violence has happened at least once. These children are at greater risk for repeating the cycle as adults by entering into abusive relationships or becoming abusers themselves. For example, a boy who sees his mother being abused is 10 times more likely to abuse his female partner as an adult. A girl who grows up in a home where her father abuses her mother is more than 6 times as likely to be sexually abused when compared to a girl who grows up in a nonabusive home.

Children who witness or are victims of emotional, physical, or sexual abuse are at higher risk for health problems as adults. These can include mental-health conditions, such as depression and anxiety. They may also include diabetes, obesity, heart disease, poor self-esteem, and other problems.

Can Children Recover from Witnessing or Experiencing Domestic Violence or Abuse?

Each child responds differently to abuse and trauma. Some children are more resilient, and some are more sensitive. How successful a child is at recovering from abuse or trauma depends on several things, including having:

- A good support system or good relationships with trusted adults
- High self-esteem
- Healthy friendships

Although children will probably never forget what they saw or experienced during the abuse, they can learn healthy ways to deal with their emotions and memories as they mature. The sooner a child gets help, the better her or his chances for becoming a mentally and physically healthy adult.

How Can You Help Your Children Recover after Witnessing or Experiencing Domestic Violence?

You can help your children by:

- **Helping them feel safe.** Children who witness or experience domestic violence need to feel safe. Consider whether leaving an abusive relationship might help your child feel safer. Talk to your child about the importance of healthy relationships.

- **Talking to them about their fears.** Let them know that it is not their fault or your fault.

- **Talking to them about healthy relationships.** Help them learn from the abusive experience by talking about what healthy relationships are and are not. This will help them know what is healthy when they start romantic relationships of their own.

- **Talking to them about boundaries.** Let your child know that no one has the right to touch them or make them feel uncomfortable, including family members, teachers, coaches, or other authority figures. Also, explain to your child that she or he does not have the right to touch another person's body, and if someone tells them to stop, they should do so right away.

- **Helping them find a reliable support system.** In addition to a parent, this can be a school counselor, a therapist, or another trusted adult who can provide ongoing support. Know that school counselors are required to report domestic violence or abuse if they suspect it.

- **Getting them professional help.** Cognitive behavioral therapy (CBT) is a type of talk therapy or counseling that may work best for children who have experienced violence or abuse. CBT is especially helpful for children who have anxiety or other mental-health problems as a result of the trauma. During CBT, the therapist will work with your child to turn negative thoughts into more positive ones. The therapist can also help your child learn healthy ways to cope with stress.

Your doctor can recommend a mental-health professional who works with children that have been exposed to violence or abuse. Many shelters and domestic violence organizations also have support groups for kids. These groups can help children by letting them know they are not alone and helping them process their experiences in a nonjudgmental place.

Is It Better to Stay in an Abusive Relationship Rather Than Raise Your Children as a Single Parent?

Children do best in a safe, stable, loving environment, whether that is with one parent or two. You may think that your kids would not be negatively affected by the abuse if they never see it happen. But children can also hear the abuse, such as screaming and the sounds of hitting. They can also sense tension and fear. Even if your kids do not see you being abused, they can be negatively affected by the violence they know is happening.

If you decide to leave an abusive relationship, you may be helping your children feel safer and making them less likely to tolerate abuse as they get older. If you decide not to leave, you can still take steps to protect your children and yourself.

How Can You Make Yourself and Your Children Safe Right Now If You Are Not Ready to Leave an Abuser?

Your safety and the safety of your children are the biggest priorities. If you are not yet ready or willing to leave an abusive relationship, you can take steps to help yourself and your children now, including:

- Making a safety plan for you and your child

- Listening and talking to your child and letting them know that abuse is not okay and is not their fault

- Reaching out to a domestic violence support person who can help you learn your options

If you are thinking about leaving an abusive relationship, you may want to keep quiet about it in front of your children. Young children may not be able to keep a secret from an adult in their life. Children may say something about your plan to leave without realizing it. If it would be unsafe for an abusive partner to know ahead of time you are planning to leave, talk only to trusted adults about your plan. It is better for you and your children to be physically safe, than for your children to know ahead of time that you will be leaving.

Chapter 29

Adult Survivors
of Childhood Sexual Abuse

The great paradox of childhood sexual abuse is that, while it has become more prominent in the public consciousness, it remains shrouded in secrecy. Media coverage of high-profile disclosures and investigations provide evidence that childhood sexual abuse does exist in "good" families and "trusted" institutions, at all socioeconomic levels, and among all racial and ethnic groups. Frequently, we hear and read stories about survivors who are men and women from all walks of life—students, sports figures, clergy, entertainers, educators, police officers, judges, politicians, and healthcare practitioners. They are our friends and neighbors, our colleagues, and sometimes even ourselves or members of our own families. Despite this prevalence, most childhood sexual abuse survivors are invisible to us, particularly given that it is estimated that fewer than half disclose their abuse to anyone. Some are silent because they fear reprisal from their abusers; others worry they will not be believed or that they will be blamed or even punished. Still, others say nothing because they harbor the erroneous belief that they are responsible for their abuse.

This chapter includes text excerpted from "Sensitive Practice for Health Care Practitioners: Lessons from Adult Survivors of Childhood Sexual Abuse," Substance Abuse and Mental Health Administration (SAMHSA), 2009. Reviewed March 2019.

191

Female Survivors of Childhood Sex Abuse

Gender socialization affects both children's responses to sexual abuse and how the experience affects them in adulthood. Throughout the research for this chapter, survivor participants described ways in which gender socialization shaped their interactions with healthcare practitioners.

Although many would argue that gender socialization has changed considerably in the past century, many female children continue to be encouraged to be nonaggressive, submissive, and "nice." They receive multiple messages that to be female is to be less valued and less powerful than males, and that the appropriate role for females is to please others, especially males.

These aspects of normative female socialization may exacerbate girls' tendency to be submissive and to blame themselves for negative experiences involving adults, which can leave many female survivors believing that they are bad people who are responsible for the abuse and that their bodies, which they have come to hate, somehow caused the abuse.

A female abuse survivor may also be mistrustful of authority figures, which stems from having been betrayed by the trusted adult who abused her. This helps to explain the difficulty that some survivors have trusting healthcare practitioners and why they experience healthcare encounters as distressing. It also helps explain why so many female survivors report symptoms of depression and anxiety. Girls learn that it is important for females to be objects of male sexual desire and that appearing young and innocent is sexually appealing. "We dress fashion models up to look child-like and sexually provocative and set this standard for all women," writes Calgary social worker Lois Sapsford. Girls may also learn that to be valued, they must be sexually "pure;" at the same time, they receive the contradictory message that they should be not only beautiful but also "sexy." Sexual abuse objectifies a girl's body to serve the needs of her abuser and may leave her believing that her sole value is as a sexual object. The message that females should be sexually "pure" along with the stigma attached to sexual abuse contributes to some female survivors' perceptions of themselves as "damaged goods" and to the shame and guilt that many describe. This may be manifested in a survivor's ambivalence about her body and reticence to seek care for health problems.

The historical and current societal factors that encourage people in our society to deny or minimize the significance of child sexual abuse also affect female survivors' perceptions about the wisdom of disclosing their experience. Many women participants talked about their fear of not being believed; some gave examples of being told directly that they must be lying or imagining things.

Another aspect of female gender socialization is the message that it is the female who is responsible for setting limits on sexual behavior, which contributes to women survivors fearing that they will be blamed for what happened, even though the sexual behavior occurred when they were children and the perpetrator was older and more powerful. One healthcare practitioner responded to a woman's disclosure of past abuse by asking, "How did you let it happen?"

These societal messages strongly discourage women survivors from sharing their experience with healthcare practitioners, which in turn impedes the clinician's ability to assess all factors that may contribute to health problems.

Male Survivors of Childhood Sex Abuse

The men in the studies repeatedly reported feeling invisible as survivors of childhood sexual abuse. Among the major factors contributing to the invisibility of male childhood sexual abuse, survivors are: (a) the widespread lack of knowledge about the prevalence of childhood sexual abuse of boys; (b) incongruence between society's notions of masculinity and victimhood; and (c) the fact that services for childhood sexual abuse survivors, which grew out of the second wave of feminism, were historically designed for women and not for men.

For a man to acknowledge that he has been sexually abused is an admission of vulnerability in a society that has few models for the expression of masculine vulnerability. Indeed, applying the label victim of sexual abuse to a man juxtaposes vulnerability with masculinity, an uneasy pairing that further contributes to the underrecognition and underreporting of childhood sexual abuse among boys and men.

The socialization of men to be strong and independent complicates the situation for male survivors who consider sharing their history of abuse with a healthcare practitioner. As Michel Dorais puts it in his book *Don't Tell: The Sexual Abuse of Boys*, the "masculine conception of virility is incompatible with the factual experience of having been a victim of sexual abuse, or needing help following such a trauma." Men in our study spoke about their need to appear "tough" and "in control," despite feeling anxious and fearful during encounters with healthcare practitioners.

Some participants also spoke about their difficulty in identifying and expressing their feelings. Women appear to be more aware of the names of things, such as, "I am feeling depressed" or "I have been having a real struggle for the past couple of weeks, and these are the circumstances."

There is a pervasive belief that boys and men are rarely victimized and that a central feature of masculinity is the ability to protect oneself; failure to do so is seen as evidence of weakness and can be a source of great male shame. Thus, the "dissonance between the male role expectation and the experience of victimization" may seriously compromise the healthcare of male survivors, often because their feelings of shame and unworthiness affect their ability to seek care.

Most of the men in the studies expressed the belief that different reactions to male and female childhood sexual abuse survivors shape their help-seeking behaviors and, in turn, influence how healthcare practitioners treat them. In general, the participants suggested that healthcare providers are skeptical about men who disclose sexual abuse and tend to take their experiences less seriously than those of their female counterparts. In addition, some regard sexual abuse by a woman as something that the "fortunate" male survivor should have enjoyed. Ramona Alaggia and Guy Holmes and colleagues of the University of Toronto reiterate that such perceptions are common. The media also contribute to these views by framing the sexual abuse of boys by adult women as a "sexual relationship." The fact that boys are more often sexually abused by a female than girls may fuel the myth that sex between boys and women is normative rather than abusive and perpetuates the "male gender role of seeking early sexual experiences with women." Notwithstanding the general progress made in addressing homophobia in our society, some of the men in the study talked about their fear that healthcare practitioners would think they were homosexual if they revealed their history of childhood sexual abuse. Others talked about how their abuse experiences had led them to develop strong negative feelings about individuals (including healthcare practitioners) whom they perceived to be homosexual.

Such reactions can be seen as internalized homophobia. These fears may also reflect the pervasiveness of the myth in our society that childhood sexual abuse causes boys and girls to become gay or lesbian.

Specific Behaviors and Feelings Arising during Healthcare Encounters

Distrust of authority figures. Throughout this project, survivors told how, as children, they experienced violation at the hands of an authority figure and how the distrust from these past experiences affects their interactions with healthcare practitioners. Although this distrust originates in the past and should not be taken as a personal affront, survivors constantly scrutinize healthcare providers for evidence that they are taking active and ongoing steps to demonstrate their trustworthiness. It is crucial to recognize that some survivors may associate a healthcare practitioner's attempts to verbally assure them that they are safe with the perpetrator's empty assurance of safety during their abuse.

Fear and anxiety. Many survivors spoke at length about their tremendous fear and anxiety during healthcare encounters. The experiences of waiting, being in close contact with authority figures, and not knowing what is to come all resonated with past abuse. Some survivor participants said that they were even afraid of being abused by the healthcare practitioner.

Discomfort with persons who are the same gender as their abuser(s). For some survivors, the gender of a person in a position of authority is a powerful "trigger" that can leave them feeling vulnerable and unsafe. This strong reaction prevents some survivors from seeking care from practitioners who are the same gender as their abuser.

Triggers. Examinations or treatments may "trigger" or precipitate flashbacks; a specific memory; or overwhelming emotions, such as fear, anxiety, terror, grief, or anger. A flashback is an experience of reliving something that happened in the past and usually involves intense emotion. Some survivors are particularly susceptible to flashbacks and some are overwhelmed by them.

Dissociation. Survivor participants also spoke about dissociating during interactions with healthcare providers. The *Diagnostic and Statistical Manual of Mental Disorders, Fourth Edition* (Text Revised) (*DSM-IV-TR*) explains dissociation as "a disruption in the usually integrated functions of consciousness, memory, identity, or perception of the environment" that may be sudden or gradual, transient or chronic. Some authors liken it to a state of divided consciousness in which aspects of the self that are normally integrated become fragmented. Dissociation is also understood to be a process that exists on a continuum, with one end being "common experiences, such as daydreaming and lapses in attention; through déjà vu phenomena; to a pathological failure to integrate thoughts, feelings, and actions." *DSM-IV-TR* states that "dissociative states are a common and accepted expression of cultural activities or religious experience in many societies," and in these cases, they do not usually lead to the "significant distress, impairment, or help-seeking behavior" that is required for them to be diagnosed as a disorder. A common experience of dissociation that most of us can relate to is highway hypnosis, in which an individual driving a car suddenly realizes that he or she cannot remember all or part of the trip. The International Society for the Study of Trauma and Dissociation takes the position that traumatic experiences play an important role in the development of various pathological dissociative disorders. Many believe that dissociation is an effective strategy for coping (in the immediate situation) with extreme stress, such as childhood sexual abuse. However, if it becomes a long-term coping mechanism, it may contribute to a variety of mental-health problems and interfere with relationships, self-concept, identity development, and adaptive functioning.

A number of the survivor participants told that they do not have consistent control over this mechanism through which they "escape" from a current (usually stressful) situation; some even report that for many years they were unaware of their tendency to dissociate. When they are in a dissociative state, some individuals experience themselves as being outside their bodies, watching the present situation from a distance. Others simply go silent, stare blankly into the distance, or seem unaware of their surroundings. When the dissociative episode is over, individuals may have no memory of what occurred and may have difficulty orienting themselves back to the present.

Physical pain. For some survivors, the experience of acute and/or chronic physical pain may be associated with past abuse. This association can manifest itself in various ways (e.g., some individual have learned to ignore or dissociate from pain, while others are hypersensitive to it).

Ambivalence about the body. Many survivors feel hate, shame, and guilt about their bodies. As children, many believed that something about them or their bodies invited or caused the abuse. This belief is reinforced if the survivor enjoyed some aspects of the abuse (e.g., special attention, physiological arousal). This shame and guilt may lead some survivors to feel ambivalent about and disconnected from their bodies.

The conflict between the need to seek healthcare for a physical problem and the ambivalence or dislike of one's body can affect treatment. For example, an individual may ignore symptoms that might contribute to an accurate diagnosis, explain an individual's response to treatment, or interfere with the ability to self-monitor the effects of an intervention or medication.

Conditioning to be passive. Abuse can teach children to avoid speaking up or questioning authority figures. In adulthood, survivors may then have difficulty expressing their needs to a healthcare practitioner who is perceived as an authority figure.

Self-harm. Self-harm (e.g., scratching, cutting, or burning the skin) is a way that some survivors attempt to cope with long-term feelings of distress. Healthcare practitioners may see evidence of self-harm in the form of injuries or scars on the arms, legs, or abdomen. Self-harm may take more subtle forms as well, such as ignoring health teachings or recommendations for treatment or symptom management (e.g., refusing to pace one's activity in response to pain or fatigue, or failing to adhere to a diabetic treatment regime).

There are many reasons why survivors harm themselves. It may serve to distract them from emotional pain, focus the pain to one area of the body, or interrupt an episode of dissociation or numbness. Some survivors may harm themselves to regain a sense of control or ownership of their bodies. For others, it may be a punishment or an effort to atone for wrongs they believe they have committed. Dusty Miller, a psychotherapist, argues that self-harm is one example of a range of self-destructive behaviors that can be thought of as an unconscious effort to reenact past trauma.

Chapter 30

Posttraumatic Stress Disorder in Adult Survivors

Chapter Contents

Section 30.1

Posttraumatic Stress Disorder

This section contains text excerpted from the following sources:
Text in this section begins with excerpts from "Post-Traumatic
Stress Disorder," Office on Women's Health (OWH), U.S.
Department of Health and Human Services (HHS), August 28, 2018;
Text beginning with the heading "Signs and Symptoms" is excerpted
from "Post-Traumatic Stress Disorder," National Institute
of Mental Health (NIMH), February 2016.

Posttraumatic stress disorder (PTSD) happens when people who
have experienced or witnessed a traumatic event continue to experience symptoms for more than a month that make it difficult to live
their lives normally. Traumatic events can include physical or sexual
assault, war, natural disasters, car accidents, or any event experienced
as deeply scary and upsetting. Although PTSD is often associated
with military service members, PTSD may develop after any type of
traumatic event.

People with PTSD may continue to experience the traumatic event
through flashbacks, nightmares, or memories they cannot control.
These thoughts can create serious emotional pain for the person and
can cause problems at home, work, school, or relationships. Most often,
the traumatic event happened to the person with PTSD, but sometimes
PTSD can happen to a person who witnesses someone else experiencing
a trauma. People who develop PTSD usually experience symptoms
soon after the traumatic event, but sometimes symptoms do not appear
for months or years afterward.

Signs and Symptoms

Not every traumatized person develops ongoing (chronic) or even
short-term (acute) PTSD. Not everyone with PTSD has been through
a dangerous event. Some experiences, such as the sudden, unexpected
death of a loved one, can also cause PTSD. Symptoms usually begin
early, within three months of the traumatic incident, but sometimes
they begin years afterward. Symptoms must last more than a month
and be severe enough to interfere with relationships or work to be
considered PTSD. The course of the illness varies. Some people recover
within six months, while others have symptoms that last much longer.
In some people, the condition becomes chronic.

A doctor who has experience helping people with mental illnesses, such as a psychiatrist or psychologist, can diagnose PTSD.

To be diagnosed with PTSD, an adult must have all of the following for at least one month:

- At least one re-experiencing symptom
- At least one avoidance symptom
- At least two arousal and reactivity symptoms
- At least two cognition and mood symptoms

Re-experiencing symptoms include:

- Flashbacks—reliving the trauma over and over, including physical symptoms, such as a racing heart or sweating
- Bad dreams
- Frightening thoughts

Re-experiencing symptoms may cause problems in a person's everyday routine. The symptoms can start from the person's own thoughts and feelings. Words, objects, or situations that are reminders of the event can also trigger re-experiencing symptoms.

Avoidance symptoms include:

- Staying away from places, events, or objects that are reminders of the traumatic experience
- Avoiding thoughts or feelings related to the traumatic event
- Things that remind a person of the traumatic event can trigger avoidance symptoms. These symptoms may cause a person to change his or her personal routine. For example, after a bad car accident, a person who usually drives may avoid driving or riding in a car.

Arousal and reactivity symptoms include:

- Being easily startled
- Feeling tense or "on edge"
- Having difficulty sleeping
- Having angry outbursts

Arousal symptoms are usually constant, instead of being triggered by things that remind one of the traumatic events. These symptoms can make the person feel stressed and angry. They may make it hard to do daily tasks, such as sleeping, eating, or concentrating.

Cognition and mood symptoms include:

- Trouble remembering key features of the traumatic event
- Negative thoughts about oneself or the world
- Distorted feelings, such as guilt or blame
- Loss of interest in enjoyable activities

Cognition and mood symptoms can begin or worsen after the traumatic event, but are not due to injury or substance use. These symptoms can make the person feel alienated or detached from friends or family members.

It is natural to have some of these symptoms after a traumatic event. Sometimes people have very serious symptoms that go away after a few weeks. This is called "acute stress disorder," or ASD. When the symptoms last more than a month; seriously affect one's ability to function; and are not due to substance use, medical illness, or anything except the event itself, they might be PTSD. Some people with PTSD do not show any symptoms for weeks or months. PTSD is often accompanied by depression, substance abuse, or one or more of the other anxiety disorders.

Risk Factors

Anyone can develop PTSD at any age. This includes war veterans; children; and people who have been through a physical or sexual assault, abuse, accident, disaster, or other serious events. According to the National Center for PTSD, about 7 or 8 out of every 100 people will experience PTSD at some point in their lives. Women are more likely to develop PTSD than men, and genes may make some people more likely to develop PTSD than others.

Not everyone with PTSD has been through a traumatic event. Some people develop PTSD after a friend or family member experiences danger or harm. The sudden, unexpected death of a loved one can also lead to PTSD.

It is important to remember that not everyone who lives through a traumatic event develops PTSD. In fact, most people will not develop the disorder.

Many factors play a part in whether a person will develop PTSD. Some examples are listed below. Risk factors make a person more likely to develop PTSD. Other factors, called "resilience factors," can help reduce the risk of the disorder.

Risk Factors and Resilience Factors for PTSD

Some factors that increase the risk for PTSD include:

• Living through dangerous events and traumas

• Getting hurt

• Seeing another person hurt, or seeing a dead body

• Childhood trauma

• Feeling horror, helplessness, or extreme fear

• Having little or no social support after the event

• Dealing with extra stress after the event, such as loss of a loved one, pain and injury, or loss of a job or home

• Having a history of mental illness or substance abuse

Some resilience factors that may reduce the risk of PTSD include:

• Seeking out support from other people, such as friends and family

• Finding a support group after a traumatic event

• Learning to feel good about one's own actions in the face of danger

• Having a positive coping strategy, or a way of getting through the bad event and learning from it

• Being able to act and respond effectively despite feeling fear

Researchers are studying the importance of these and other risk and resilience factors, including genetics and neurobiology. With more research, someday it may be possible to predict who is likely to develop PTSD and to prevent it.

Section 30.2

FAQs about PTSD Assessment

This section includes text excerpted from "FAQs about PTSD Assessment," U.S. Department of Veterans Affairs (VA), August 13, 2015. Reviewed March 2019.

How Can You Tell If You Have PTSD?

Many people want to know how they can decide for themselves whether they have PTSD. It is natural to want to know why you are feeling or acting a certain way. However, trying to figure out on your own whether or not you have PTSD is difficult. Since many common reactions after trauma look like the symptoms of PTSD, a mental-health provider must decide if you have PTSD.

Providers who have been trained to understand the thoughts and behaviors that go along with PTSD are best able to make that decision. A provider must use her or his training and judgment to select the best test or set of questions to use. Then she or he must interpret the results of the test.

The American Psychological Association (APA) suggests that only trained professionals give tests to assess for PTSD. If you think you may have PTSD, talk to your doctor or a mental-health provider.

How Can You Find out If a Mental-Health Provider Is Able to Evaluate You for PTSD?

You can ask questions about the provider's training and experience. Here are some questions you might ask:

Mental-Healthcare Experts and Their Area of Expertise

Many providers specialize in assessing and treating people who have experienced trauma. Providers who specialize in trauma will likely have expertise in evaluating PTSD. Some providers may specialize in working with certain kinds of trauma survivors. For example, a provider may work with adult survivors of childhood traumas. You may find a provider who specializes in a different trauma area than what you need, or who does not specialize at all. A provider who has experience assessing trauma survivors is most likely to have the expertise to do a good job on your assessment.

What Formal Training Your Mental-Healthcare Provider Should Have Had That Will Allow Him to Evaluate You for PTSD?

If possible, find a professional who has completed training focused on PTSD assessment. Such providers are preferred over those trained only in general assessment.

How Is PTSD Assessed?

You should feel comfortable with the assessment methods that a provider will use. A good assessment of PTSD can be done without the use of any special equipment. Most often, providers will have you fill out surveys or they will use a standard interview in which the provider will read a series of questions from a printed document.

Who Can Request a PTSD or Trauma Measure from the National Center for PTSD?

The APA requires that anyone who gives and interprets psychological tests must have advanced training.

What Is the Difference between an Evaluation That Measures Trauma Exposure and an Evaluation That Measures PTSD?

An evaluation that measures trauma exposure looks at whether you have gone through a traumatic event. Examples of traumatic events include combat, a car accident, or child sexual abuse. Sometimes, the evaluation asks when the event happened. For example, you might be asked your age at the time of the experience. A measure of trauma exposure may also assess how you felt at the time of the event. You might be asked if you felt your life or the life of someone else was in danger.

By contrast, an evaluation that measures PTSD looks at how you felt or acted after you went through the traumatic event. You might be asked about the effect the trauma has had on your life or any symptoms you may have had since the trauma. Some PTSD evaluations also ask about other problems, such as depression or relationship problems. These other problems do not lead to a PTSD diagnosis, however.

If an Organization Is Asking for Proof of a PTSD Diagnosis, What Should You Provide?

Only the results of a complete evaluation given by a professional can determine whether you have PTSD. Any organization with which you might be dealing will likely need the results of your evaluation. Therefore, you should see a healthcare provider who has experience in this area. As a patient, you can typically request a copy of your evaluation results from the professional who completes your assessment.

If you are a veteran, the Veterans Benefits Administration has section on how to submit a compensation claim for PTSD. You can also call your local U.S. Department of Veterans Affairs (VA) Medical Center to ask about benefits. Veterans Service Organizations (VSOs) also offer free guidance on completing claims.

Chapter 31

Abuse, Trauma, and Mental Health

How Are Abuse and Trauma Related to Mental Health?

Trauma can happen after you experience an event(s) that hurt you physically or emotionally. Trauma can have lasting effects on your mental, physical, and emotional health. Experiencing abuse or other trauma puts people at risk of developing mental-health conditions, such as:

- Anxiety disorders

- Depression

- Posttraumatic stress disorder (PTSD)

- Substance-use disorders (SUDs)

- Borderline personality disorder (BPD)

Abuse may have happened during childhood or as an adult. It can be emotional, verbal, physical, or sexual. Trauma can include dangerous, frightening, or extremely stressful situations or events, such as sexual

This chapter includes text excerpted from "Abuse, Trauma, and Mental Health," Office on Women's Health (OWH), U.S. Department of Health and Human Services (HHS), August 28, 2018.

assault, war, an accident or a natural disaster, the sudden or violent death of a loved one, or a serious physical health problem.

The long-term effects of abuse or trauma can include:

- Severe anxiety, stress, or fear
- Abuse of alcohol or drugs
- Depression
- Eating disorders
- Self-injury
- Suicide

How Do You Know If Your Mental Health Is Affected by Past Abuse or Trauma?

It can be difficult to tell whether, or how much, your mental health is affected by past abuse or trauma. Sometimes, the symptoms of trauma or abuse do not start to affect your life for many months or years after the event took place. If you have any of the following symptoms, talk to your doctor or nurse or reach out for help:

- Anxiety
- Trouble sleeping
- Anger
- Depression
- Changes in mood or appetite
- Abusing drugs or alcohol

What Should You Do If You Have Been Abused or Traumatized?

The sooner you can get professional help for abuse or trauma, the sooner you can begin to get better. If you have been physically hurt, visit a hospital or doctor right away. You may also need to call the police. The doctor and the police can help document what has happened to you. This documentation may be important later if you decide to press charges against someone who attacked you.

If you are experiencing changes in how you think and feel, or are experiencing behaviors that are interfering with your ability to work or live your life normally, reach out to a mental-health professional. Find a mental-health professional near you. A mental-health professional can help make sense of any symptoms you may be having that are related to your abuse or trauma. The professional can help you find the best kinds of treatment to help manage symptoms of the abuse or trauma.

If you are in immediate danger, call 911.

You can also call helplines to talk about what happened to you or get guidance about what to do:

- **National Domestic Violence Hotline**

  Phone number: 800-799-7233

- **National Sexual Assault Hotline**

  Phone number: 800-656-4673

- **Safe Helpline** (for members of the military)

  Phone number: 877-995-5247

Abuse or trauma you have suffered is not your fault. You can get better with treatment.

How Are Abuse and Trauma Treated?

Symptoms caused by abuse or trauma can usually be treated with different types of talk therapy, medicine, or both. Therapy with a professional counselor can help you work through your feelings and learn healthy ways to cope. Medicines might include antidepressants or antianxiety medicine.

Nowadays, complementary mind and body therapies, such as mindfulness and yoga*, may be offered along with traditional treatments, such as medicines and therapy.

A mind and body practice with origins in ancient Indian philosophy. The various styles of yoga typically combine physical postures, breathing techniques, and meditation or relaxation.

Chapter 32

Intergenerational Patterns of Child Maltreatment: What the Evidence Shows

The majority of children who experience maltreatment do not become adults that abuse or neglect their own children. The review of nearly three decades of research on the topic reveals that intergenerational patterns of child abuse and neglect are far more complex and nuanced than originally understood. Although this research is limited, it is important for practitioners, administrators, and others who work with children, youth, and families to have an accurate understanding of the issue. Incorrect conclusions about the existence, extent, and causes of intergenerational maltreatment (IGM) could lead to ineffective screening tools, harmful social policies, worker bias, and poor outcomes for children and families.

Over time, a stronger research base will continue to increase the understanding of the factors that contribute to patterns of maltreatment within families. This will enable child welfare, family support, and other organizations to more effectively promote protective factors and address risk factors in ways that can benefit all families.

This chapter includes text excerpted from "Intergenerational Patterns of Child Maltreatment: What the Evidence Shows," Child Welfare Information Gateway, U.S. Department of Health and Human Services (HHS), August 2016.

This chapter briefly explores what is currently known about intergenerational patterns of maltreatment, the limits of current knowledge, implications of what is known and what remains still unknown (including promising prevention strategies), and areas for further research.

Theories to Explain Intergenerational Maltreatment

Several theories have been cited to improve understanding of intergenerational patterns of maltreatment. The most prevalent include the following:

- **Social learning theory** proposes that individuals' behavior is shaped through observation and imitation. Therefore, this theory suggests that adults' parenting will be influenced by childhood experiences of their own parents' behaviors. If individuals experience abusive or neglectful parenting, then they may develop beliefs that these behaviors are acceptable and/or effective and replicate them with their own children.

- **Attachment theory** emphasizes the importance of a quality, early attachment with a caregiver. If a caregiver is not caring and sensitive to an infant's needs (as is the case when early maltreatment occurs), the affected individual struggles to form healthy attachments into adulthood. This is theorized to increase the likelihood of abusive behavior as an adult.

- **Trauma-based models** suggest that maltreatment, like other forms of violence, produces trauma symptoms. If untreated and unresolved, these symptoms may increase the likelihood that the individual will engage in violent behavior, including child maltreatment, as an adult.

- **Ecological or transactional theories** view child maltreatment as the result of multiple influences and systems, including family, community, and societal factors.

What the Research Shows

Although many researchers have attempted to quantify and explain the persistence of child abuse and neglect across generations, many in the field agree that the current evidence base is still woefully inadequate. This is due, in part, to the fact that sample sizes, measurement tools, and the ways that key terms are defined vary greatly from study to study. Some studies base their findings on either risk or potential for abuse, via the Child Abuse Potential Inventory (CAPI), rather than actual maltreatment.

Little agreement exists about how "child maltreatment" is defined across studies. Some studies rely on participants' own perceptions of childhood experiences as abusive or neglectful, while others establish specific parameters about maltreatment type, perpetrator, and severity. Some studies assess maltreatment of the child for as short a period as the first year of life, while other, longitudinal studies include incidents of maltreatment occurring at any time before the child is 18 years of age. Finally, studies differ in how rigorously they control other factors that may impact the incidence of IGM (e.g., parental age, race, marital status, gender, socioeconomic status, community factors).

Given this diversity in approaches, it is not surprising that some studies find associations between parents' and children's experiences of maltreatment, while others do not. In the majority of studies that find evidence of IGM, estimated rates of maltreatment vary widely and range between 7 and 70 percent.

Understanding Why: Findings about Pathways

Some research looks specifically for factors that explain or account for the apparent association between a parent's experience of childhood maltreatment and the maltreatment experienced by her or his own children. These factors (referred to as "mediators" in the research) can be thought of as pathways for IGM. Identifying these pathways can help practitioners develop and select the most effective prevention strategies.

Further research is needed in this area, but some of the stronger studies identified that the following factors may partially account for intergenerational patterns:

- Mothers' social isolation and tendency to respond to minor provocations with verbal or physical aggression

- Maternal substance use

- Young parental age, parents' history of mental illness or depression, and parents living with another violent adult

- Parental age, educational achievement, psychiatric history, and poverty

- Mothers' marital status, depressive symptoms, and adult experiences of victimization

- Mothers' life stress, anxiety, and depression

- Parents' experience of intimate partner violence (IPV)

It should be noted that many of these risk factors are found in a wide variety of families, not just those in which parents experienced childhood maltreatment. Future research may reveal that these factors play a far more significant role in a child's overall risk for maltreatment than parental history.

Intervening Effectively: Findings on Protective Factors

Identifying protective factors is integral to prevention efforts. This requires studies that look closely at the high percentage of families in which there is intergenerational resilience (i.e., cases in which adults who experienced childhood maltreatment do not abuse or neglect their own children) to understand what factors help promote healthier interactions within families.

Caring and supportive relationships, in various forms, have emerged in the literature as a potential protective factor:

- Several studies published in a special issue of the *Journal of Adolescent Health* (JAH) examined the role of safe, stable, and nurturing relationships (SSNRs) in interrupting the intergenerational transmission of parenting practices, including child maltreatment. All but one of the studies found positive effects of SSNRs, including caregivers' nurturing relationships and caring parent-child attachments in both generations.

- A study found that mothers who broke the cycle of severe physical abuse were more likely to receive emotional support from a non-abusive adult during childhood, participate in therapy at some point in their lives, and have a stable and non-abusive relationship with a mate than mothers who were unable to break the cycle of abuse.

- One small study suggests that receiving nurturing during childhood, even from an abusive parent, can mitigate the effects of severe physical abuse on the likelihood of child neglect in the next generation.

Findings from a large study of 4,351 families identified other potential protective factors by distinguishing between families who maintained and those who broke the intergenerational cycle of maltreatment during an infant's first year of life. "Cycle breakers" were found to have fewer serious financial difficulties and higher levels of perceived social support compared to "maintainers," suggesting that these factors may help interrupt the cycle for parents who experienced childhood physical or sexual abuse.

Parenting practices also may play a role. One study found that parents who experienced high levels of abusive acts and injuries, but who were consistent in their discipline, were less abusive than abused parents who were inconsistent disciplinarians. Teaching parents' skills to increase their effectiveness and consistency may be a prevention pathway worth exploring.

Practical Implications

Although the current body of research provides some evidence to support an association between parents' childhood experiences of maltreatment and the likelihood that their children also will experience abuse or neglect, much more research is needed. Again, one of the most well-supported findings is that most parents who were maltreated will not abuse or neglect their own children. This fact should be reflected in agency policy governing screening and family casework practices.

Screening Considerations

In a worst-case scenario, giving theories of IGM too much weight in a screening process could create a surveillance bias (i.e., when one population is followed more closely than another and, therefore, appears to have higher rates of incidence) that submits already-traumatized parents and their children to unwarranted scrutiny and intervention. The same bias could cause workers to overlook other families in which a history of abuse is absent, but where real and present danger exists.

At least one study has uncovered evidence of such a bias. Among children who self-reported being abused or neglected, those whose parents had documented histories of childhood maltreatment were twice as likely to have been the subject of a child protective services (CPS) report as compared to children whose parents had no such history (29% to 15%).

Another study found that child maltreatment "initiators" (i.e., parents who had not themselves experienced maltreatment but who did abuse or neglect their own children) had similar risk profiles to maltreated parents who both perpetuated and broke the intergenerational cycle of maltreatment. Therefore, caseworkers should not use a general checklist of risk factors to distinguish between parents who will and who will not maltreat their children.

Already, the identification of a number of specific factors that play a role in IGM indicates that, although it may make sense to include a history of childhood abuse in screening for risk factors (and even, potentially, prioritize parents with such a history for some prevention services), this approach must be accompanied by screening for a number of other risk and protective factors that, taken together, provide a richer and more complex view of family functioning, potential for harm, and sources of resilience.

According to the current body of research, some significant factors might include the quality of parenting and attachment, substance use, IPV, trauma symptoms, financial and other life stressors, and the presence of nurturing adult relationships and social support. However, more research is needed to confirm these factors and identify others.

If there is one thing the present body of research shows, it is that this issue is complicated and that context is important, as illustrated by the following:

- Several studies have shown depression and trauma symptoms to be potential pathways for intergenerational maltreatment. However, at least one study found that, in the case of child physical abuse, depression and posttraumatic stress disorder (PTSD) reduced the likelihood of intergenerational abuse. This shows that more type-specific research is needed to deepen the understanding of the complex interactions between risk and protective factors.

- Similarly, another study found that parents with histories of neglect were at an increased risk for IGM, but parents with histories of physical abuse were not.

- In one small study, researchers found that authoritarian parenting attitudes, which have been linked to poor child outcomes in Caucasian American families, were found to protect against intergenerational patterns of abuse by African American mothers.

These are just a few examples of how studies have begun the important work of refining the field's understanding of intergenerational patterns of maltreatment in ways that may eventually lead to screening tools that are more sensitive to the nuances and context of each family's situation than what currently exists.

Preventing Intergenerational Maltreatment

To date, very little research has been conducted specifically to evaluate strategies that may prevent IGM. Prevention may, therefore, be best accomplished by continuing to invest in programs and practices that have proven effective in reducing child maltreatment in the general population, such as the following:

- **Home-visiting programs**, such as Nurse-Family Partnership (NFP), can enhance nurturing and supportive family relationships, social support, and parenting knowledge and skills.

- **Parent education programs**, such as the Triple-P–Positive Parenting Program and parent–child interaction therapy (PCIT), can give parents practical tools for more consistent and effective parenting.

Building Protective Factors

Focusing on building protective factors may reduce child abuse and neglect in all families, including those with a parent who has a history of childhood maltreatment.

Conclusion

Child maltreatment is a serious social issue with lasting consequences for children, youth, families, and communities. A thorough understanding of how and why maltreatment occurs is critical to inform prevention efforts. Research shows promise in helping the child welfare field to better understand the degree to which maltreatment is perpetuated by multiple generations within families, circumstances that contribute to these intergenerational patterns of maltreatment, and protective factors that may prevent such a cycle from continuing.

Part Five

Child Abuse Preventions, Interventions, and Treatments

Chapter 33

Preventing Child Abuse and Neglect Is a Priority

Children and families thrive when they have access to safe, stable, nurturing relationships and environments. Policies and programs that are supportive of children and families can prevent child abuse and neglect and other early adversity.

Facts about Child Abuse and Neglect

Child abuse and neglect are significant public-health problems in the United States.

- In 2016, more than 1,750 children died in the United States from abuse and neglect.

- According to child protective service (CPS) agencies, about 676,000 children were victims of child abuse or neglect in 2016, although this number likely underestimates the true occurrence.

This chapter contains text excerpted from the following sources: Text in this chapter begins with excerpts from "Child Abuse Prevention," Centers for Disease Control and Prevention (CDC), April 5, 2018; Text under the heading "Preventing Child Abuse and Neglect Is a Priority" is excerpted from "Preventing Child Abuse and Neglect: A Technical Package for Policy, Norm, and Programmatic Activities," Centers for Disease Control and Prevention (CDC), 2016.

- 1 in 4 children has experienced abuse or neglect at some point in their lives, and 1 in 7 experienced abuse or neglect in the past year.

- The total lifetime cost associated with just 1 year of confirmed cases of child abuse or neglect is $124 billion.

Exposure to child abuse and neglect and other adverse childhood experiences (ACEs) cause toxic stress that can disrupt early brain development and harm the nervous and immune systems. Exposure to childhood adversity can increase a person's risk for future violence, unhealthy behaviors, poor health, and wellness, and it can limit life opportunities. This impact can be long-lasting and may continue across future generations.

Child Abuse and Neglect Are Preventable

Children's lives are shaped by their experiences, including what happens in their environment (such as homes, schools, and neighborhoods) and the types of relationships they have with parents, teachers, and other caregivers. Healthy relationships and environments act as a buffer against adverse experiences and are necessary to ensure the long-term physical and emotional well-being of children.

Preventing Child Abuse and Neglect Is a Priority

Child maltreatment includes all types of abuse and neglect of a child under the age of 18 by a parent, caregiver, or another person in a custodial role (e.g., clergy, coach, teacher) that results in harm, potential for harm, or threat of harm to a child. There are 4 common types of child maltreatment:

- **Physical abuse** is the use of physical force, such as hitting, kicking, shaking, burning, or other shows of force, against a child.

- **Sexual abuse** involves inducing or coercing a child to engage in sexual acts. It includes behaviors, such as fondling, penetration, and exposing a child to other sexual activities.

- **Emotional abuse** refers to behaviors that harm a child's self-worth or emotional well-being. Examples include name calling, shaming, rejection, withholding love, and threatening.

- **Neglect** is the failure to meet a child's basic physical and emotional needs. These needs include housing, food, clothing, education, and access to medical care.

Child abuse and neglect are highly prevalent. Self-report data suggest that at least 1 in 7 children has experienced child abuse and/or neglect in the last year. Not all children, however, experience abuse and neglect at the same rates. Younger children are more likely to experience fatal abuse and neglect, while 14- to 17-years-old are more likely to experience nonfatal abuse and neglect. Race, ethnicity, and family income are other factors that may affect a child's exposure. Child protective services (CPS) data show high rates of victimization among African American children. African American children experience abuse and neglect at rates that are nearly double those for White children. These differences are generally attributed to various community and societal factors, including poverty, as well as differences in reporting and investigation. Children living in families with a low socioeconomic status (SES) have rates of child abuse and neglect that are 5 times higher than those of children living in families with a higher SES. Irrespective of data source, definitions, and measures, the true magnitude of child abuse and neglect is likely underestimated, and children of all ages, races, and ethnicities deserve safe, stable, nurturing relationships and environments to achieve maximal health and life potential.

Child abuse and neglect are associated with several risk factors. The risk for child abuse and neglect perpetration and victimization is influenced by a number of individual, family, and environmental factors, all of which interact to increase or decrease risk over time and within specific contexts. Risk factors for victimization include child age and special needs that may increase caregiver burden (e.g., developmental and intellectual disabilities, mental-health issues, and chronic physical illnesses). Risk factors for perpetration include young parental age, single parenthood, large number of dependent children, low parental income, parental substance abuse, parental mental-health issues, parental history of abuse or neglect, social isolation, family disorganization, parenting stress, intimate partner violence (IPV), poor parent-child relationships, community violence, and concentrated neighborhood disadvantage (e.g., high poverty and residential instability, high unemployment rates). Although risk factors provide information about who is most at risk for being a victim or a perpetrator of child abuse and neglect, they are not direct causes and cannot predict who will be a victim or a perpetrator.

Factors that protect or buffer children from being abused or neglected are known as "protective factors." Supportive family environments and social networks consistently emerge as protective factors; however, other factors, such as parental employment, adequate housing, and access to healthcare and social services, may also serve to protect against child abuse and neglect. Unfortunately, no single factor reveal the entire story about how and why child abuse and neglect occurs, and the risk and protective factors differ depending on the type of child abuse and neglect being studied.

Chapter 34

Preventing Child Sexual Abuse

Any one sign does not mean that a child was sexually abused, but the presence of several suggests that you should begin asking questions and consider seeking help.

Behavior you may see in a child or adolescent:

- Has nightmares or other sleep problems without an explanation

- Seems distracted or distant at odd times

- Has a sudden change in eating habits

- Refuses to eat

- Loses or drastically increases appetite

- Has trouble swallowing

- Sudden mood swings, such as rage, fear, insecurity, or withdrawal

This chapter contains text excerpted from the following sources: Text in this chapter begins with excerpts from "Learn the Warning Signs—Recognizing Sexual Abuse," The Dru Sjodin National Sex Offender Public Website (NSOPW), U.S. Department of Justice (DOJ), November 1, 2012. Reviewed March 2019; Text under the heading "What You Can Do" is excerpted from "Preventing Child Sexual Abuse," Child Welfare Information Gateway, U.S. Department of Health and Human Services (HHS), 2019.

- Leaves "clues" that seem likely to provoke a discussion about sexual issues

- Develops new or unusual fear of certain people or places

- Refuses to talk about a secret shared with an adult or older child

- Writes, draws, plays, or dreams of sexual or frightening images

- Talks about a new older friend

- Suddenly has money, toys, or other gifts without reason

- Thinks of self or body as repulsive, dirty, or bad

- Exhibits adult-like sexual behaviors, language, and knowledge

All of the warning signs listed above are general indicators of sexual abuse in children. Many children do not actually disclose what happened; it is up to attentive adults to recognize hints. However, if you suspect a child has been abused by seeing these indications, or if she or he hints at abuse or outright discloses sexual abuse, seek help.

Behavior more typically found in adolescents (teens) include:

- Self-injury (cutting, burning)

- Inadequate personal hygiene

- Drug and alcohol abuse

- Sexual promiscuity

- Running away from home

- Depression, anxiety

- Suicide attempts

- Fear of intimacy or closeness

- Compulsive eating or dieting

Warning Signs That Might Suggest Someone Is Sexually Abusing a Child

The following behaviors could be a cause for concern:

- Making others uncomfortable by ignoring social, emotional, or physical boundaries or limits

- Refusing to let a child set any of his or her own limits; using teasing or belittling language to keep a child from setting a limit

- Insisting on hugging, touching, kissing, tickling, wrestling with, or holding a child even when the child does not want this physical contact or attention

- Turning to a child for emotional or physical comfort by sharing personal or private information or activities that are normally shared with adults

- Frequently pointing out sexual images or telling inappropriate or suggestive jokes with children present

- Exposing a child to adult sexual interactions without apparent concern

- Having secret interactions with teens or children (e.g., games; sharing drugs, alcohol, or sexual material), or spending excessive time e-mailing, text-messaging, or calling children or youth

- Being overly interested in the sexuality of a particular child or teen (e.g., talks repeatedly about the child's developing body or interferes with normal teen dating)

- Insisting on or managing to spend unusual amounts of uninterrupted time alone with a child

- Seeming "too good to be true" (e.g., frequently babysits different children for free, takes children on special outings alone, buys children gifts or gives them money for no apparent reason)

- Frequently walking in on children/teens in the bathroom

- Allowing children or teens to consistently get away with inappropriate behaviors

What You Can Do

To prevent child sexual abuse, it is important to keep the focus on adult responsibility while teaching children skills to help them protect themselves. Consider the following tips:

- Take an active role in your children's lives. Learn about their activities and people with whom they are involved. Stay alert for possible problems.

- Watch for "grooming" behaviors in adults who spend time with your child. Warning signs may include frequently finding ways to be alone with your child, ignoring your child's need for privacy

227

(e.g., in the bathroom), or giving gifts or money for no particular occasion.

- Ensure that organizations, groups, and teams that your children are involved with minimize one-on-one time between children and adults. Ask how staff and volunteers are screened and supervised.

- Make sure your children know that they can talk to you about anything that bothers or confuses them.

- Teach children accurate names of private body parts and the difference between touches that are "okay" and "not okay."

- Empower children to make decisions about their bodies by allowing them age-appropriate privacy and encouraging them to say "no" when they do not want to touch or be touched by others—even in nonsexual ways.

- Teach children to take care of their own bodies (e.g., bathing or using the bathroom) so they do not have to rely on adults or older children for help.

- Educate children about the difference between good secrets (such as birthday surprises) and bad secrets (those that make the child feel unsafe or uncomfortable).

- Monitor children's use of technology, including cell phones, social networking sites, and messaging. Review their friend's lists regularly and ask about any people you don't recognize.

- Trust your instincts. If you feel uneasy about leaving your child with someone, do not do it. If you are concerned about possible sexual abuse, ask questions.

- If your child tells you that she or she has been abused, stay calm, listen carefully, and never blame the child. Thank your child for telling you. Report the abuse right away.

Chapter 35

Child Maltreatment Prevention Initiatives

Child maltreatment prevention efforts have grown and changed substantially over the last half-century. They have moved beyond a public awareness approach to one that emphasizes the vital role of community, early intervention services, and caregiver education to help keep children safe from abuse and neglect. There is growing recognition that child maltreatment is a substantial public-health concern, as well as a serious social problem. Research suggests investments in prevention go beyond protecting children from maltreatment to also preventing maltreatment's devastating consequences, such as debilitating and lifelong physical and mental-health problems, considerable treatment and healthcare costs, and lost opportunities in education and work. This chapter presents prevention as the most important means of keeping children safe from abuse and neglect, and highlights current best practices and emerging trends in the child protection field.

Scope of the Problem

Although child maltreatment prevention programs and services in the United States have made great strides toward preventing child

---

This chapter includes text excerpted from "Child Maltreatment Prevention: Past, Present, and Future," Child Welfare Information Gateway, U.S. Department of Health and Human Services (HHS), July 2017.

abuse and neglect, several million children continue to be referred to child protective services (CPS) every year. Over three-fourths of maltreatment cases, each year are the result of neglect, including physical, emotional, educational, or medical neglect. Maltreatment reporting statistics from the National Child Abuse and Neglect Data System (NCANDS) show that the number of children receiving an investigation or alternative response rose nine percent from fiscal year (FY) 2011 to FY 2015. During this same period, substantiated child maltreatment cases rose almost four percent, and fatalities rose almost six percent. Other key findings for FY 2015 include the following:

- Approximately 4.0 million referrals alleging child maltreatment were made to CPS agencies.

- Referrals involved roughly 7.2 million children, and subsequent investigations verified that approximately 683,000 of these children were victims of maltreatment.

- Most of these children were victims of neglect (75.3%), with physical abuse (17.2%) and sexual abuse (8.4%) being the next most frequent types of child maltreatment.

- Infants under the age of 1 experienced the highest rate of victimization (24.2 per 1,000 children).

- Professionals were the reporters in most (63.4%) of the cases of alleged abuse and neglect, with the largest numbers of reports by professionals coming from education personnel (18.4%), legal and law enforcement personnel (18.2%), and social services staff (10.9%).

- African American children experienced the highest rate of victimization (14.5 per 1,000 children in the population of the same race or ethnicity), followed by American Indian or Alaska Native children (13.8 per 1,000 children), Hispanic children (8.4 per 1,000 children), and White children (8.1 per 1,000 children).

Child abuse and neglect can have a multitude of long-term effects on a child's physical, psychological, and behavioral health. In addition to the devastating health consequences of child maltreatment, the economic costs are massive in terms of healthcare and hospitalization expenses, treatment and counseling, incarceration, and lost productivity. Prevent Child Abuse America estimated the cost of child maltreatment in 2012—including both direct and indirect costs—to be $80 billion. The enormous societal consequences of child abuse and neglect make it imperative for the child welfare field to continue building on its knowledge and implementation of evidence-informed prevention practices.

History of Child Maltreatment Prevention

Child maltreatment was recognized as a growing social concern in the 1960s.

Recognizing a Problem

Modern child maltreatment prevention efforts can be traced to pediatrician Henry Kempe's 1962 article on battered child syndrome (BCS), which attributed the excessive use of physical punishment or failure to meet a child's basic physical or emotional needs to parents or caregivers who were experiencing undue stress or serious depression in their day-to-day lives. Kempe's work persuaded federal and state policymakers to support the adoption of a formal reporting system, and by 1967, every state and the District of Columbia (DC) had enacted laws regarding the referral of suspected cases of child abuse or neglect to a public agency. Then, the Child Abuse Prevention and Treatment Act (CAPTA) of 1974 authorized federal funds to improve state responses to child abuse and neglect. It also instituted new reporting laws for states to determine which individuals (child welfare, education, medical, mental health, child care, law enforcement, religious personnel, or—in some states—any individual) must report suspected cases of maltreatment (physical or emotional abuse, neglect, exploitation, or sexual abuse).

The new reporting laws led to an increase in cases, and the 1980s ushered in a significant increase in education efforts to raise public awareness of child abuse and neglect, including child sexual abuse and emotional neglect.

Gradual Move toward Prevention and Early Intervention

The Children's Bureau (CB) within the U.S. Department of Health and Human Services' (HHS) Administration on Children, Youth and Families (ACYF) funded research and demonstration grants as early as 1966 to explore the causes of child maltreatment and possible prevention measures, which paved the way for expanded efforts in the next decades. The focus on child maltreatment prevention gradually expanded beyond public education to early intervention. This included an emphasis on home visitation programs for new, at-risk mothers to teach basic caregiving skills and to help parents and primary caregivers bond with their children to encourage healthy child development and a positive home environment. These programs demonstrated gains in access to preventive healthcare, improved parental functioning, and early identification of developmental delays. In 2008, the Children's Bureau funded 17 cooperative agreement grants to expand home visiting, and in 2011, home visiting was formally incorporated into the formula grants of the Maternal, Infant, and Early Childhood Home Visiting (MIECHV) program within the Health Resources and Services Administration (HRSA), part of HHS.

There are numerous home visiting models in practice nowadays. Home visits have been recognized as a cost-effective means of promoting infant and child health, preventing maltreatment, and improving family functioning.

Emergence of Child Maltreatment Protective Factors

The 1990s saw the expanded use of family support services to help communities reduce child abuse and neglect. The Family Preservation and Support Services Program Act of 1993 authorized nearly $1 billion over five years to provide services for families in crisis, including counseling, respite care, and intensive in-home assistance programs. Other forms of family support services—parent support groups, drop-in family centers, and child care—as well as services to help reunify families after out-of-home placements, were also included.

In 2000, the Institute of Medicine (IOM) and the National Research Council (NRC) issued a groundbreaking study, From Neurons to Neighborhoods: The Science of Early Childhood Development (SECD), which underscored the critical influence of a child's social environment on brain development. The study highlighted the importance of early positive relationships with parents, caregivers, extended family, and community members and the harmful consequences of abusive or neglectful relationships or early exposure to violence. This was the impetus for energized prevention and early intervention efforts.

Promoting social supports or protective factors to help families overcome negative conditions or experiences—and an emphasis on community-based efforts to help improve social environments for children and families—became a focal point for child welfare policy in the early 2000s. This shifted the emphasis in prevention efforts from avoiding negative outcomes to actively pursuing positive outcomes through front-end investments in early intervention, education, and community-building.

The 2003 amendments to CAPTA funded a variety of child abuse prevention activities that promoted protective factors through Community-Based Child Abuse Prevention (CBCAP) programs. That same year, the Center for the Study of Social Policy (CSSP) identified a list of 5 protective factors it deemed necessary to help families offset parenting stress and make children and families safer:

- Parental resilience

- Social connections

- Concrete support in times of need

- Knowledge of parenting and child development

- Development of social and emotional competence in children

The CSSP protective factors gave policymakers and social workers a more positive focus and generated new energy in prevention programming. In 2005, the Office on Child Abuse and Neglect (OCAN) within the Children's Bureau began to incorporate protective factors into its annual Prevention Resource Guide. In 2007, OCAN added a sixth protective factor to the Prevention Resource Guide: nurturing and attachment. This new protective factor recognized the profound effect that the earliest relationship with the primary caregiver has on the safety and well-being of the developing child.

A variety of child maltreatment prevention and treatment programs were funded through additional amendments to CAPTA in 2010, including substance-use treatment programs, domestic violence services, and a variety of trainings and programs that support unaccompanied homeless youth and diverse population groups. In 2012, ACYF undertook an extensive review of protective factors research in order to inform the development of programs and policies to improve outcomes for the following ACYF-served populations:

- Abused and neglected infants, children, or youth, or those at risk of maltreatment

- Children exposed to domestic violence

- Youth in or transitioning out of foster care

- Runaway and homeless youth

- Pregnant or parenting teens

As a part of this review, ACYF identified 10 protective factors: self-regulation, relational skills, problem-solving skills, involvement in positive activities, parenting competencies, caring adults, positive peers, positive community, positive school environments, and economic opportunities.

Prevention Today

The current approach to child maltreatment prevention relies on enhancing the role of communities in strengthening protective factors in a child's environment and providing prevention services targeted toward different segments of the population. An example of the current emphasis on community-oriented prevention can be seen in the Doris Duke Charitable Foundation's (DDCF) shift from a parent education approach to a place-based approach, stressing the role of communities in promoting a child's well-being. The focus on overall child well-being reflects advances in child development research and a greater understanding of the negative outcomes that children experience when they lack stable and nurturing relationships with a parent or caregiver.

Targeting Prevention Services

Child maltreatment prevention services can be organized into a framework of primary, secondary, and tertiary programs. Primary prevention programs are directed at the general population to prevent maltreatment before it occurs; secondary prevention programs are targeted to individuals or families deemed to be at greater risk for potential abuse or neglect, and tertiary programs are directed at families in which maltreatment has already occurred. To create a comprehensive approach to preventing child maltreatment, communities and agencies develop plans that incorporate protective factors through primary, secondary, and tertiary programs. State CBCAP funds can be used for primary and secondary prevention services, while state child welfare programs fund tertiary services. Increasingly, the child welfare field is placing more emphasis on primary prevention as a strategy for preventing maltreatment and its harmful and costly consequences. In a 2016 report to Congress, HHS emphasized the role of primary prevention activities in preventing child maltreatment and the importance of establishing a strong infrastructure for tackling those problems that most threaten children's well-being, including poverty, substance-use disorders (SUD), mental illness, and domestic violence.

Figure 35.1. *Levels of Prevention Services*

The Division of Violence Prevention (DVP) within the National Center for Injury Prevention and Control (NCIPC) of the Centers for Disease Control and Prevention (CDC) promotes primary prevention through its Essentials for Childhood Framework, which highlights four major steps that communities can take to implement safe, stable, and nurturing relationships and environments for children and families:

- Greater awareness of child maltreatment and a commitment to prevent it

- Use of data to inform actions

- Programs to create the context for healthy children and families

- Policy that develops such a context

The CDC also highlights the following strategies as key to preventing child abuse and neglect at the community, societal, and individual levels:

- Strengthening economic supports for families

- Changing social norms to support parents and positive parenting practices

- Providing quality care and education in infancy and early childhood

- Enhancing parenting skills to promote healthy child development

- Intervening when necessary to lessen the potential for harm and prevent future risk

Identifying and Implementing Quality Programs

Child maltreatment prevention programs may fall under several different categories, including public awareness efforts, parent education and support groups, and community prevention efforts. Communities are increasingly relying on evidence-based practices (EBPs) when choosing programs and interventions to ensure the best outcomes for children and families and the highest return on public investment. This chapter describes select primary, secondary, and tertiary prevention programs and the use of EBPs, including specific state efforts. It also looks at incorporating cultural competence to yield optimal results for families and children.

Quality Prevention Programs

There are numerous programs agencies can implement to prevent child maltreatment at the primary, secondary, and tertiary levels. The Triple P—Positive Parenting Program (Triple P) is an example of a successful primary prevention strategy that provides a parenting and family support system for parents or caregivers of children from birth through the age of 16 to prevent and treat children's behavioral and emotional problems. It aims to foster positive family environments by building parenting skills and confidence.

A study that randomly assigned counties to a trial or control group found that making Triple P universally available to all parents in a county (not just those parents at risk for maltreating their children) was associated with the following results for children between birth and eight years of age:

- Fewer hospitalizations or emergency room (ER) visits due to child maltreatment injuries

- Fewer out-of-home placements

- Fewer substantiated cases of maltreatment

Additional promising primary prevention programs include the following:

- Period of PURPLE Crying is designed to help new parents and caregivers understand the scientific basis for an infant's prolonged crying and offers helpful coping and parenting tips.

- Stewards of Children is a sexual-abuse prevention program offered by Darkness to Light (D2L), a nonprofit organization that seeks to empower and educate adults about preventing child sexual abuse.

- Adults and Children Together (ACT)/Parents Raising Safe Kids is an eight-week program to educate parents and other adults who care for children to create environments that protect children from violence early in their lives.

- Parents as Teachers is a home visiting-based program for families during pregnancy and up to their children's entry into kindergarten. It is designed to increase parent knowledge of early childhood development and improve parenting practices, promote early detection of developmental delays and health issues, prevent child abuse and neglect, and encourage school readiness and success.

The following are examples of secondary prevention programs:

- The Incredible Years (IY) provides three separate curricula for parents, teachers, and children (between the ages of four and eight years) to promote social and emotional competence and eliminate or treat behavioral or emotional problems. IY has demonstrated positive impacts on parents who self-reported a history of child maltreatment.

- SafeCare (SC) is an in-home training program that teaches parents and caregivers how to interact with children in a positive manner, respond appropriately to challenging behaviors, recognize home hazards, and respond when a child is sick or injured.

- Combined Parent-Child Cognitive-Behavioral Therapy (CPC-CBT) is a strengths-based therapy (SBT) program for children between the ages of 3 and 17 and their parents (or caregivers) in families with a history of coercive parenting.

- The Effective Black Parenting Program (EBPP) was created for families with children between the ages of 0 and 18 to teach general parenting strategies and basic parenting skills and address topics such as single parenting and drug abuse prevention in a culturally sensitive manner.

Examples of tertiary prevention programs include the following:

- Attachment and Biobehavioral Catch-up (ABC) is for caregivers with infants or toddlers between the ages of six months and two years who have experienced early maltreatment or a disruption in care. ABC helps caregivers provide a nurturing, responsive, and predictable environment to improve children's behavior and ability to self-regulate.

- Early Pathways (EP) is a home-based therapy program designed for children six years of age and younger with significant behavior and/or emotional problems. The program teaches parents and primary caregivers, effective strategies for strengthening a child's positive behaviors, while reducing challenging ones.

- Promoting First Relationships (PFR) is a home visiting intervention for infants and young children between the ages of zero and three and their primary caregivers to build caregivers' confidence in parenting skills and enrich their commitment to the children.

- Parent–child interaction therapy (PCIT) is for children between the ages of two and seven years with behavior and parent-child relationship problems. It was designed to help parents or caregivers reduce children's negative behaviors (e.g., defiance, aggression), increase children's social skills and cooperation, and improve parent-child attachment.

Relying on Evidence-Based Practices

As the emphasis on proven interventions increases in the child welfare field, it is important to keep in mind that an intervention that proves particularly successful in one area or with one population might not be the best choice for another. Interventions should be carefully selected with the target population in mind to help ensure success and sustainability. Below are five nationally recognized EBP registries that rate various prevention programs designed to keep children, youth, and families safe:

- Blueprints for Healthy Youth Development

- California Evidence-Based Clearinghouse (CEBC) for Child Welfare

- Home Visiting Evidence of Effectiveness (HomVEE)

- CrimeSolutions.gov
- National Registry of Evidence-Based Programs and Practices (NREPP)

Importance of Cultural Competence

It is important that policymakers and practitioners consider cultural concerns in prevention efforts by giving attention to how parents engage in their cultural communities, how culture shapes parenting approaches, and the implications culture may have for targeted child maltreatment prevention and intervention programs. The National Academy of Sciences (NAS) identified the integration of culture into research and practice as one of the major challenges in preventing child maltreatment. By increasing the diversity of the child welfare workforce and developing and promoting culturally responsive interventions, the child welfare field can become more attuned to different ethnicities.

A Look to the Future: Challenges and Trends

A growing recognition of the long-term health consequences of child maltreatment will likely drive continued interest in programs and services that strengthen families and individuals and reduce the incidence of abuse and neglect. This highlights efforts to educate communities about the harmful consequences of adverse childhood experiences (ACEs), better integrate prevention programming across the multiple social service sectors, combat addiction, and increase the use of EBPs to ensure the best outcomes for children and families.

Reducing Adverse Childhood Experiences

ACEs are negative experiences in childhood that can have lifelong consequences for a person's physical and psychological health by taking a powerful toll on the developing brain. The toxic stress from ACEs has the potential to exact enormous consequences on both the individual and society. Research from the CDC and the Center on the Developing Child at Harvard University correlates early life ACEs with long-term negative outcomes for children and families. Although the initial research occurred nearly 20 years ago, ACEs are still receiving heightened attention in child maltreatment prevention efforts. ACEs data are frequently collected in research on child maltreatment and related areas, including through the CDC's Behavioral Risk Factor Surveillance System (BRFSS) data-collection effort.

239

Importance of Cross-System Integration and Collaboration

The incidence of child maltreatment is deeply influenced by poverty, violence, and substance use. While separate programs to alleviate these issues are helpful in preventing maltreatment, system-wide collaboration and data sharing across multiple service sectors—child welfare, juvenile justice, early childhood, education, public health, and the behavioral and mental-health fields—are essential to improving child and family safety and well-being on a broad scale. Because of the diversity of and within families and communities, relevant agencies and service providers need to find unique ways of engaging families and ensuring they have access to comprehensive prevention-related supports. Tailoring protective-factor approaches to specific at-risk populations, such as homeless youth, may also yield more positive outcomes.

Through a 2016 Program Instruction, ACF highlighted how state CBCAP programs can collaborate with a variety of other agencies and programs to strengthen child maltreatment prevention efforts. Examples of agencies or programs that CBCAP programs could partner with include the Administration on Intellectual and Developmental Disabilities (AIDD); Temporary Assistance for Needy Families (TANF); Head Start, Early Head Start, and other child-care and early intervention programs; faith-based and community organizations; and family support programs.

Addressing the Addiction Dilemma

Another major concern is the rampant heroin and prescription painkiller epidemic in the United States, which has resulted in increasing instances of child neglect and a new set of challenges for an already overwhelmed child welfare system. From FY 2006 to FY 2012, there was a 20-percent decline in the number of children entering foster care, but there was an 8-percent increase in the number of children entering care from FY 2012 to FY 2015. Additionally, the percentage of removals where parental substance use was cited as a contributing factor increased 13 percent from FY 2012 (28.5%) to FY 2015 (32.2%). HHS reported that state child welfare directors often attributed the increased number of placements in foster care to the dramatic rise in substance use, specifically opioid and methamphetamine abuse. The directors also reported that there are fewer opportunities to place children with relatives because this addiction epidemic often affects entire families and neighborhoods. This considerably limits the number of placement options. They also noted that the addiction epidemic has strained their agencies and increased the need for community leadership and cross-service collaboration.

The Comprehensive Addiction and Recovery Act (CARA), which was signed into law in 2016, significantly expanded access to addiction treatment services and medications to reverse drug overdoses.

Greater Reliance on Evidence-Based Practices and Statistics

The child protection field is moving toward a greater reliance on EBPs, increased use of qualitative and quantitative research methods, and a growing awareness of the need for model fidelity. Even with the significant progress that has been achieved in child maltreatment research, the NAS has called for a coordinated, national research infrastructure with high-level federal support.

The Children's Bureau continues to fund several projects whose primary purpose is to improve the use of EBPs in prevention work. Federal program instructions for CBCAP programs emphasize that the lead CBCAP agencies should describe the criteria they will use to develop, or select and fund, evidence-informed or evidence-based prevention programs and activities. To assist CBCAP lead agencies and their partners in this effort, the Family Resource Information, Education, and Network Development Service (FRIENDS) National Center for CBCAP was established to provide training and technical assistance in evidence-informed and evidence-based practices demonstrated to have reduced child maltreatment.

Conclusion

The use of statistical techniques to predict the likelihood of child welfare outcomes is another growing trend in child maltreatment prevention. Referred to as "predictive analytics," this practice relies on assessing current or past data points to predict likely child welfare outcomes. Supporters of this technique hope to use the data to predict and prevent child maltreatment by targeting services to children and families most at risk of harm and improving their safety, permanency, and well-being outcomes. The CDC is exploring the benefits and limitations of predictive analytics and its utility for child welfare, including its potential use in primary prevention efforts.

Chapter 36

Safe Youth, Safe Schools

Schools are expected to be, and usually are, safe havens for learning, but unintentional injuries and violence can occur, disrupting the educational process and negatively affecting the school and surrounding community.

New haircuts, new clothes, and backpacks stuffed with markers, pencils, and binders—everything a child needs to start a new school year. As millions of students return to school, teachers plan their school supply list, and parents carefully make sure their child is prepared with each and every item. Safety should also be on everyone's back-to-school list.

Parents, students, educators, and community members can all take action to keep children safe in and away from school.

Get to School Safely

Children face an increased risk for pedestrian injuries during the school year. You can help by learning more about these risks and steps you can take to promote pedestrian safety in your community.

Motor vehicle injuries are the greatest public-health problem facing children today. In fact, motor vehicle crashes are the leading cause of death for children between the ages of 0 and 12 in the United States. Keep children safe by using an age- and size-appropriate restraint system.

This chapter includes text excerpted from "Safe Youth, Safe Schools," Centers for Disease Control and Prevention (CDC), August 4, 2017.

Teen drivers are nearly 3 times more likely to be in a fatal crash than drivers over the age of 20. Crash risk is particularly high during a teen's first year of driving. They should be encouraged to learn about strategies that help a new driver arrive at school safely, including Graduated Driver Licensing (GDL) systems and parent-teen driving agreements.

School Safety

While U.S. schools remain relatively safe, any amount of violence is unacceptable. Parents, teachers, and administrators expect schools to be safe havens of learning. Acts of violence can disrupt the learning process and have a negative effect on students, the school itself, and the broader community.

Youth violence can take different forms, such as fighting, bullying, threats with weapons, and gang-related violence. It is a leading cause of death and injuries of young people between the ages of 10 and 24 in the United States.

Sexual violence begins early in life. 80 percent of female victims experienced their first rape before the age of 25, and about 40 percent experienced their first rape before the age of 18. Most victims do not tell friends and family about the abuse, and suffer alone. Those who do disclose the violence may be stigmatized by friends, family, and their community.

Suicide is a serious public-health problem that affects all age groups, including youth. It is the second leading cause of death among youth and young adults between the ages of 10 and 24, with nearly 6,000 lives lost among this group each year.

The Centers of Disease Control and Prevention's (CDC) *A Comprehensive Technical Package for the Prevention of Youth Violence and Associated Risk Behaviors* offers strategies that represents the best available evidence to prevent or reduce public-health problems, such as youth violence.

The School Health Index (SHI), also available from the CDC, is a self-assessment and planning tool that enables school administrators to identify strengths and weaknesses of health and safety policies and programs; develop an action plan for improving student health and safety; and to involve teachers, parents, students, and the community in improving school services.

Safety during Sports and Physical Activity

Each year in the United States, emergency departments treat more than 200,000 children, who are 14 years of age and younger, for playground-related injuries. Learn about risks and how to avoid severe injuries associated with playgrounds, such as making sure that surfaces under equipment are safe, soft, and well-maintained.

A child can take a spill, knock her or his head, and get a concussion in any number of school settings ranging from the hallway, the playground, the cafeteria, in school sports activities, and beyond. Heads Up to Schools: Know Your Concussion ABCs is a flexible set of materials that was developed for professionals working with grades K-12 and helps principals, school nurses, teachers, or other school professionals identify and respond to concussions and learn strategies to help support students returning to school after a concussion.

Additional Resources

The **U.S. Department of Education (ED)** seeks to ensure equal access to education and to promote educational excellence nationwide. The agency provides parents, teachers, and school administrators with various resources on school safety and youth violence prevention.

The **National Organizations for Youth Safety (NOYS)** is a coalition comprised of national organizations and federal agencies that serve youth. The primary focus is on youth safety and health. The NOYS website includes information about membership, research, and resources concerning youth safety.

Protect the Ones You Love: Child Injuries Are Preventable is a CDC initiative to raise parents' awareness about the leading causes of child injury in the United States and how they can be prevented. Working together, we can keep our children safe and help them live to their full potential.

Safe Kids Worldwide is an international, nonprofit organization solely dedicated to preventing unintentional childhood injury. Safe Kids Worldwide promotes changes in attitudes, behaviors, laws, and the environment to prevent accidental injury to children.

The **National Center for Safe Routes to Schools (NCSRTS)** helps states and communities enable and encourage children to safely walk and bicycle to school, working with parents; schools; community leaders; and local, state, and federal governments to improve the health and well-being of children. The organization also coordinates and provides technical support for the U.S. Walk to School Day.

StopBullying.gov is the federal government's one-stop-shop for information about bullying, including what bullying is (and is not), state laws on bullying and cyber-bullying, the warning signs for bullying, and how to prevent bullying by engaging the community.

STRYVE, or **Striving To Reduce Youth Violence Everywhere**, is a national initiative led by the CDC to prevent youth violence before it starts. STRYVE seeks to increase awareness that youth violence can, and should be, prevented and to promote the use of prevention strategies based on the best available evidence.

Chapter 37

Prevention of Maltreatment of Children with Disabilities

Children with disabilities are at least three times more likely to be abused or neglected than their peers without disabilities, and they are more likely to be seriously injured or harmed by maltreatment. Even among children with disabilities, the risk of maltreatment varies by disability type.

This chapter describes the scope of the problem, risk factors, and strategies for prevention. It examines the problem in terms of statistics and research; covers critical issues encountered when assessing a child with a disability for maltreatment; and provides information about promising prevention, collaboration, and training approaches.

Background and Research
Statistics Regarding Children with Disabilities

Estimates vary regarding the number of children with disabilities in the general population, depending on how disability is defined. According to the latest U.S. Census Bureau (2011) statistics, 5.2 percent of school-aged children (between the ages of 5 and 17) have a disability. According to federal child maltreatment data, 12.7 percent of child maltreatment victims had a reported disability in 2014; that

This chapter includes text excerpted from "The Risk and Prevention of Maltreatment of Children With Disabilities," Child Welfare Information Gateway, U.S. Department of Health and Human Services (HHS), January 2018.

number increased to 14.1 percent in 2015. A recent study in Minnesota estimated that greater than ⅓ of children reported for maltreatment possess some type of disability. Of those children in foster care in the United States, about ⅓ have a disability.

Statistics on the number of children with disabilities in child welfare, however, are difficult to obtain for many reasons. Until the 2010 reauthorization of CAPTA, state child welfare agencies were not required to report disability information to the federal government. This authorization mandates that states report (1) the number of children under three years of age who are involved in a substantiated case of child maltreatment and are eligible to be referred for early intervention services and (2) the number of children who were actually referred for those services.

Although the reauthorization of CAPTA systematized data collection through the National Child Abuse and Neglect Data System, it does not require information regarding types of disabilities or the number of children with disabilities who are older than the age of three when they enter the child welfare system. In many ways, however, accurate statistics on the number of children with disabilities are necessary for the development of public health services for this population.

Maltreatment Risk by Disability Type

Not all forms of disability carry the same level of risk, and not all children diagnosed with the same type of disability experience maltreatment equally. For example, children with disabilities that affect conduct, such as attention-deficit hyperactivity disorder (ADHD), may be vulnerable to physical abuse by parents or caregivers who may become frustrated by their behavior. Children who rely on adults for their care, as well as children who are nonverbal or hearing impaired, may be more likely than others to experience neglect or sexual abuse. Knowing the characteristics of children's disabilities can help child welfare professionals and service providers comprehend the barriers that these children face; better recognize and respond to those challenges; and obtain a more informed perspective of each child's social, familial, and individual contexts.

Risk and Protective Factors

While no single risk factor indicates that a child will necessarily be the victim of abuse or neglect, research reveals that children with disabilities face an assortment of factors that place them at higher risk of maltreatment than children without disabilities. Children with disabilities and their families often encounter societal risk factors that may increase their risk for maltreatment, such as isolation, discrimination, and lack of support. Additionally, they may be at heightened risk for maltreatment due to risk factors related to the characteristics of families, parents, children, and specific disabilities. This section describes those risk factors and highlights maltreatment in institutional and nonfamilial settings as well as protective factors.

Family or Parental Risk Factors

It is important for professionals to understand the effects that raising a child with disabilities can have on family dynamics. Such knowledge can help child welfare professionals and/or service providers assess risk factors (e.g., stress), the family support system, challenges to effective family functioning, and the additional risks that poverty may present.

- **Stress and physical health:** Providing additional care and supervision for children with disabilities can increase the stress placed on families caring for children with special needs. Causes of stress can include additional financial costs, the physical and emotional health of parents or caregivers, and concerns about the future. High levels of stress and concern about their own well-being can lessen parents' abilities to provide appropriate care for their children and may lead to maltreatment. Thus, child welfare professionals or service providers should emphasize to parents or caregivers the importance of attending to their physical and mental-health needs, as well as the needs of their children.

- **Lack of support:** The increased time and resources often required to care for children with disabilities may leave parents socially isolated. A limited ability to connect with other parents and social isolation, in general, may leave these parents unaware that their children are at increased risk of maltreatment, and they may be unprepared to identify and protect their children from risky situations. Helping connect parents with opportunities for social interaction, such as peer-to-peer networking and support groups, may help them better protect their children and reduce negative emotions.

- **Family functioning:** Families may experience feelings of loss for not having a child who has developed "normally." Additionally, parents may have to expend a significant amount of time and energy attending medical and therapy appointments and providing additional in-home care.

- **Poverty:** Regardless of disabilities, children who come from economically disadvantaged families are more likely to suffer maltreatment than children from financially stable homes. Low-income families often live in areas with high crime rates, poor-quality housing, underperforming schools, and a lack of quality services—all of which can make it difficult to create a nurturing home environment. Caregiving demands placed on parents of children with chronic conditions, such as physical and intellectual disabilities, are predictors of serious stress, a known risk factor for maltreatment. Additional stressors due to low-income, housing instability, unsafe neighborhoods, and poor social connections can add to the risk of maltreatment, as can poverty accompanied by depression and substance use.

To be effective, child welfare professionals must understand that families from these communities are disproportionally families of color who have likely experienced multigenerational trauma and negative experiences with public systems. Because availability of quality services and lack of awareness of resources can create barriers to accessing services, child welfare professionals should be aware of what resources are available in the community to help these children and families; if certain resources are not available, professionals can engage, support, and connect parents or caregivers to readily available quality services that are easy to access and culturally appropriate.

Child and Disability Risk Factors

Numerous risk factors for maltreatment may be related to the characteristics of the children or their disabilities. For example, disabilities may result in feelings of isolation and powerlessness in children. These feelings may prevent them from avoiding or reporting an abusive situation. Children with disabilities may have a limited ability to protect themselves or to understand what maltreatment is or whether they are experiencing it. Further compounding this, children with disabilities who rely on caregivers for their daily needs may experience a lack of independence and privacy and not know when the behavior is inappropriate.

Having a disability makes a child more vulnerable to maltreatment, but studies have shown that children with certain disabilities are more prone to maltreatment than others. For example, compared with children born without medical complications, children born with congenital anomalies, such as spina bifida or Down syndrome (DS), have an increased likelihood of maltreatment during the first month of life. The type of maltreatment children experience is likely to be specifically related to their disabilities. For example, perpetrators may withhold medical care from children who need it or inappropriately restrict movement of children who have problems with movement control.

Risk Factors for Institutional and Nonfamilial Maltreatment

Although maltreatment is most often perpetrated by family members, children with disabilities are also at risk when being cared for by others. School-age children with disabilities who are victims of substantiated maltreatment are more than twice as likely to be placed in out-of-home care as those without disabilities. Older youth with disabilities have higher rates of placement instability, longer stays in foster care, and decreased the likelihood of reunification. Children with disabilities may face an increased risk of sexual abuse due to their placement in isolating environments (e.g., group homes, long-term-care facilities, hospitals) that allow easy access by others. These types of settings may undergo frequent staff turnover, which can lead to a decreased opportunity for staff to become familiar with the children and recognize changes in their behavior or demeanor indicative of maltreatment.

Disabilities and Transitioning to Independent Living

Given that approximately one-third of children in foster care have a disability, it is likely that many of the youth transitioning from the child welfare system to independent living possess some type of disability. To ease their transitions, child welfare professionals who work with such youth can help connect them with appropriate services, such as pairing them with mentors or disability advocacy organizations.

Protective Factors

Child welfare professionals also should be aware of protective factors associated with children with disabilities. Protective factors are conditions or attributes in individuals, families, or communities that can mitigate or eliminate risk factors that decrease the health and well-being of children and families. For example, an increased willingness on the part of parents to engage with various service professionals (a protective factor) could safeguard children who would otherwise be at risk of maltreatment.

Children may have impairments in some areas of development but experience strengths in others. Child welfare professionals and caregivers who are knowledgeable about children's strengths can tailor services that maximize those strengths while seeking to bolster others. A focus on strengths can help improve children's self-esteem. When child welfare professionals work with families of children who have disabilities, this type of strengths-based approach allows the child to feel supported and can reduce the risk of maltreatment. Building strong, positive relationships with families and focusing on caregivers' strengths can also improve parents' confidence and self-esteem, which can reduce stress and other risk factors of abuse.

Assessing for Disabilities

Systematic assessments for disabilities can improve casework practice. Comprehensive assessments go beyond simply stating whether a child has a disability. They help child welfare and related professionals know whether children are functioning with a severe, moderate, or mild impairment that may otherwise go undetected and paint a more complete picture of how a disability affects children, such as how they function across the cognitive, behavioral, social, and daily-living domains. Comprehensive assessments also can help child welfare professionals identify nuanced risk factors that indicate children's vulnerability to abuse and neglect. Understanding how children's disabilities affect their daily functioning enables parents, caregivers, and child welfare professionals to build on strengths, identify vulnerabilities, and connect children to services that are most beneficial.

Child welfare professionals who suspect children in their caseloads have a disability can make a referral to early intervention services or a developmental disability agency for a thorough assessment. Part C of Individuals with Disabilities Education Act (IDEA) is a federal grant program that assists states in providing comprehensive early intervention services for infants and toddlers. Part C requires child welfare professionals to refer families and children, between birth and two years of age with substantiated maltreatment allegations, for a disability assessment and evaluation. Lack of identification—or a misidentification—of a disability may result in the referral or provision of inappropriate services or failure to provide needed services. Early identification can help alleviate future behavioral and educational issues among children with disabilities and a history of maltreatment. It is important that child welfare professionals become familiar with the provisions outlined in the IDEA regulation so they can best serve children with disabilities and their families.

Assessing for Maltreatment

Regardless of the type of maltreatment experienced or the disability a child presents with, some children may have difficulty communicating their experience of maltreatment due to the symptoms of their disability or the lack of a connection to a trusted adult. Adults may believe that children with disabilities are unable to accurately convey the type of abuse or neglect they experienced. However, treating each child as an individual, avoiding assumptions about a child's abilities, and offering multiple and varied opportunities to report maltreatment can assist children with disabilities in communicating any maltreatment they may have experienced. In fact, research has shown that even children with communication difficulties or trouble expressing needs, feelings, or other issues are able to accurately convey their experiences of distress and know what happened to them.

Ideally, child welfare professionals and service providers should confer with disability professionals or a multidisciplinary group of knowledgeable consultants to obtain expert advice before interviewing children about possible maltreatment. This may be particularly helpful in cases where it is difficult to distinguish between maltreatment and a disability. For example, a child may exhibit withdrawal due to a disability or due to the effects of maltreatment.

Other issues, such as children's communication limitations or behavioral challenges, may affect assessments for maltreatment. In these situations, child welfare professionals, in consultation with disability professionals, may need to adapt the structure or location of the interviews. Interviewers should account for the developmental and mobility abilities of the child, as well as the severity of the injuries and underlying medical conditions that could hamper victims from disclosing what happened.

Promising Practices

The following section highlights various prevention methods, collaborative responses, and training tips that may help professionals

253

improve their interactions with families, caregivers, children, educators, and other associated agencies and service providers.

Prevention

Although many communities have initiatives to prevent the maltreatment of all children, further efforts are necessary to provide additional protections and awareness regarding the maltreatment of children with disabilities. This section looks at prevention strategies focused at the community, family, and child levels.

Community-Level Prevention

Child welfare professionals can build upon general child maltreatment prevention efforts by incorporating the following strategies to raise awareness of the maltreatment of children with disabilities and help change societal attitudes about children with disabilities.

Ensure community members are aware of the heightened risk. Community members may not realize that children with disabilities are at an increased risk for maltreatment or understand how they can better identify, support, and protect children with disabilities who have been or are at risk for maltreatment.

Help others see children with disabilities, as valued and unique individuals. Child welfare professionals can counteract negative attitudes by discussing the strengths of children with disabilities and their families and the unique perspectives they bring to their communities. They also can help develop leadership skills in parents and family members of children with disabilities so they can be powerful advocates for promoting the safety of their children and all children in the community.

Promote the inclusion of children with disabilities in everyday life. Child welfare professionals can identify and address physical and social accessibility barriers for children with disabilities and their families (e.g., access to public buildings and parks, equal opportunities to participate in sports or social events) to promote greater exposure and decrease isolation.

Encourage communities to share the responsibility for the well-being of children with disabilities. Through regular contact with schools, neighbors, faith-based organizations, and businesses that interact with families, child welfare professionals and service providers can encourage greater community involvement to create a larger support network for children with disabilities and their families. Education systems are key to prevention and intervention efforts due to their frequent contact with children with disabilities and their families. They can also help create and promote policies and educational opportunities that support the well-being of this population.

Family-Focused Prevention

Parents and other caregivers spend the most time with their children; therefore, it is important to connect them with prevention programs that help them raise their children without resorting to maltreatment. Interventions that encourage positive interactions between parents and caregivers and children with disabilities can improve parent responsiveness and increase appropriate expectations and limit setting.

Parents should educate themselves about their child's disability, as well as care for their own mental health and well-being. Connecting parents to services, such as social support groups and respite care, may allow them to better understand their own mental and physical well-being and reduce stress, improve attachment, and reduce the risk of maltreatment. The following are examples of general prevention services to which child welfare professionals can connect families.

- **Home visiting:** Professional or paraprofessional staff can visit families to provide them support and services in their homes. The visitor partners with the family to assess the family's strengths and needs and enhance their protective factors.

- **Parenting classes:** Given the large presence of children with disabilities involved with child welfare, even general parenting classes should include a focus on parenting children with disabilities and accessing supports and services.

- **Support groups:** Parents can share their experiences in a supportive group setting and trade information on resources, address issues related to their children's disabilities, and create informal support networks. In addition to connecting parents to national support organizations, such as Parents Anonymous or Circle of Parents, child welfare professionals can help parents identify supports specific to their children's disabilities, when possible.

- **Respite care:** Whether it is planned or offered during times of crisis, taking a break from the demands of caring for a child with disabilities can help parents reduce stress and the risk of abuse or neglect.

Child-Focused Prevention

Teaching children with disabilities about the risks of abuse and neglect, as well as improving their ability to advocate for themselves, can help reduce maltreatment among this population. If appropriate, it is also important to keep the child's parent or primary caregiver engaged in making decisions about the various intervention options. Summarized below are some additional prevention strategies to keep in mind when working with children with disabilities.

- **Help children protect themselves:** Child welfare professionals should try to involve children at risk of maltreatment in group-based educational opportunities about abuse and neglect. This could include involving children in opportunities to learn about their body parts and functions, what constitutes abuse and neglect, how to communicate with a trusted adult if the need arises, and distinguishing between appropriate and inappropriate social interactions. This can help children identify abuse, respond to it, and tell others. When involving children with disabilities, child welfare professionals should ensure programs are inclusive and appropriate to children's ability levels, cultures, and genders. Professionals should also remember that children with disabilities possess a wide variety of strengths and may need alternative methods of instruction.

- **Maximize children's communication skills and tools:** Children may need opportunities to practice using effective communication skills. Child welfare professionals can model healthy relationships and positive interactions with other children and adults and encourage others involved in children's lives to do the same. Increasing children's verbal development and communication skills can help them advocate for their own needs and report maltreatment if it does occur.

- **Reduce children's social isolation:** Children with disabilities may have limited involvement in developmentally appropriate activities (e.g., clubs, sports, jobs) that can help reduce social isolation. Youth with disabilities who are involved with the child welfare system are two times less likely to participate in these types of activities than their peers without disabilities. Child welfare professionals can help ensure children with disabilities feel welcomed and included in these activities and throughout their communities. Service providers can work with multidisciplinary teams of parents, foster parents, educators, and others to identify opportunities and assist caretakers in enrolling their children in appropriate activities and supporting them as they form and strengthen relationships with peers and trusted adults.

Collaborative Responses

Service coordination and collaboration between the numerous professionals who serve children with disabilities and their families are critical to addressing their multiple needs. For example, child welfare professionals can partner with professionals in the fields of medicine, early childhood education, developmental disabilities, mental health, and nutrition. Child welfare professionals and service providers should also include families whenever possible. To improve collaboration and coordination of services, the following strategies should be considered.

- **Use a team approach:** Include families in joint meetings with other professionals to plan services and share information on case progress. Engaging and involving the family and caretakers help implement needed services. For example, as required by IDEA, all families of children with disabilities should have 2 plans, an individualized family service plan (IFSP) and an individualized education program (IEP). The IFSP (for children from between birth and 2 years of age) focuses on the services that a family needs to enhance the development of their child. It is broader than the IEP and puts more focus on the family. School-aged children with disabilities (between the ages of 3 and 21) should also have an IEP, which assesses strengths and needs and determines appropriate educational services and support provided in schools. The IFSP and IEP should be developed collaboratively with the children's parents and other key stakeholders to best address goal setting, as well as the planning, coordination, and monitoring of services.

- **Collaborate and share information between agencies:** Collaboration is key to increasing communication between multiple agencies and systems. It may help them develop a joint mission or vision statement, which can unite agencies around a common goal. Having well-defined roles and shared priorities and resources helps promote stronger partnerships among service providers. Additionally, developing multidisciplinary teams to work across the various providers is crucial to conducting assessments, finding placements, identifying needs, and delivering appropriate services. Some agencies or systems have found success in inviting a disability specialist to colocate within the agency to ensure children receive the needed developmental assessments and to encourage collaboration and ongoing case support.

Training

Families commonly encounter service providers who have limited training in and knowledge of working with children with disabilities. Training regarding disabilities is not offered sufficiently to child welfare service providers, making it difficult for many providers to identify and assess disabilities and maltreatment. Service providers may be unable to identify the unmet needs of children with disabilities and their families or connect them to appropriate services. Training topics could include an introduction to the relevant policies, programs, and services that are in place to support children with disabilities, as well as effective ways to communicate about disabilities to help gather pertinent information from the family, the child, and other service providers.

Funded by the Administration on Intellectual and Developmental Disabilities, the National Network of University Centers for Excellence in Developmental Disabilities Education, Research, and Service (UCEDDs) supports universities in every state to carry out interdisciplinary training, technical assistance, research, and information dissemination.

Evidence-Informed Interventions

Using evidence-informed interventions to reduce parental stress is an effective way to help decrease the potential for child maltreatment when working with families with children with disabilities. Each of the following programs focuses on positive ways of addressing the behavior of children with disabilities and decreasing the stress associated with parenting a child with emotional or behavioral problems.

The Stepping Stones Triple P—Positive Parenting Program is a family-centered model of parenting to help prevent emotional and behavioral issues in children with disabilities. It helps parents develop ways to manage their children's behavior problems and developmental issues in order to increase parents' competence and communication.

The Parent Management Training—Oregon Model is aimed at caregivers of children with antisocial behavior. It teaches parents to encourage positive behaviors through the use of praise and incentives, limit setting, and family problem-solving skills.

Parent–child interaction therapy is aimed at addressing disruptive behaviors in preschool-aged children by teaching parents how to work with their children to decrease negative behaviors, increase prosocial practices, and improve parenting skills to decrease parental stress.

The Incredible Years teaches parents about family-based problem solving and positive child relationships and attachment to increase understanding of their children's developmental abilities.

Family group decision-making centers on the belief that children and their parents are part of a larger family group and recognize the need for both to be involved in decision-making about the children's safety, permanency, and well-being.

Conclusion

Children with disabilities experience a higher rate of abuse and neglect than children without disabilities. They are disproportionally represented in the child welfare system; however, due to time and budget constraints, training for child welfare professionals and service providers on how to best serve children with disabilities and their families may not be available. Awareness of the characteristics of different disabilities in relation to the risks of maltreatment and the supports each child needs may help child welfare professionals provide services that assist children in meeting their cognitive, behavioral, social, and daily living needs. Promising strategies are available to prevent the maltreatment of children with disabilities, and opportunities exist to improve collaboration between child welfare and disability agencies to respond more effectively to children and families in this population. Child welfare professionals can play a key role in developing networks of support for children with disabilities and their families, identifying and addressing family strengths and needs so children with disabilities can live in safe and supportive homes, and educating children about abuse and neglect so they are better able to protect themselves.

Chapter 38

Infant Safe Haven Laws

Many state legislatures have enacted legislation to address infant abandonment and endangerment in response to a reported increase in the abandonment of infants in unsafe locations, such as public restrooms or trash receptacles. Beginning in Texas in 1999, "Baby Moses laws," or infant safe haven laws, have been enacted as an incentive for mothers in crisis to safely relinquish their babies to designated locations where the babies are protected and provided with medical care until a permanent home is found. Safe haven laws generally allow the parent, or an agent of the parent, to remain anonymous and to be shielded from criminal liability and prosecution for child endangerment, abandonment, or neglect in exchange for surrendering the baby to a safe haven.

To date, all 50 states, the District of Columbia (DC), and Puerto Rico have enacted safe haven legislation. The focus of these laws is protecting newborns from endangerment by providing parents an alternative to criminal abandonment, and therefore, the laws are generally limited to very young children. For example, in approximately 11 states and Puerto Rico, only infants who are 72 hours old or younger may be relinquished to a designated safe haven. Approximately 19 states accept infants up to one month old. Other states specify varying age limits in their statutes.

This chapter includes text excerpted from "Infant Safe Haven Laws," Child Welfare Information Gateway, U.S. Department of Health and Human Services (HHS), December 2016.

261

Who May Leave a Baby at a Safe Haven?

In most states with safe haven laws, either parent may surrender her or his baby to a safe haven. In 4 states and Puerto Rico, only the mother may relinquish her infant. Idaho specifies that only a custodial parent may surrender an infant. In the DC, an infant may be relinquished only by a custodial parent who is a resident of the District. In approximately 11 states, an agent of the parent (someone who has the parent's approval) may take a baby to a safe haven for a parent. In California, Kansas, and New York, if the person relinquishing the infant is someone other than a parent, she or he must have legal custody of the child. 8 states do not specify the person who may relinquish an infant.

Safe Haven Providers

The purpose of safe haven laws is to ensure that relinquished infants are left with persons who can provide the immediate care needed for their safety and well-being. To that end, approximately 16 states and Puerto Rico require parents to relinquish their infants only to a hospital, emergency medical services provider, or healthcare facility. In 27 states, fire stations also are designated as safe haven providers. Personnel at police stations or other law enforcement agencies may accept infants in 25 states. In 5 states, emergency medical personnel responding to 911 calls may accept an infant. In addition, 5 states allow churches to act as safe havens, but the relinquishing parent must first determine that church personnel are present at the time the infant is left.

Responsibilities of Safe Haven Providers

The safe haven provider is required to accept emergency protective custody of the infant and to provide any immediate medical care that the infant may require. In 14 states and the DC, when the safe haven receiving the baby is not a hospital, the baby must be transferred to a hospital as soon as possible. The provider is also required to notify the local child welfare department that an infant has been relinquished.

In 24 states and the DC, the provider is required to ask the parent for family and medical history information. In 17 states and the DC, the provider is required to attempt to give the parent or parents information about the legal repercussions of leaving the infant and information about referral services. In 4 states, a copy of the infant's numbered identification bracelet may be offered to the parent as an aid to linking the parent to the child if reunification is sought at a later date.

Immunity from Liability for Providers

In 43 states and the DC, safe haven laws protect providers who accept custody of relinquished infants from liability for anything that might happen to the infant while in their care, unless there is evidence of major negligence on the part of the provider.

Protections for Parents

In approximately 16 states and the DC, anonymity for the parent or agent of the parent is expressly guaranteed in statute. In 27 states and Puerto Rico, the safe haven provider cannot compel the parent or agent of the parent to provide identifying information. In addition, 15 states provide an assurance of confidentiality for any information that is voluntarily provided by the parent.

In addition to the guarantee of anonymity, most states provide protection from criminal liability for parents who safely relinquish their infants. Approximately 34 states, the DC, and Puerto Rico do not prosecute a parent for child abandonment when a baby is relinquished to a safe haven. In 16 states, safe relinquishment of the infant is an affirmative defense in any prosecution of the parent or her/his agent for any crime against the child, such as abandonment, neglect, or child endangerment.

The privileges of anonymity and immunity are forfeited in most states if there is evidence of child abuse or neglect.

Consequences of Relinquishment

Once the safe haven provider has notified the local child welfare department that an infant has been relinquished, the department assumes custody of the infant as an abandoned child. The department has responsibility for placing the infant, usually in a pre-adoptive home, and for petitioning the court for termination of the birth parents' parental rights. Before the baby is placed in a pre-adoptive home, 14 states and the DC require the department to request the local law enforcement agency to determine whether the baby has been reported as a missing child. In addition, 5 states require the department to check the putative father registry before a termination of parental rights petition can be filed.

Approximately 20 states and the DC have procedures in place for a parent to reclaim the infant, usually within a specified time period and before any petition to terminate parental rights has been granted. 5 states also have provisions for a non-relinquishing father to petition for custody of the child. In 18 states and Puerto Rico, the act of surrendering an infant to a safe haven is presumed to be a relinquishment of parental rights to the child, and no further parental consent is required for the child's adoption.

Chapter 39

Child Abuse Prevention and Treatment Act

The key federal legislation addressing child abuse and neglect is the Child Abuse Prevention and Treatment Act (CAPTA), originally enacted on January 31, 1974 (P.L. 93–247). This act has been amended several times and was last reauthorized on December 20, 2010, by the CAPTA Reauthorization Act of 2010 (P.L. 111–320). Most recently, certain provisions of the act were amended on May 29, 2015, by the Justice for Victims of Trafficking Act (JVTA) of 2015 (P.L. 114–22) and on July 22, 2016, by the Comprehensive Addiction and Recovery Act (CARA) of 2016 (P.L. 114–198).

CAPTA provides federal funding and guidance to states in support of prevention, assessment, investigation, prosecution, and treatment activities and also provides grants to public agencies and nonprofit organizations, including Indian tribes and tribal organizations, for demonstration programs and projects. Additionally, CAPTA identifies the federal role in supporting research, evaluation, technical assistance, and data collection activities; establishes the Office on Child Abuse and Neglect; and establishes a national clearinghouse of information relating to child abuse and neglect. CAPTA also sets forth a federal definition of child abuse and neglect. In 2015, the federal definitions

This chapter includes text excerpted from "About CAPTA: A Legislative History," Child Welfare Information Gateway, U.S. Department of Health and Human Services (HHS), August 2017.

of "child abuse and neglect" and "sexual abuse" were expanded by the JVTA to include a child who is identified as a victim of sex trafficking or severe forms of trafficking in persons.

Summary of Legislative History

CAPTA was originally enacted in P.L. 93–247. The act was later amended by the Child Abuse Prevention and Treatment and Adoption Reform Act of 1978 (P.L. 95–266, 4/24/78). The law was completely rewritten in the Child Abuse Prevention, Adoption, and Family Services Act of 1988 (P.L. 100–294, 4/25/88). It was further amended by the Child Abuse Prevention Challenge Grants Reauthorization Act of 1989 (P.L. 101–126, 10/25/89) and the Drug-Free School Amendments of 1989 (P.L. 101–226, 12/12/89).

The Community-Based Child Abuse and Neglect Prevention (CBCAP) grants program was originally authorized by sections 402 through 409 of the Continuing Appropriations Act for FY 1985 (P.L. 98–473, 10/12/84). The Child Abuse Prevention Challenge Grants Reauthorization Act of 1989 (P.L. 101–126) transferred this program to the Child Abuse Prevention and Treatment Act, as amended.

A new title III, certain preventive services regarding Children of Homeless Families or Families at Risk of Homelessness, was added to the Child Abuse and Neglect Prevention and Treatment Act by the Stewart B. McKinney Homeless Assistance Act Amendments of 1990 (P.L. 101–645, 11/29/90).

CAPTA was amended and reauthorized by the Child Abuse, Domestic Violence, Adoption, and Family Services Act of 1992 (P.L. 102–295, 5/28/92) and amended by the Juvenile Justice and Delinquency Prevention Act Amendments of 1992 (P.L. 102–586, 11/4/92).

CAPTA was amended by the Older American Act Technical Amendments of 1993 (P.L. 103–171, 12/2/93) and the Human Services Amendments of 1994 (P.L. 103–252, 5/19/94).

CAPTA was further amended by the Child Abuse Prevention and Treatment Act Amendments of 1996 (P.L. 104-235, 10/3/96), which amended Title I; replaced the Title II, Community-Based Family Resource Centers program, with a new Community-Based Family Resource and Support Program; and repealed Title III, Certain Preventive Services Regarding Children of Homeless Families or Families at Risk of Homelessness.

CAPTA was reauthorized and amended by the Keeping Children and Families Safe Act of 2003 (P.L. 108–36, 6/25/03), which amended Title I and replaced Title II, Community-Based Family Resource and

Support Program, with Community-Based Grants for the Prevention of Child Abuse and Neglect. CAPTA also was amended and reauthorized by the CAPTA Reauthorization Act of 2010 (P.L. 111–320, 12/20/10), which amended both Titles I and II.

CAPTA was further amended by the JVTA of 2015 (P.L. 114–22, 5/29/15). Effective since May 2017, states are required, as part of their CAPTA state plans, to have provisions and procedures in place:

1. Requiring identification and assessment of all reports involving children known or suspected to be victims of sex trafficking

2. For training child protective services (CPS) workers about identifying, assessing, and providing comprehensive services for children who are sex trafficking victims, including efforts to coordinate with state law enforcement; juvenile justice; and social service agencies, such as runaway and homeless youth shelters. It also expanded the federal definition of "child abuse and neglect" and "sexual abuse" to include a child who is identified as a victim of sex trafficking or severe forms of trafficking in persons.

CAPTA was most recently amended by the Comprehensive Addiction and Recovery Act of 2016 (P.L. 114–198, 7/22/16). Title V, Section 503 of the act modified the CAPTA state plan requirement for infants born and identified as being affected by substance abuse or withdrawal symptoms or fetal alcohol spectrum disorder (FASD) by adding criteria to state plans to ensure the safety and well-being of infants following the release from the care of healthcare providers, to address the health and substance-use disorder (SUD) treatment needs of the infant and affected family or caregiver, and to develop the plans of safe care for infants affected by all substance abuse (not just illegal-substance abuse, as was the requirement prior to this change).

Chapter 40

Sex Offender Registration and Notification Act

Title 1 of the Adam Walsh Child Protection and Safety Act of 2006 established a comprehensive, national sex offender registration system called the "Sex Offender Registration and Notification Act" (SORNA). SORNA aims to close potential gaps and loopholes that existed under prior laws and to strengthen the nationwide network of sex offender registrations.

Purposes of the Sex Offender Registration and Notification Act

Sex offender registration and notification programs are important for public safety purposes. Sex offender registration is a system for monitoring and tracking sex offenders following their release into the community. The registration provides important information about convicted sex offenders to local and federal authorities and the public, such as the offender's name, current location, and past offenses. Currently, the means of public notification includes sex offender websites in all states, the District of Columbia (DC), and some territories. Some states involve other forms of notice.

This chapter includes text excerpted from "Sex Offender Registration and Notification Act (SORNA)," U.S. Department of Justice (DOJ), March 6, 2018.

Within a specified timeframe, each jurisdiction is required to comply with the federal standards outlined in the SORNA. Jurisdictions include all 50 states, the DC, the principal U.S. territories, and federally recognized Indian tribes.

Failure to Register

It is a federal crime for an individual to knowingly fail to register or update her or his registration as required pursuant to the SORNA. For example, a sex offender is required to update their registration in each jurisdiction they reside, are employed, or attend school. Offenders convicted of this crime face statutory penalties.

Role of the Chief Executive Officer

The chief executive officers (CEO) work with the High Technology Investigative Unit (HTIU), the Federal Bureau of Investigation (FBI), and United States Attorneys' Offices around the country to investigate and prosecute sex offenders who fail to register pursuant to the SORNA.

In addition, CEOs' attorneys conduct trainings to educate law enforcement officials, investigators, prosecutors, and others about the national sex offender registration system. Moreover, CEOs design, implement, and support strategies, legislative proposals, and policy initiatives relating to the enforcement of SORNA.

Chapter 41

How You Can Help Someone Who Is Being Abused or Neglected

Every child deserves a safe, loving family and to have her or his basic needs—such as food, clothing, and shelter—met. Most parents try their best to provide these things for their children, but unfortunately, not all parents do, and not all children are cared for and safe. Some children may not be safe because their parent or other caregiver, such as a grandparent, aunt, uncle, or babysitter, is harming them. Others may not be safe because there is not a responsible adult to watch or take care of them. When children are not safe because of what a parent or other caregiver does or does not do, this could be child abuse or neglect.

How Do You Know If Someone Is Being Abused or Neglected?

It is often really hard—even for adults—to know if a child is being harmed. Sometimes, we may see it happening with our own eyes, such as if we notice an adult hitting a child. But other times,

This chapter includes text excerpted from "How You Can Help Someone Who Is Being Abused or Neglected," Child Welfare Information Gateway, U.S. Department of Health and Human Services (HHS), September 2018.

271

we may only see signs of what could be happening. These signs may mean a child is being hurt by an adult, but there could be other causes too.

The list below gives a few signs that a child may be abused or neglected, but you should remember two things. First, a child who shows these signs may not necessarily be abused or neglected by an adult, but these signs may be reasons to be concerned and for you to talk with an adult. Second, this list is not complete. There are many other signs of abuse and neglect too.

These are examples of signs a child may be abused or neglected or otherwise needs help:

- The child has injuries (bruises, burns, cuts, etc.) that she or he cannot or will not explain, or the explanation does not make sense.

- The child is frightened of her or his parents or other adults.

- The child hurts pets or other animals.

- The child spends a lot of time at home without a parent or other caregiver (if the child is young).

- The child uses alcohol or drugs.

- The child avoids going home or spending time with a particular adult.

- The child often comes to school in dirty clothes.

Sometimes you also may just get a feeling that something is not right about how a parent or other caregiver treats a child or how a friend is acting. If you are concerned about someone, you should talk to a trusted adult, such as a parent, teacher, or school counselor.

The child also may tell you she or he is being harmed. If someone does tell you she or he is being abused or neglected, here are a few tips about how you can react:

- Listen to what the child has to say.

- Tell the child you care and want to help.

- Let the child know she or he is not alone.

- Let the child know what is happening is not his or her fault.

- Encourage the child to talk to a trusted adult to get help.

What Should You Do If Someone Is Being Abused or Neglected?

If you suspect or know that a child is being abused or neglected, there are ways you can help. If you or someone else is in immediate and serious danger, you should call 911. In other cases, you can find a trusted adult to talk with. You do not need to be 100 percent sure that a child is being abused or neglected to talk with someone. You should share your worries, and the adult can help determine what to do next. You also can encourage the child to talk to a trusted adult.

Many times, there is a trusted adult already in your life—such as a parent, teacher, school counselor, or coach—that you can approach. You can tell this trusted adult what your concerns are or what you have witnessed. Give a complete, honest description of what you know. This may be a difficult conversation to have, but remember the reason you are having it: to keep someone (maybe you) safe. The adult can help figure out what can be done.

Some children and youth may not have an adult that they trust enough to talk with about their concerns, or they may have told an adult who does not believe them. In this case, there are national and local hotlines they can call for help. The Childhelp National Child Abuse Hotline has counselors available 24 hours every day to talk with children and adults about abuse and neglect. To reach a Childhelp counselor, call 800-422-4453, and then press 1.

Other Questions You Might Have

Here are answers to other questions that might come up in these situations:

Is Telling Someone Else Just Tattling or Snitching?

No. There is a big difference between telling someone about a child who is being hurt and tattling. Children usually tattle to get another child in trouble for not following a rule. Telling someone about abuse or neglect—or even bullying—is about keeping a child safe. You are not tattling when you report abuse or neglect to someone.

What Will Happen after You Tell Someone?

After you talk with a trusted adult or call a hotline, that person may contact a local agency, often called "child protective services" or

"CPS." The workers at CPS are trained to help make sure that children and families are safe. When they receive a call, CPS workers review the information and figure out if they need to investigate. If so, they may talk with the family, the child, or others to help determine what is making the child unsafe. CPS workers can help parents or other caregivers get services, education, or other assistance so they can learn to better care for their children in their own homes. If a child is in danger at that moment or has been seriously hurt by a parent or other caregiver, the CPS worker may need to have the child stay with another relative or in foster care, which is a temporary home for the child to live. In these situations, the CPS worker will work with the family so that the child can return to live with the parent or other caregivers when CPS determines they will be safe and properly treated.

Will I Get in Trouble for Telling Someone?

If you are being honest about what you have noticed, you will not get in trouble, even if the child was not actually being abused or neglected. You do not have to be absolutely sure about whether a child is being abused or neglected when you talk with someone about your concerns. You told someone because you really thought the child was in danger. However, if someone purposely lies to CPS when reporting abuse or neglect, they could get in trouble.

Will the Other Child Get Upset with Me for Telling Someone Else?

Children often tell each other secrets, or you may see or hear something that was supposed to be a secret. A friend or classmate may tell you they are being harmed and ask you not to tell anyone. When a child is being harmed, this is a secret that must be shared, and telling a trusted adult is the right move. It is possible the child could be upset you told, but she or he is probably feeling a lot of different emotions at that time. The child may feel scared because he or she is being hurt. The child may feel ashamed or embarrassed that someone else knows about what happened. The child may be confused because someone she or he cares about is harming them. The child may feel guilty because he or she told someone else about "family business." All these feelings are normal, but you should still tell someone. By talking with a trusted adult, you are showing the child that you care, and it could lead to the family getting help to keep everyone safe.

Why Do Parents Abuse or Neglect Their Children?

There are many reasons why a parent or other caregiver may abuse or neglect a child, but no matter what, it is never the child's fault. Adults who hurt children may have trouble controlling their anger. They also may not know about children's needs or have unrealistic expectations about how children grow and develop (for example, thinking a baby should be potty trained by the age of one). Adults also may have problems, such as using drugs or having mental-health issues, that affect how they make decisions. Of course, there are many other reasons an adult may abuse or neglect a child, and not every parent who has the problems mentioned here will harm their children. No matter the reason an adult harm a child, it is important that the family receives help to make sure it stops.

Chapter 42

Legal Interventions in Suspected Child Abuse Cases

Chapter Contents

Section 42.1

How the Child Welfare System Works

This section includes text excerpted from "How the Child
Welfare System Works," Child Welfare Information
Gateway, U.S. Department of Health and Human
Services (HHS), February 2013. Reviewed March 2019.

The child welfare system is a group of services designed to promote
the well-being of children by ensuring safety, achieving permanency,
and strengthening families to care for their children successfully.
While the primary responsibility for child welfare services rests with
the states, the federal government plays a major role in supporting
states in the delivery of services through funding of programs and
legislative initiatives.

The primary responsibility for implementing federal child and family legislation rests with the Children's Bureau, within the Administration on Children, Youth, and Families (ACYF); the Administration
for Children and Families (ACF); and the U.S. Department of Health
and Human Services (HHS). The Children's Bureau works with state
and local agencies to develop programs that focus on preventing child
abuse and neglect by strengthening families, protecting children from
further maltreatment, reuniting children safely with their families,
or finding permanent families for children who cannot safely return
home.

Most families first become involved with their local child welfare system because of a report of suspected child abuse or neglect
(sometimes called "child maltreatment"). Child maltreatment is
defined by the Child Abuse Prevention and Treatment Act (CAPTA)
as "serious harm (neglect, physical abuse, sexual abuse, and emotional abuse or neglect) caused to children by parents or primary
caregivers, such as extended family members or babysitters." Child
maltreatment also can include harm that a caregiver allows to
happen or does not prevent from happening to a child. In general,
child welfare agencies do not intervene in cases of harm to children
caused by acquaintances or strangers. These cases are the responsibility of law enforcement.

The child welfare system is not a single entity. Many organizations in each community work together to strengthen families and
keep children safe. Public agencies, such as departments of social
services or child and family services, often contract and collaborate

with private child welfare agencies and community-based organizations to provide services to families, such as in-home family preservation services, foster care, residential treatment, mental-health care, substance-abuse treatment, parenting skills classes, domestic violence services, employment assistance, and financial or housing assistance.

Child welfare systems are complex, and their specific procedures vary widely by state. Child welfare systems typically:

- Receive and investigate reports of possible child abuse and neglect

- Provide services to families that need assistance in the protection and care of their children

- Arrange for children to live with kin or with foster families when they are not safe at home

- Arrange for reunification, adoption, or other permanent family connections for children leaving foster care

What Happens When Possible Abuse or Neglect Is Reported?

Any concerned person can report suspicions of child abuse or neglect. Most reports are made by "mandatory reporters"—people who are required by state law to report suspicions of child abuse and neglect. As of August 2012, statutes in approximately 18 states and Puerto Rico require any person who suspects child abuse or neglect to report it. These reports are generally received by child protective services (CPS) workers and are either "screened in" or "screened out." A report is screened in when there is sufficient information to suggest an investigation is warranted. A report may be screened out if there is not enough information on which to follow up, or if the situation reported does not meet the state's legal definition of abuse or neglect. In these instances, the worker may refer the person reporting the incident to other community services or law enforcement for additional help.

What Happens after a Report Is "Screened In"?

CPS caseworkers, often called "investigators" or "assessment workers," respond within a particular time period—which may be anywhere from a few hours to a few days, depending on the type of maltreatment alleged—the potential severity of the situation, and requirements under state law. They may speak with the parents and other people in contact with the child, such as doctors, teachers, or child care providers. They also may speak with the child, alone or in the presence of caregivers, depending on the child's age and level of risk. Children who are believed to be in immediate danger may be moved to a shelter, a foster home, or a relative's home during the investigation and while court proceedings are pending. An investigator also engages the family, assessing strengths and needs and initiating connections to community resources and services.

Some jurisdictions now employ an alternative, or differential, response system.

In these jurisdictions, when the risk to the children involved is considered low, the CPS caseworker focuses on assessing family strengths, resources, and difficulties and on identifying supports and services needed, rather than on gathering evidence to confirm the occurrence of abuse or neglect.

At the end of an investigation, CPS caseworkers typically make one of two findings—unsubstantiated (unfounded) or substantiated (founded). These terms vary from state to state. Typically, a finding of unsubstantiated means there is insufficient evidence for the worker to conclude that a child was abused or neglected, or what happened does not meet the legal definition of child abuse or neglect. A finding of substantiated typically means that an incident of child abuse or neglect, as defined by state law, is believed to have occurred. Some states have additional categories, such as "unable to determine," that suggest there was not enough evidence to either confirm or refute that abuse or neglect occurred.

The agency will initiate a court action if it determines that the authority of the juvenile court (through a child protection or dependency proceeding) is necessary to keep the child safe. To protect the child, the court can issue temporary orders placing the child in shelter care during the investigation, ordering services, or ordering certain individuals to have no contact with the child. At an adjudicatory hearing, the court hears evidence and decides whether maltreatment occurred and whether the child should be under the continuing jurisdiction of the court. The court then enters a disposition, either at that hearing or at a separate hearing, which may result in the court ordering a parent to comply with services necessary to alleviate the abuse or neglect. Orders can also contain provisions regarding visitation between the parent and the child, agency obligations to provide the parent with services, and services needed by the child.

What Happens in Substantiated (Founded) Cases

If a child has been abused or neglected, the course of action depends on state policy, the severity of the maltreatment, an assessment of the child's immediate safety, the risk of continued or future maltreatment, the services available to address the family's needs, and whether the child was removed from the home and a court action to protect the child was initiated. The following general options are available:

- **No or low risk.** The family's case may be closed with no services if the maltreatment was a one-time incident, the child is considered to be safe, there is no or low risk of future incidents, and any services the family needs will not be provided through the child welfare agency but through other community-based resources and service systems.

- **Low to moderate risk.** Referrals may be made to community-based or voluntary in-home child welfare services if the CPS worker believes the family would benefit from these services and the child's present and future safety would be enhanced. This may happen even when no abuse or neglect is found if the family needs, and is willing, to participate in services.

- **Moderate to high risk.** The family may again be offered voluntary in-home services to address safety concerns and help reduce the risks. If these are refused, the agency may seek intervention by the juvenile dependency court. Once there is a judicial determination that abuse or neglect occurred, the juvenile dependency court may require the family to cooperate with in-home services if it is believed that the child can remain safely at home, while the family addresses the issues contributing to the risk of future maltreatment. If the child has been seriously harmed, is considered to be at high risk of serious harm, or the child's safety is threatened, the court may order the child's removal from the home or affirm the agency's prior removal of the child. The child may be placed with a relative or in foster care.

What Happens to Parents

Caregivers who are found to have abused or neglected a child are generally offered support and treatment services or are required by a juvenile dependency court to participate in services that will help keep their children safe. In cases of low risk, in-home services and supports may be provided, including parent education, child care, counseling, safety planning, and more.

In more severe cases or fatalities, police are called on to investigate and may file charges in criminal court against the perpetrators of child maltreatment. In many states, certain types of abuse, such as sexual abuse and serious physical abuse, are routinely referred to law enforcement.

Whether or not criminal charges are filed, the name of the person committing the abuse or neglect may be placed on a state child maltreatment registry if abuse or neglect is confirmed. A registry is a central database that collects information about maltreated children and individuals who are found to have abused or neglected those children. These registries are usually confidential and used for internal child protective purposes only. However, they may be used in background checks for certain professions that involve working with children to protect children from contact with individuals who may mistreat them.

What Happens to Children

Depending on the severity of the case, children may remain at home or be removed into foster care.

In-Home

In low-risk cases, children may remain in their own homes with their families, and the families may receive in-home services and supports. These may include parent education, safety planning, counseling, and more. Families may also be connected with community services that provide concrete help (e.g., housing, food), as well as services such as therapy, parent training, and support groups.

Out-of-Home

Most children in foster care are placed with relatives or foster families, but some may be placed in a group or residential setting. While a child is in foster care, she or he attends school and should receive medical care and other services as needed. The child's family also receives services to support their efforts to reduce the risk of future maltreatment and to help them, in most cases, be reunited with their child. Visits between parents and their children and between siblings are encouraged and supported, following a set plan.

Every child in foster care should have a permanency plan. Families typically participate in developing a permanency plan for the child and a service plan for the family, and these plans guide the agency's work. Family reunification, except in unusual and extreme circumstances, is the permanency plan for most children. In some cases, when prospects for reunification appear less likely, a concurrent permanency plan is developed. If the efforts toward reunification are not successful, the plan may be changed to another permanent arrangement, such as adoption or transfer of custody to a relative.

Section 42.2

Court Appointed Special Advocates for Children

This section includes text excerpted from "Representation of Children in Child Abuse and Neglect Proceedings," Child Welfare Information Gateway, U.S. Department of Health and Human Services (HHS), December 2017.

Representation of Children in Child Abuse and Neglect Proceedings

The federal Child Abuse Prevention and Treatment Act (CAPTA) requires states to document in their state plan provisions for appointing a guardian ad litem (GAL) to represent the child's best interests in every case of abuse or neglect that results in a judicial proceeding. The GAL may be an attorney or a court-appointed special advocate (CASA)—or both—who has received appropriate training. The GAL represents the child at all judicial proceedings related to the case and has the responsibility to perform the following tasks:

- Obtain firsthand a clear understanding of the situation and needs of the child

- Make recommendations to the court concerning the best interests of the child

At the state level, statutes specify when the court must appoint a representative—and whom the court may appoint—for a child who is involved in an abuse and neglect proceeding. As described in the National Council of Juvenile and Family Court Judges' Enhanced Resource Guidelines: Improving Court Practice in Child Abuse and Neglect Cases, there are a number of ways that a child's interests can be represented. In some instances, two or more of these representatives may work on the same case:

- A GAL may be appointed to investigate and advocate for the child's best interests.

- An attorney may be appointed specifically to advocate for the child's position and expressed wishes before the court.

- A CASA may be appointed to assist the court by investigating a child's circumstances and providing recommendations on meeting the child's needs. In some cases, a CASA may serve as the child's GAL, as described in CAPTA.

Making the Appointment

For this section, statutes regarding requirements for providing legal representation for children involved in cases of child abuse or neglect that result in judicial proceedings were collected from across all states, the District of Columbia, and the U.S. territories, and an analysis of the information informs the discussion that follows. All states, the District of Columbia, American Samoa, Guam, the Northern Mariana Islands, Puerto Rico, and the U.S. Virgin Islands provide in their statutes for the appointment of representation for a child involved in a child abuse or neglect proceeding. Approximately 41 states, the District of Columbia, American Samoa, Guam, the Northern Mariana Islands, Puerto Rico, and the Virgin Islands provide for the appointment of a GAL to represent the best interests of the child. In 15 of these states, the District of Columbia, and the Virgin Islands, the GAL must be an attorney. In Montana, a CASA, who may or may not be an attorney, can be appointed as the child's GAL. In other states, volunteers who may or may not be attorneys may serve as GALs.

16 states require the appointment of an attorney for the child; 7 states require both an attorney and GAL. Oregon requires the appointment of a CASA. In Wisconsin, a child has the right to counsel, and she or he may not be removed from the home unless counsel has been appointed. If the child is under the age of 12, the court may appoint

a GAL instead of counsel. In 4 states, if the GAL is not an attorney, counsel may be appointed to represent the GAL.

In all cases, the appointment of a GAL, attorney, or CASA is made by the court that has jurisdiction over the child abuse or neglect proceedings. In Louisiana, the attorney may be provided by a Child Advocacy Program. In Maryland, the court appoints an attorney with whom the Department of Human Resources has contracted to provide legal services. In Washington, the court may select a GAL from a rotational registry of qualified GALs.

The Use of Court-Appointed Special Advocates

Approximately 37 states, the District of Columbia, and the Virgin Islands allow for the appointment of a CASA. In 16 of these states, the CASA may serve as the GAL. In 14 states, the District of Columbia, and the Virgin Islands, the CASA may be appointed in addition to the GAL. A CASA may be appointed in addition to an attorney in 8 states. In Connecticut, Louisiana, and New Mexico, a CASA may be assigned to assist the court, while in Missouri, Rhode Island, and Utah a CASA may be selected to assist the court or the child's GAL.

Qualifications and Training

Approximately 46 states, the District of Columbia, and the Virgin Islands address the qualifications and training required for a person who can be assigned to represent a child involved in a child abuse or neglect proceeding. In the states that require the appointment of an attorney for the child, 6 of these states do not require additional specific training, while 3 states express in general terms that a child's counsel have training and experience that is appropriate to the role. 7 states have certain requirements that must be met before an attorney may be appointed as a child's counsel, either in terms of the content of training, the number of hours of training, or both.

For attorneys serving as GALs, training requirements vary considerably from state to state. In 3 states, additional training is not specified. In 14 states, laws require attorneys to receive training specific to their roles as GALs. For example, Florida requires training to be provided by the Statewide Guardian ad Litem Office. In Georgia, the requirement for training can be satisfied within the state's existing continuing legal education obligations. Laws in 7 states and the District of Columbia provide more specific requirements about the content of training, including knowledge about the needs and protection of children; applicable statutory, regulatory, and case law; and the roles, responsibilities, and duties when representing the best interests of a child.

For non-attorneys acting as GALs and CASAs, the laws in many states provide more detailed training requirements. Typically, an initial training program must be completed before a person may be assigned to a child's case, followed by ongoing in-service training. The training programs are designed to ensure that the child's advocate possesses the knowledge and skills to represent the child's best interests competently. Topics covered in these programs may include the following:

- Child abuse and neglect
- Early childhood, child, and adolescent development
- Roles and responsibilities of the child's advocate
- Cultural awareness
- The juvenile court process
- Federal, state, and local laws, regulations, and rules
- Interview techniques and information gathering
- Documentation and report writing

9 states specify that the training provided to CASAs must comply with standards set by the National Court Appointed Special Advocates Association.

In addition to training requirements, volunteers are screened and interviewed prior to acceptance in a GAL or CASA program. 20 states and the Northern Mariana Islands require criminal background checks. Checks of the state's child abuse and neglect registry are required in 12 states. California, Florida, and Idaho require checks of the state's sex offender registry.

Specific Duties

The primary responsibility of a GAL is to represent the best interests of a child in child abuse and neglect proceedings. The laws in 42 states, the District of Columbia, American Samoa, Guam, the Northern Mariana Islands, and the Virgin Islands list specific duties that may be required as part of that responsibility. These duties include, but are not limited to, the following:

- Meeting face to face with the child on a regular basis, including before all hearings
- Conducting an independent investigation of the circumstances of the case
- Attending all hearings and staffings related to the case
- Monitoring cases to ensure that court orders for services have been fulfilled
- Submitting written reports to the court

The GAL also is expected to make recommendations to the court about specific actions that would serve the best interests of the child. Sometimes, the GAL's determination of best interests may conflict with the child's expressed wishes. In 26 states, the District of Columbia, Guam, and the Virgin Islands, the GAL is obligated to communicate the child's wishes to the court along with her or his own recommendations. In 14 states, the District of Columbia, and Guam, the court may appoint a separate counsel to represent the child's wishes.

The statutes in 15 states list specific duties for a CASA who is appointed in addition to an attorney or GAL. Typically, these duties may include the following:

- Investigating the case to provide independent, factual information to the court

- Monitoring the case to ensure compliance with court orders

- Determining whether appropriate services are being offered to the child and family

- Preparing regular written reports for the court and parties to the case

Compensating the Representative

Most states, the District of Columbia, American Samoa, and Guam provide in statute that reasonable compensation should be paid to attorneys and GALs who are appointed to represent a child. In Arkansas, the child's attorney is contracted through a state agency, while in Colorado, Kentucky, and Oregon, attorney expenses are paid by either a state agency or a specially designated fund. In California and Connecticut, the child's attorney and GAL are assigned by the public defender's office, which also has the responsibility to pay the fees of the attorney and GAL.

In 33 states, the District of Columbia, American Samoa, and Guam, fees and expenses for attorney and/or GAL services are paid by the court handling the case. In 7 states and American Samoa, these costs are funded by the state; in 13 states, expenses are paid by the county. To the extent that they are able to pay, the court in 22 states and Guam may require the parent or guardian of the child or other appropriate party to reimburse the court for any attorney or GAL fees that have been paid. In Tennessee and American Samoa, the person found responsible for the abuse or neglect is required to pay these expenses.

Since they serve as volunteers, CASAs are not compensated. However, in Maine and Missouri, they may be reimbursed for any expenses they incur.

Chapter 43

Reporting Child Abuse

Chapter Contents

Section 43.1

How to Report Suspected Child Maltreatment

This section includes text excerpted from "How to Report
Suspected Child Maltreatment," Child Welfare Information
Gateway, U.S. Department of Health and Human Services (HHS),
December 13, 2014. Reviewed March 2019.

If you suspect a child is being abused or neglected, or if you are a
child who is being maltreated, contact your local child protective services (CPS) office or law enforcement agency (LEA), so professionals
can assess the situation. Many states have a toll-free number to call
to report suspected child abuse or neglect.

Anyone can report suspected child abuse or neglect. Reporting
abuse or neglect can protect a child and get help for a family; it may
even save a child's life. In some states, any person who suspects child
abuse or neglect is required to report it.

The Child Welfare Information Gateway provides resources to promote child welfare, but it is not a hotline for reporting suspected child
abuse or neglect nor is it equipped to accept reports of this nature.
Information Gateway is not equipped to offer crisis counseling. As a
service of the Children's Bureau (CB) in the U.S. Department of Health
and Human Services (HHS), Information Gateway does not have the
authority to intervene or advise in personal situations.

Childhelp® is a national organization that provides crisis assistance
and other counseling and referral services. The Childhelp National
Child Abuse Hotline is staffed 24 hours a day, 7 days a week, with
professional crisis counselors who have access to a database of 55,000
emergency, social service, and support resources. All calls are anonymous. Contact them at 800-422-4453.

Section 43.2

Mandatory Reporters of Child Abuse and Neglect

This section includes text excerpted from "Mandatory Reporters of Child Abuse and Neglect," Child Welfare Information Gateway, U.S. Department of Health and Human Services (HHS), August 2015. Reviewed March 2019.

All states, the District of Columbia (DC), American Samoa, Guam, the Northern Mariana Islands, Puerto Rico, and the U.S. Virgin Islands have statutes identifying persons who are required to report suspected child maltreatment to an appropriate agency, such as child protective services (CPS), a law enforcement agency, or a state's toll-free child abuse reporting hotline.

Professionals Required to Report

Approximately 48 states, the DC, American Samoa, Guam, the Northern Mariana Islands, Puerto Rico, and the Virgin Islands designate professions whose members are mandated by law to report child maltreatment. Individuals designated as mandatory reporters typically have frequent contact with children. Such individuals may include:

- Social workers
- Teachers, principals, and other school personnel
- Physicians, nurses, and other healthcare workers
- Counselors, therapists, and other mental-health professionals
- Child care providers
- Medical examiners or coroners
- Law enforcement officers

Some other professions frequently mandated across the states include commercial film or photograph processors (in 12 states, Guam, and Puerto Rico) and computer technicians (in 6 states). Substance-abuse counselors are required to report in 14 states, and probation or parole officers are mandatory reporters in 17 states. Directors, employees, and volunteers at entities that provide organized activities for children, such as camps, day camps, youth centers, and recreation centers, are required to report in 13 states.

The DC includes animal control or humane officers. Illinois includes both domestic violence workers and animal control or humane officers as mandatory reporters. Court-appointed special advocates are mandatory reporters in 11 states. Members of the clergy now are required to report in 27 states and Guam.

11 states now have faculty, administrators, athletics staff, other employees, and volunteers at institutions of higher learning—including public and private colleges, universities, and vocational and technical schools—designated as mandatory reporters.

Reporting by Other Persons

In approximately 18 states and Puerto Rico, any person who suspects child abuse or neglect is required to report it. Of these 18 states, 16 states and Puerto Rico specify certain professionals who must file a report, but also require all persons to report suspected abuse or neglect, regardless of profession. New Jersey and Wyoming require all persons to report without specifying any professions. In all other states, territories, and the DC, any person is permitted to report. These voluntary reporters of abuse are often referred to as "permissive reporters."

Institutional Responsibility to Report

The term "institutional reporting" refers to situations in which the mandated reporter is working (or volunteering) as a staff member of an institution, such as a school or hospital, and she or he gains knowledge that leads her or him to suspect that abuse or neglect has occurred. Many institutions have internal policies and procedures for handling reports of abuse, and these usually require the person who suspects abuse to notify the head of the institution of the suspected abuse and report it to CPS or other appropriate authorities. Statutes in 33 states, the DC, and the Virgin Islands provide procedures that must be followed in those cases. In 18 states, the DC, and the Virgin Islands, any staff member who suspects abuse must notify the head of the institution when the staff member feels that abuse or possible abuse should be reported to an appropriate authority. In 9 states, the DC, and the Virgin Islands, the staff member who suspects abuse notifies the head of the institution first, and then the head, or his or her designee, is required to make the report. In

9 states, the individual reporter must make the report to the appropriate authority first, and then notify the institution that a report has been made.

Laws in 15 states make clear that, regardless of any policies within the organization, the mandatory reporter is not relieved of her or his responsibility to report. In 17 states, an employer is expressly prohibited from taking any action to prevent or discourage an employee from making a report.

Standards for Making a Report

The circumstances under which a mandatory reporter must make a report vary from state to state. Typically, a report must be made when the reporter, in her or his official capacity, suspects or has reason to believe that a child has been abused or neglected. Another standard frequently used is in situations in which the reporter has knowledge of, or observes a child being subjected to, conditions that would reasonably result in harm to the child. In Maine, a mandatory reporter must report when she or he has reasonable cause to suspect that a child is not living with the child's family.

Mandatory reporters are required to report the facts and circumstances that led them to suspect that a child has been abused or neglected. They do not have the burden of providing proof that abuse or neglect has occurred. Permissive reporters follow the same standards when electing to make a report.

Privileged Communications

Mandatory reporting statutes also may specify when a communication is privileged. "Privileged communications" is the statutory recognition of the right to maintain confidential communications between professionals and their clients, patients, or congregants. To enable states to provide protection to maltreated children, the reporting laws in most states and territories restrict this privilege for mandated reporters. All but three states and Puerto Rico currently address the issue of privileged communications within their reporting laws, either affirming the privilege or denying it (i.e., not allowing the privilege to be grounds for failing to report). For instance:

- The physician-patient and husband-wife privileges are the most common to be denied by states.

- The attorney-client privilege is most commonly affirmed.

- The clergy-penitent privilege is also widely affirmed; although that privilege usually is limited to confessional communications and, in some states, denied altogether.

In Louisiana, a mental health or social services practitioner is not required to report if the practitioner is engaged by an attorney to assist in the provision of legal services to a child.

Inclusion of the Reporter's Name in the Report

Most states maintain toll-free telephone numbers for receiving reports of abuse or neglect. Reports may be made anonymously to most of these reporting numbers, but states find it helpful to their investigations to know the identity of reporters. Approximately 19 states, the DC, American Samoa, Guam, and the Virgin Islands currently require mandatory reporters to provide their names and contact information, either at the time of the initial oral report or as part of a written report. The laws in Connecticut, Delaware, and Washington allow child protection workers to request the name of the reporter. In Wyoming, the reporter does not have to provide her or his identity as part of the written report, but if the person takes and submits photographs or X-rays* of the child, her or his name must be provided.

A type of high-energy radiation. In low doses, X-rays are used to diagnose diseases by making pictures of the inside of the body.

Disclosure of the Reporter's Identity

All jurisdictions have provisions in the statute to maintain the confidentiality of abuse and neglect records. The identity of the reporter is specifically protected from disclosure to the alleged perpetrator in 41 states, the DC, American Samoa, Guam, the Northern Mariana Islands, and Puerto Rico. This protection is maintained even when other information from the report may be disclosed.

Release of the reporter's identity is allowed in some jurisdictions under specific circumstances or to specific departments or officials—for example, when information is needed for conducting an investigation or family assessment or upon a finding that the reporter knowingly made a false report (in Alabama, Arkansas, Connecticut, Kentucky, Louisiana, Minnesota, Nevada, South Dakota, Vermont, and Virginia). In some jurisdictions (California, Florida, Minnesota, Tennessee, Texas, Vermont, the DC, and Guam), the reporter can waive confidentiality and give consent to the release of her or his name.

Chapter 44

Therapy Options for Children Impacted by Abuse

Chapter Contents

Section 44.1

Cognitive Behavioral Therapy for Physical Abuse

This section includes text excerpted from "Alternatives for Families: A Cognitive-Behavioral Therapy (AF-CBT)," Child Welfare Information Gateway, U.S. Department of Health and Human Services (HHS), January 2013. Reviewed March 2019.

Families that experience conflict, coercion, and/or physical abuse create a substantial risk to children's development of significant psychiatric, behavioral, and adjustment difficulties, including aggression, poor interpersonal skills/functioning, and emotional reactivity. Caregivers in such families often report punitive or excessive parenting practices, frequent anger and hyperarousal, and negative child attributions, among other stressful conditions. During the past four decades, research has documented the effectiveness of several behavioral and cognitive behavioral methods, many of which have been incorporated in alternatives for families: a cognitive-behavioral therapy (AF-CBT).

AF-CBT is an evidence-supported intervention that targets:

- Diverse individual child and caregiver characteristics related to conflict and intimidation in the home

- The family context in which aggression or abuse may occur. This approach emphasizes training in intra- and interpersonal skills designed to enhance self-control and reduce violent behavior. AF-CBT has been found to improve functioning in school-aged children, their parents (caregivers), and their families following a referral for concerns about parenting practices, including child physical abuse, as well as a child's behavior problems.

This section is intended to build a better understanding of the characteristics and benefits of AF-CBT, formerly known as "abuse-focused cognitive behavioral therapy." The information provided in this section may help parents, foster parents, and other caregivers understand what they and their children can gain from AF-CBT and what to expect during treatment. In addition, this section may be useful to others with an interest in implementing or participating in effective strategies for the treatment of family conflict, child physical abuse, coercive parenting, and children with externalizing behavior problems.

What Makes Alternatives for Families: A Cognitive Behavioral Therapy Unique?

AF-CBT is designed to intervene with families referred for conflict or coercion, verbal or physical aggression by caregivers (including the use of excessive physical force or threats), behavior problems in children/adolescents, or child physical abuse. The treatment program has been expanded to accommodate children and adolescents with physical abuse or discipline-related trauma symptoms, such as posttraumatic stress disorder (PTSD).

AF-CBT addresses both the risk factors and the consequences of physical, emotional, and verbal aggression in a comprehensive manner. Thus, AF-CBT seeks to address specific clinical targets among caregivers that include heightened anger or hostility, negative perceptions or attributions of their children, and difficulties in the appropriate and effective use of parenting practices, such as ineffective or punitive parenting practices. Likewise, AF-CBT targets children's difficulties with anger or anxiety, trauma-related emotional symptoms, poor social and relationship skills, behavioral problems that include aggression, and dysfunctional attributions. At the family level, AF-CBT addresses coercive family interactions by teaching skills to improve positive family relations and reduce family conflict.

Reflects a Comprehensive Treatment Strategy

The diversity of family circumstances and individual problems associated with family conflict points to the need for a comprehensive treatment strategy that targets both the contributors to caregivers' behavior and children's subsequent behavioral and emotional adjustment. Treatment approaches that focus on several aspects of the problem (for example, a caregiver's parenting skills, a child's anger, or family coercion) may have a greater likelihood of reducing re-abuse and more fully remediating mental-health problems. Therefore, AF-CBT adopts a comprehensive treatment strategy that addresses the complexity of the issues more completely.

Integrates Several Therapeutic Approaches

AF-CBT combines elements drawn from the following:

- Cognitive therapy, which aims to change behavior by addressing a person's thoughts or perceptions, particularly thinking patterns that create distorted views

- Behavioral and learning theory, which focuses on modifying habitual responses (e.g., anger, fear) to identified situations or stimuli

- Family therapy, which examines patterns of interactions among family members to identify and alleviate problems, and offers strategies to help reframe how problems are viewed

- Developmental victimology, which describes how the specific effects of exposure to traumatic or abusive experiences may vary for children at different developmental stages and across the life span

- Psychology of aggression, which describes the processes by which aggression and coercion develop and are maintained, which can help to understand one's history as both a contributor to and victim of aggressive behavior

AF-CBT pulls together many techniques currently used by practitioners, such as behavior and anger management, affect regulation, problem-solving, social skills training, cognitive restructuring, and communication. The advantage of this program is that all of these techniques, relevant handouts, training examples, and outcome measures are integrated in a structured approach that practitioners and supervisors can easily access and use.

Treats Children and Parents Simultaneously

During AF-CBT, school-aged children (between the ages of 5 and 15) and their caregivers participate in separate but coordinated therapy sessions, often using somewhat parallel treatment materials. In addition, children and parents attend joint sessions together at various times throughout treatment. This approach seeks to address individual and parent-child issues in an integrated fashion.

Discourages Aggressive or Violent Behavior

The AF-CBT approach is designed to promote appropriate and prosocial behavior, while discouraging coercive, aggressive, or violent behavior from caregivers, as well as children. Consistent with cognitive-behavioral approaches, AF-CBT includes procedures that target three related ways in which people respond to different circumstances:

- Cognition (thinking)

- Affect (feeling)

- Behavior (doing)

AF-CBT includes training in various psychological skills in each of these response channels that are designed to promote self-control and to enhance interpersonal effectiveness.

Tailors Treatment to Meet Specific Needs and Circumstances

AF-CBT begins with a multisource assessment to identify the nature of the problems the child is experiencing, specific parental and family difficulties that may be contributing to family conflict, and the child's and family's strengths that may help influence change. Tailoring the treatment to the family's specific strengths and challenges is key to efficient outcomes.

Treatment Phases and Key Components

AF-CBT is a short-term treatment typically provided once or twice a week, which may require 18 to 24 hours of service (or longer, based on individual needs) over 4 to 12 months (although treatment may last as long as determined necessary). Treatment includes separate individual sessions with the child and caregiver/parent and joint sessions with at least both of them. Where necessary, family interventions may be applied before, during, or after the individual services. The treatment program for children, caregivers, and families incorporates the use of specific skills, roleplaying exercises, performance feedback, and home practice exercises.

Generally, the goals of AF-CBT treatment are to:

- Reduce conflict and increase cohesion in family

- Reduce use of coercion (hostility, anger, verbal aggression, threats) by the caregiver and other family members

- Reduce use of physical force (aggressive behavior) by the caregiver, child, and, as relevant, other family members

- Promote nonaggressive (alternative) discipline and interactions

- Reduce child physical abuse risk or recidivism (prevention of child welfare system involvement or repeated reports/allegations)

- Improve the level of child's safety/welfare and family functioning

Treatment Phases

AF-CBT includes three treatment phases, each with key content that is designed to be relevant for both the caregiver and child. The sequence for conducting the treatment generally proceeds from teaching intrapersonal (e.g., cognitive, affective) skills first, followed by interpersonal skills (e.g., behavioral). Although AF-CBT has primarily been used in outpatient and home settings, the treatment has been delivered in inpatient and residential settings when there is some ongoing or potential contact between the caregiver and the child.

Key Components

AB-CBT includes specific therapy elements for children, parents, and families.

Treatment for School-Aged Children

The school-aged child-directed therapy elements include:

- Promoting engagement and treatment motivation by identifying individualized goals

- Identifying the child's exposure to and views of positive experiences and upsetting ones (family hostility, coercion, and violence), including the child's perceptions of the circumstances and consequences of the physical abuse or other conflicts

- Educating the child on topics related to child welfare, safety/ protection, service participation, and common reactions to abuse and family conflict

- Training in techniques to identify, express, and manage emotions appropriately (e.g., anxiety management, anger control)

- Processing the child's exposure to incidents involving force or family conflict to understand and challenge any dysfunctional thoughts/views that encourage the use of aggression or support self-blame

- Training in interpersonal skills to enhance social competence and developing social support plans

- For those with significant PTSD symptoms, conducting imaginal exposure and helping to articulate the meaning of what happened to the child

Treatment for Parents or Caregivers

Parent-directed therapy elements include:

- Education about relevance of the CBT model and physical abuse

- Establishing a commitment to limit physical force

- Encouraging discussion of any incidents involving the use of force within the family

- Reviewing the child's exposure to emotional abuse in the family and providing education about the parameters of abusive experiences (causes, characteristics, and consequences), in order to understand the context in which they occurred

- Teaching affect management skills to help identify and manage reactions to abuse-specific triggers, heightened anger, anxiety, and depression to promote self-control

- Identifying and addressing cognitive contributors to abusive behavior in caregivers (i.e., misattributions, high expectations, etc.) and/or their consequences in children (i.e., views supportive of aggression, self-blame, etc.) that could maintain any physically abusive or aggressive behavior

- Teaching parents strategies to support the child and encourage positive behavior using active/listening attention, praise, and rewards

- Training in effective discipline guidelines and strategies (e.g., planned ignoring, withdrawal of privileges, time out,) as alternatives to the use of physical force

- If the caregiver is ready, working on a clarification letter to be read to the child

Treatment for Families or the Parent and Child

Parent-child or family therapy elements include:

- Conducting a family assessment using multiple methods and identifying family treatment goals

- Encouraging a commitment to increasing the use of positive behavior as an alternative to the use of force

- Conducting a clarification session in which the caregiver can support the child by providing an apology, taking responsibility for the abuse/conflict, and showing a commitment to safety plans and other rules in order to keep the family safe and intact

- Training in communication skills to encourage constructive interactions

- Training in nonaggressive problem-solving skills with home practice applications

- Involving community and social systems, as needed

Target Population

AF-CBT is most appropriate for use with physically, emotionally, and/or verbally abusive or coercive parents and their school-aged children. AF-CBT has also been adapted for children diagnosed with behavior problems or disorders, including conduct disorder and oppositional defiant disorder. Often, the children experience behavioral dysfunction, especially aggression, as a result of abuse. AF-CBT may also help high-conflict families who are at risk for physical abuse/aggression.

Thus, AF-CBT is recommended for use with families that exhibit any or all of the following:

- Caregivers whose disciplinary or management strategies range from mild physical discipline to physically aggressive or abusive behaviors, or caregivers who exhibit heightened levels of anger, hostility, or explosiveness

- Children who exhibit significant externalizing or aggressive behavior (e.g., oppositionality, antisocial behavior), with or without significant physical abuse/discipline-related trauma symptoms (e.g., anger, anxiety, PTSD)

- Families who exhibit heightened conflict or coercion or who pose threats to personal safety

Limitations for Use of Alternatives for Families: A Cognitive Behavioral Therapy

Parents with psychiatric disorders that may significantly impair their general functioning or their ability to learn new skills (e.g., substance-use disorders (SUDs), major depression) may benefit from alternative or adjunctive interventions designed to address these problems. In addition, children or parents with very limited intellectual functioning, or very young children, may require more simplified services or translations of some of the more complicated treatment concepts. Children with psychiatric disorders, such as significant attention deficit disorder (ADD) or major depression, may benefit from additional interventions. Sexually abused children may respond better to trauma-focused therapy.

Effectiveness of Alternatives for Families: A Cognitive Behavioral Therapy

The effectiveness of AF-CBT is supported by a number of outcome studies, and AF-CBT has been recognized by other experts as a "model" or "promising" treatment program.

Demonstrated Effectiveness in Outcome Studies

During the past four decades, many of the procedures incorporated into AF-CBT have been evaluated by outside investigators as effective in:

- Improving child, parent, and/or family functioning

- Promoting safety and/or reducing abuse risk or reabuse among various populations of parents, children, and families

These procedures have included the use of stress management and anger-control training, cognitive restructuring, parenting skills training, psychoeducational information regarding the use and impact of physical force and hostility, social skills training, imaginal exposure, and family interventions focusing on reducing conflict. Foundational studies by Kolko showed the effectiveness of the individual components of AF-CBT when compared to routine community services with abusive families in terms of improved child, parent, and family outcomes. A study by Kolko, Iselin, and Gully documents the sustainability and clinical benefits of AF-CBT in an existing community clinic serving physically abused children and their families.

Recognition as an Evidence-Based Practice

Based on systematic reviews of available research and evaluation studies, several groups of experts and agencies have highlighted AF-CBT as a model program or promising treatment practice:

- AF-CBT is rated a three, which is a Promising Practice, by the California Evidence-Based Clearinghouse (CEBC) for Child Welfare.

- AF-CBT is featured in the Chadwick Center's (2004) Closing the Quality Chasm in Child Abuse Treatment: Identifying and Disseminating Best Practices.

- AB-CBT is featured in Trauma-Informed Interventions: Clinical and Research Evidence and Culture-Specific Information Project, published by the National Child Traumatic Stress Network (NCTSN) and the Medical University of South Carolina.

- It is approved as an evidence-based treatment (EBT) by the Los Angeles County Office of Mental Health.

- It is included in EBT dissemination efforts being conducted by the Effective Providers for Child Victims of Violence Program of the American Psychological Association

- AF-CBT is included as a promising EBT in the website maintained by the U.S. Office of Justice Programs (OJP).

- It is included in EBT dissemination activities by the Defending Childhood Initiative sponsored by the Attorney General's Office, U.S. Department of Justice (DOJ).

- It is currently being disseminated by the NCTSN in a National Learning Collaborative on AF-CBT.

What to Look for in a Therapist

Caseworkers who are considering a family's referral for AF-CBT should become knowledgeable about commonly used treatments before recommending a treatment provider to families. Parents or caregivers should receive as much information as possible on the treatment options available to them. If AF-CBT appears to be an appropriate treatment model for a family, the caseworker should look for a provider who has received adequate training, supervision, and consultation in the AF-CBT model. If feasible, both the caseworker and the family should have an opportunity to interview potential AF-CBT therapists prior to beginning treatment. AF-CBT can be provided in multiple settings—in the home, in clinics, or other community settings—and the average length of services varies depending on the client's needs, goals, and progress.

Alternatives for Families: A Cognitive Behavioral Therapy Training

Mental-health professionals with at least some advanced training in psychotherapy skills and methods and experience working with physically abusive caregivers and their children are eligible for training in AF-CBT. Training generally involves:

- An initial didactic workshop training (3 days)
- Follow-up case consultation calls during "action plan" periods (6 to 12 months)
- Review of session performance samples for integrity/competency
- Booster retraining and advanced case review (1 day)
- Review of community metrics and progress report

Questions to Ask Treatment Providers

In addition to appropriate training and thorough knowledge of the AF-CBT model, it is important to select a treatment provider who is sensitive to the particular needs of the child, caregiver, and family. Caseworkers recommending an AF-CBT therapist should ask the treatment provider to explain the course of treatment, the role of each family member in treatment, and how the family's specific cultural considerations will be addressed. The child, caregiver, and family should feel comfortable with and have confidence in the therapist.

Some specific questions to ask regarding AF-CBT include:

- Will the child and parent each receive individualized therapy using corresponding (coordinated) treatment protocols?
- Will social learning principles be used to address the thoughts, emotions, and behaviors of the child and parent?
- Is there a focus on enhancing the parent-child relationship and improving parental discipline practices?
- Is the practitioner sensitive to the cultural background of the child and family?
- Is there a standard assessment process used to gather baseline information on the functioning of the child and family and to monitor their progress in treatment over time?
- Is this the most appropriate treatment for this child and family?

Section 44.2

Parent–Child Interaction Therapy with At-Risk Families

This section includes text excerpted from "Parent–Child Interaction Therapy with At-Risk Families," Child Welfare Information Gateway, U.S. Department of Health and Human Services (HHS), January 2013. Reviewed March 2019.

Parent–child interaction therapy (PCIT) is a family-centered treatment approach that has proven to be effective for abused and at-risk children between the ages of two and eight and their caregivers—birth parents, adoptive parents, or foster or kin caregivers. During PCIT, therapists coach parents while they interact with their children, teaching caregivers strategies that will promote positive behaviors in children who have disruptive or externalizing behavior problems. Research has shown that, as a result of PCIT, parents learn more effective parenting techniques, the behavior problems of children decrease, and the quality of the parent-child relationship improves.

This section is intended to build a better understanding of the characteristics and benefits of PCIT. It may help parents, foster parents, and other caregivers understand what they and their children can gain from PCIT and what to expect during treatment. It also may be useful to others with an interest in implementing or participating in effective parent-training strategies.

What Makes Parent–Child Interaction Therapy Unique?

Introduced in the 1970s as a way to treat young children with serious behavioral problems, PCIT has since been adapted successfully for use with populations who have experienced trauma due to child abuse or neglect. The distinctiveness of this approach lies in the use of live coaching and the treatment of both parent and child together. PCIT is the only evidence-based practice in which the parent and child are treated together throughout the course of all treatment sessions. As a result, it is a more intensive parenting intervention and most applicable for children with serious behavioral problems, parents with significant limitations (e.g., substance abuse, limited intellectual ability, mental-health problems), and/or parents at risk for child maltreatment. In randomized testing, including families identified by the child welfare system, PCIT has consistently demonstrated success in improving parent–child interactions. Benefits of the model, which have been experienced by families along the child welfare continuum, such as at-risk families and those with confirmed reports of maltreatment or neglect, are described below.

Reduces Behavior Problems in Young Children by Improving Parent–Child Interaction

PCIT was originally designed to treat children between the ages of two and eight with disruptive or externalizing behavior problems, including conduct and oppositional defiant disorders. These children are often described as negative, argumentative, disobedient, and aggressive.

PCIT addresses the negative parent–child interaction patterns that contribute to the disruptive behavior of young children. Through PCIT, parents learn to bond with their children and develop more effective parenting styles that better meet their children's needs. For example, parents learn to model and reinforce constructive ways for dealing with emotions, such as frustration. Children, in turn, respond to these healthier relationships and interactions. As a result, children treated with PCIT typically show significant reductions in behavior problems at home and at school.

Treats the Parent and Child Together

While many treatment approaches target either parents or children, PCIT focuses on changing the behaviors of both the parent and child together. Parents learn to model positive behaviors that children can learn from and are trained to act as "agents of change" for their children's behavioral or emotional difficulties. Sitting behind a one-way mirror and coaching the parent through an "ear bug" audio device, therapists guide parents through strategies that reinforce their children's positive behavior. In addition, PCIT therapists are able to tailor treatment based on observations of parent–child interactions. As such, PCIT can help address specific needs of each parent and child.

Decreases the Risk for Child Physical Abuse and Breaks the Coercive Cycle

PCIT has been found effective for physically abusive parents with children between the ages of 2 and 12. PCIT is appropriate where physical abuse occurs within the context of child discipline, as most physical abuse does. While child behavior problems and child physical abuse often co-occur, PCIT may help change the parental response to challenging child behaviors, regardless of the type of behavior problem.

Foundational research has shown that many complex factors contribute to abusive behaviors, including a coercive relationship between the parent and child. Abusive and at-risk parents often interact in negative ways with their children, use ineffective and inconsistent discipline strategies, and rely too much on punishment. These same parents rarely interact in positive ways with their children (e.g., rewarding good behavior). At the same time, some physically abused and at-risk children learn to be aggressive, defiant, noncompliant, and resistant to parental direction. The reciprocal negative behaviors of the parent and child create a harmful cycle that often escalates to the point of severe corporal punishment and physical abuse. The negative behaviors of the parent—screaming and threatening—reinforce the negative behaviors of the child—such as unresponsiveness and disobedience—which further aggravates the parent's behavior and may result in violence. PCIT helps break this cycle by encouraging positive interaction between parent and child and training parents in how to implement consistent and nonviolent discipline techniques when children act out.

Parents and caretakers completing PCIT typically:

- Show more positive parenting attitudes and demonstrate improvements in the ways that they listen to, talk to, and interact with their children

- Report less stress

- Use less corporal punishment and physically coercive means to control their children

- In addition, parent satisfaction with PCIT is typically high.

Offers Support for Caregivers Including Foster Parents

PCIT is now recognized as a way to help support foster parents caring for children with behavioral problems by enhancing the relationship between foster parents and foster children and by teaching foster parent's behavior management skills. In addition to reporting decreases in child behavior problems, foster parents frequently report less parental stress following PCIT and high levels of satisfaction with the program. One benefit of providing foster parents with PCIT skills is that they can use these same effective parenting skills with future generations of foster children.

Uses Live Coaching

PCIT is a behavioral parent-training model. What makes PCIT different from other parent training programs is the way skills are taught, as it uses live coaching of parents and children together. Live coaching provides immediate prompts to parents while they interact with their children. During the course of this hands-on treatment, parents are guided to demonstrate specific relationship-building and discipline skills.

The benefits of live coaching are significant:

- Parents are provided with opportunities to practice newly taught skills.

- Therapists can correct errors and misunderstandings on the spot.

- Parents receive immediate feedback.

- Parents are offered support, guidance, and encouragement as they learn.

- Treatment gains (e.g., increases in child compliance) are recognized by the parent "in the moment"—which supports continued use of effective parenting skills.

Adaptations for Various Populations

While PCIT was originally applied to Caucasian families, it has been adapted for use with various populations and cultures, including:

- Families in which child abuse has occurred

- Trauma victims/survivors

- Children with prenatal exposure to alcohol

- Children aged 18 to 60 months with externalizing behaviors who were born prematurely

- Children with developmental delays and/or mental retardation

- Older children

- Foster parents and maltreated children

- African American families

- Latinx and Spanish-speaking families

- Native American families

Limitations of Parent–Child Interaction Therapy

While PCIT is very effective in addressing certain types of problems, there are clear limitations to its use. For the following populations, PCIT may not be appropriate or specific modifications to treatment may be needed:

- Parents who have limited or no ongoing contact with their child

- Parents with serious mental-health problems that may include auditory or visual hallucinations or delusions

- Parents who are hearing impaired and would have trouble using the ear bug device, or parents who have significant expressive or receptive language deficits

- Sexually abusive parents, or parents engaging in sadistic physical abuse, or parents with substance-abuse issues

Key Components

PCIT is typically provided in 10 to 20 sessions, with an average of 12 to 14 sessions, each lasting about 1 to 1.5 hours. Occasionally, additional treatment sessions are added as needed.

The PCIT curriculum uses a 2-phase approach addressing:

1. Relationship enhancement

2. Discipline and compliance

Initially, the therapist discusses the key principles and skills of each phase with the parents. Then, the parents interact with their children and try to implement the particular skills. The therapist typically observes from behind a one-way mirror while communicating with the parent, who wears a small wireless earphone. Although not optimal, clinicians who do not have access to a one-way mirror and ear bug may provide services using in-room coaching. Specific behaviors are tracked on a graph over time to provide parents with feedback about the achievement of new skills and their progress in positive interactions with their child.

Phase 1: Relationship Enhancement (Child-Directed Interaction)

The first phase of treatment focuses on improving the quality of the relationship between the parent and the child. This phase emphasizes building a nurturing relationship and a secure bond between the parent and child. Phase I sessions are structured so that the child selects a toy or activity, and the parent plays along while being coached by the therapist. Because parents are taught to follow the child's lead, this phase also is referred to as "child-directed interaction" (CDI).

During phase I sessions, parents are instructed to use positive reinforcement. In particular, parents are encouraged to use skills represented in the acronym "PRIDE:"

- **Praise.** Parents provide praise for a child's appropriate behavior—for example, telling them, "good job cleaning up your crayons"—to help encourage the behavior and make the child feel good about her or his relationship with the parent.

- **Reflection.** Parents repeat and build upon what the child says to show that they are listening and to encourage improved communication.

- **Imitation.** Parents do the same thing that the child is doing, which shows approval and helps teach the child how to play with others.

- **Behavioral description.** Parents describe the child's activity (e.g., "You are building a tower with blocks") to demonstrate interest and build vocabulary.

- **Enjoyment.** Parents are enthusiastic and show excitement about what the child is doing.

Parents are guided to praise wanted behaviors, such as sharing, and to ignore unwanted or annoying behaviors, such as whining (unless the behaviors are destructive or dangerous). In addition, parents are taught to avoid criticisms or negative words—such as "No," "Do not," "Stop," "Quit," or "Not"—and instead concentrate on positive directions. In addition to the coached sessions, parents are given homework sessions of five minutes each day to practice newly acquired skills with their child. Once the parent's skill level meets the program's identified criteria, the second phase of treatment is initiated.

Phase II: Discipline and Compliance (Parent-Directed Interaction)

The second phase of PCIT concentrates on establishing a structured and consistent approach to discipline. During this phase, also known as "parent-directed interaction" (PDI), the parent takes the lead. Parents are taught to give clear, direct commands to the child and to provide consistent consequences for both compliance and noncompliance. When a child obeys the command, parents are instructed to provide labeled or specific praise (e.g., "Thank you for sitting quietly"). When a child disobeys, however, the parents initiate a timeout procedure. The timeout procedure typically begins with the parent issuing the child a warning and a clear choice of action (e.g., "Put your toys away, or go to timeout") and may advance to sending the child to a timeout chair.

Parents are coached in the use of these skills during a play situation where they must issue commands to their child and follow through with the appropriate consequence for compliance/noncompliance. In addition, parents are provided with strategies for managing challenging situations outside of therapy (for example, when a child throws a tantrum in the grocery store or hits another child). Parents also are given homework in this phase to aid in skill acquisition.

Assessments

In addition to clinical interviews, PCIT uses a combination of observational and standardized assessment measures to assess interactions between parent and child, child behaviors, and parental perception of stress related to being a parent, as well as the parents' own perceptions of the difficulty of their child's behaviors and their interactions with their child. Assessments are conducted before, during, and after treatment.

Effectiveness of Parent–Child Interaction Therapy

The effectiveness of PCIT is supported by a growing body of research and increasingly identified on inventories of model and promising treatment programs.

Demonstrated Effectiveness in Outcome Studies

At least 30 randomized clinical outcome studies and more than 10 true randomized trials have found PCIT to be useful in treating at-risk families and children with behavioral problems. Research findings include the following:

- **Trauma adaptation.** PCIT is now commonly referred to in the cluster of trauma-informed strategies. Trauma adaption to the model was examined in a study of PCIT in meeting the needs of mother-child dyads exposed to interpersonal violence (IPV) by reducing children's behavior problems and decreasing mothers' distress.

- **Reductions in the risk of child abuse.** In a study of 110 physically abusive parents, only one-fifth (19%) of the parents participating in PCIT had re-reports of physically abusing their children after 850 days, compared to half (49%) of the parents attending a typical community parenting group. Reductions in the risk of abuse following treatment have been confirmed in other studies among parents who had abused their children.

- **Improvements in parenting skills and attitudes.** Research reveals that parents and caretakers completing PCIT typically demonstrate improvements in reflective listening skills, use more prosocial verbalization, direct fewer sarcastic comments and critical statements at their children, improve physical closeness to their children, and show more positive parenting attitudes.

- **Improvements in child behavior.** A review of 17 studies that included 628 preschool-aged children identified as exhibiting a disruptive behavior disorder concluded that involvement in PCIT resulted in significant improvements in child behavior functioning. Commonly reported behavioral outcomes of PCIT included both less frequent and less intense behavior problems as reported by parents and teachers; increases in clinic-observed compliance; reductions in inattention and hyperactivity; decreases in observed negative behaviors, such as whining or crying; and reductions in the percentage of children who qualified for a diagnosis of disruptive behavior disorder.

- **Benefits for parents and other caregivers.** Examining PCIT effectiveness among foster parents participating with their foster children and biological parents referred for treatment because of their children's behavioral problems, researchers found decreases in child behavior problems and caregiver distress for both groups.

313

- **Lasting effectiveness.** Follow-up studies report that treatment gains are maintained over time.

- **Usefulness in treating multiple issues.** Adapted versions of PCIT also have been shown to be effective in treating other issues, such as separation anxiety, depression, self-injurious behavior, attention deficit hyperactivity disorder (ADHD), and adjustment following divorce.

- **Adaptability for a variety of populations.** Studies support the benefits of PCIT across genders and across a variety of ethnic groups.

Recognition as an Evidence-Based Practice

Based on systematic reviews of available research and evaluation studies, a number of expert groups have highlighted PCIT as a model program or promising treatment practice, including:

- The California Evidence-Based Clearinghouse (CEBC) for Child Welfare

- The National Child Traumatic Stress Network

- National Crime Victims Research and Treatment Center (NCVC) and the Center for Sexual Assault and Traumatic Stress; Office for Victims of Crime (OVC), U.S. Department of Justice (DOJ)

Implementation of Parent–Child Interaction Therapy in a Child Welfare Setting

When introducing PCIT as a referral option that child welfare workers may consider for children and families in their caseload, administrators will want to ensure that workers have a clear understanding of how PCIT works, the values that drive it, and its effectiveness. Training for child welfare staff on the basics of PCIT, how to screen at-risk children with behavior problems, and how to make appropriate referrals can expedite families' access to effective treatment options.

Parent–Child Interaction Therapy Training

Mental-health professionals with at least a master's degree in psychology, social work, or a related field are eligible for training in PCIT. Training involves 40 hours of direct training, with ongoing supervision and consultation for approximately 4 to 6 months, working with at least two PCIT cases through completion. Fidelity to the model is assessed throughout the supervision and consultation period.

Questions to Ask Treatment Providers

In addition to the appropriate training, it is important to select a treatment provider who is sensitive to the individual and cultural needs of the child, caregiver, and family. Caseworkers recommending a PCIT therapist should ask the treatment provider to explain the course of treatment, the role of each family member, and how the family's cultural background will be addressed. Family members should be involved in this discussion to the extent possible. The child, caregiver, and family should feel comfortable with and have confidence in, the therapist with whom they will work.

Some specific questions to ask a potential therapist regarding PCIT include:

- How will the parent be involved in this process?

- What is the nature of your PCIT training? When were you trained? By whom? How long was the training? Do you have access to follow-up consultation? What resource materials on PCIT are you familiar with? Are you clinically supervised by (or do you participate in a peer supervision group with) others who are PCIT trained?

- Why do you feel that PCIT is the appropriate treatment model for this child? Would the child benefit from other treatment methods after they complete PCIT (i.e., group or individual therapy)?

- What techniques will you use to help the child manage her or his emotions and related behaviors?

- Do you use a standard assessment process to gather baseline information on the functioning of the child and family and to monitor their progress in treatment over time?

- Do you have access to the appropriate equipment for PCIT (one-way mirror, ear bug, video equipment)? If not, how do you plan to structure the sessions to ensure that the PCIT techniques are used according to the model?

- Is there any potential for harm associated with treatment?

Chapter 45

Therapy Options for Adult Survivors of Childhood Abuse

Comprehensive Treatment for Adult Survivors of Child Abuse and Neglect

The high prevalence of histories of childhood abuse among individuals with substance-use disorders (SUDs), as well as their frequent need for mental-health services, has important implications for treatment planning and implementation. Clients with SUDs who were abused or neglected as children may be more prone to relapse than those without such histories. The Drug Abuse Treatment Outcome Study (DATOS) found that an important factor in predicting treatment success was the number of services received, such as case management, parenting education, and counseling for childhood abuse and posttraumatic stress disorder (PTSD). Clients receiving additional services, such as these were statistically more likely to stay in recovery.

Some estimates suggest that up to two-thirds of all those in substance-abuse treatment report that they were physically, sexually,

This chapter includes text excerpted from "Substance Abuse Treatment for Persons with Child Abuse and Neglect Issues," National Center for Biotechnology Information (NCBI), August 17, 2003. Reviewed March 2019.

or emotionally abused during childhood, whereas as many as 80 percent of people referred to mental-health services have histories of childhood abuse. Because an abuse history and a diagnosis of PTSD increase the risk of relapse, it is advisable to address these issues at some point during the course of substance-abuse treatment. Although many clients need to address substance-abuse issues before they are able to receive and benefit from treatment for past trauma, some need attention to the trauma before they can achieve sobriety. For some, it is during sobriety when they begin to experience symptoms of PTSD (such as flashbacks and nightmares) or recall memories of long-forgotten or repressed experiences of past abuse. As these uncomfortable and sometimes debilitating symptoms and memories emerge, many individuals return to using substances in an attempt to suppress their problems and manage their emotional pain. If abstinence can be achieved and maintained without directly dealing with traumatic issues, it should be encouraged because abstinence will likely better prepare clients to face issues related to past trauma. However, if clients mention traumatic issues or suffer from intrusive memories or other reactions related to the trauma, the counselor should be prepared to address them, initially from an educational perspective that offers clients reassurance.

Treatment Techniques

Seminal writings about the therapist's contribution to the therapeutic interaction suggest that certain characteristics are essential for effective treatment across therapeutic modalities: (1) unconditional positive regard or nonpossessive warmth, (2) a nonjudgmental attitude or accurate empathy, and (3) sincerity. Although many would argue that these are not sufficient for positive outcomes, there is evidence that these characteristics are important to establishing a working alliance with the client. For example, research has shown that an empathic therapist style is associated with more positive long-term outcomes.

For effective treatment, clients must be motivated for change. A counselor may need to address motivation before change can occur. For the counselor, the pace of some clients may seem so slow that it appears the clients are avoiding the issue. Nevertheless, the counselor must respect the clients' boundaries regarding how much and when to talk about abuse or neglect. To force the issue or to confront clients about abuse would be to reenact the violating role of the perpetrator. In dealing with clients with histories of child abuse and neglect, the counselor must strike a delicate balance between allowing clients to talk about the abuse when they are ready and not appearing to maintain the conspiracy of silence that so often surrounds issues of child abuse.

The counselor also must be prepared for the possibility that clients may disclose their childhood abuse or neglect without being asked about it. Disclosure of past abuse or neglect sometimes happens spontaneously in counseling sessions, without any intentional elicitation from the counselor or pre-planning on the part of clients. In some cases, clients believe that the sooner they address the abuse, the sooner they can resolve it. Exposure to the issue in the media may have led others to believe that this is typical, that is, "what they are supposed to do." Still, others feel a sense of urgency because they know they are allowed only a limited period of treatment. They may attempt to pressure treatment providers into addressing abuse issues prematurely—before they have adequate coping skills to manage the potential effects of such exploration. However, counselors must maintain appropriate pacing and teach clients to develop skills in self-soothing techniques so they can manage uncomfortable or volatile feelings.

When working with adult survivors of childhood abuse, the counselor can help clients situate the abuse in the past, where it belongs, while keeping the memory of it available to work with in therapy. Emphasizing a distinction between the emotions of the client as child victim and the choices available to the adult client can help this process. Recognizing this separation, clients can learn to tolerate memories of the abuse while accepting that at least some of its sequelae will probably remain.

Regardless of how or when clients talk about their abuse histories, the counselor must handle such disclosures with tact and sensitivity. Children who have been abused, especially at a young age by parents or other caretakers, will usually find it difficult to trust adults. When children's first and most fundamental relationship—that between themselves and one or both parents—has been betrayed by physical, emotional, or sexual abuse, they are likely to grow up feeling mistrustful of others and hypervigilant about the possibility of repeated betrayals. This vigilance is, in many ways, a resilient strength for children, who lack many of the protective resources of adults. As adults, however, it often stands in the way of forming intimate and trusting relationships. The counselor must take care not to tear down this defense prematurely, because to do so may result in discrediting or invalidating the experience of the abuse and, in some cases, may be perceived as abusive in itself. Patience and consistency help to reassure clients of the counselor's trustworthiness. Counselors should not assume that they have the clients' confidence simply because a disclosure has been made; with victims of childhood abuse, trust is often gained in small increments over time.

When the treatment does focus on issues of past abuse, the Consensus Panel recommends that the counselor support clients for what they can recall while reassuring them that it is quite normal to have uncertainties or not to remember all of what happened in the past. More important than the accuracy of the memory is the emotional reaction to, and consequences of, the experience; memories over time may be distorted, especially when remembered through the eyes of a child, but the feelings they engender are the most significant aspect of the experience. This last point is especially important because many survivors fear that if they disclose their histories, whomever they tell will deny that it happened. Even if the counselor finds clients' accounts difficult to believe, they can look for and respond to the emotional truth of it.

Moreover, the counselor should remember that until some degree of abstinence is achieved, clients' perceptions of reality are likely to be limited and their judgment poor. When clients disclose histories of past abuse before abstinence has been achieved, the counselor should note the information on childhood abuse and neglect, realizing that it will be important to explore this matter more thoroughly when clients have achieved a period of abstinence. When the topic is revisited later, the counselor should explain what parts of the story are the same and what parts differ, because this information may be therapeutically important. It is not unusual for trauma survivors to remember more with the retelling of their stories; however, the counselor should make note of major inconsistencies in order to discuss them with clients over the course of treatment. For example, the abuse may have been perpetrated by someone other than the person whom the client first remembered. Information such as this can have an extremely important bearing on family counseling, as well as other aspects of treatment.

Working from a Position of Supportive Neutrality

Counseling techniques for treating substance abuse in clients with a history of child abuse or neglect include interviewing from a stance of supportive neutrality. By asking, for example, what clients believe was both good and bad about the substance abuse, the counselor explores clients' perspectives and elicits rather than conveys information. The counselor's goal should be to motivate clients to explore their own issues and determine for themselves how the history of abuse relates to their substance abuse. Clients' motivations—for dealing with either abuse or substance abuse—will waver, but that is part of the process.

Group Therapy

Although group treatment, including 12-step programs and group therapy, is generally the treatment of choice for individuals who abuse substances, some individuals with childhood abuse issues may not do well in group settings. They may either find themselves unable to function or else try to undermine the group process to protect themselves from painful issues they would rather not face. This kind of behavior may point to hidden issues that the counselor should explore further. If childhood abuse issues surface during a group session (as they often do), they should not be ignored, nor should clients be discouraged from talking about such issues. However, trauma itself should not be the focus of treatment for a SUD.

The length, intensity, and type of treatment may need to be altered for clients if childhood abuse or neglect issues surface during treatment. If possible, clients with these issues should be given the chance to participate in groups that focus on the specific issue of adult survivors. Trauma-related groups are not generally recommended during the early stages of treatment for a SUD, when clients are still trying to achieve abstinence; however, groups that are designed to teach and educate clients about trauma and substance abuse can, at times, be quite helpful. (Exceptions can be made, however, for clients who continue to relapse during this early stage of treatment.) Survivors of childhood abuse should participate in a trauma-focused group only after clients' "safety and self-care are securely established, their symptoms are under reasonable control, their social supports are reliable, and their life circumstances permit engagement in a demanding endeavor."

In some cases, the first clue about the possibility of childhood abuse may be that a client is constantly undermining the group process, or the client may simply withdraw, becoming silent or dropping out of the group. Group therapy can be done effectively with this population, but counselors should keep in mind the population and the issues being dealt with and adjust goals accordingly. The group process can be an excellent way to help these individuals begin to address their attachment issues and—in a safe, controlled environment—practice disclosure and providing support to others. Adult survivors who are severely dissociative may have a hard time in any group setting. It is important that these clients are offered a symptom management program in which they can learn to use coping mechanisms other than dissociation. Clients with dissociative disorders may be very suggestible and easily disturbed by peer discussion of stressful experiences. This is not only a problem for the survivor in question but can also be disruptive and distressing to the group.

The appropriateness of group therapy for substance-abuse treatment should be assessed for each client. As a general rule, though, groups that provide education, support, and counseling about substance abuse, trauma, and posttraumatic reactions are preferable in the early stages of treatment to groups that try to provide more in-depth therapy. For example, intensive group psychotherapy is generally not beneficial for new clients in the primary stages of treatment, which should focus on more general substance-abuse issues.

Gender-Specific Groups for Survivors of Sexual Abuse

Clinical experience indicates that groups structured specifically for women or men are more beneficial, especially during the early stages of substance-abuse treatment. After clients have become more stabilized and can better empathize and share with others, mixed-gender groups may be more appropriate and can offer special opportunities for individuals to work through their issues differently. Some clients, however, may never be comfortable in mixed groups, and this should not necessarily be viewed as a measure of progress. Gender-specific groups are equally beneficial for abuse survivors in treatment, particularly if the abuse issues are identified early.

Research shows that women especially tend to do better in groups specific to women, although men may benefit from male-only groups as well. It is also helpful for sexual minorities (e.g., gay, lesbian, transgendered) to have their own groups when possible. Women who have been victims of sexual abuse perpetrated by men may find it more difficult to discuss that abuse with men present. However, in gender-specific groups women may be more willing to discuss their abuse than men. All-male groups may need more assistance from the counselor to begin discussing this topic.

Women and men have different conflicts and issues when dealing with their abuse experiences, but both might be affected by traditional societal views of gender roles. The difficulty that many men face in acknowledging past abuse is sometimes compounded by the conflict between perceiving themselves as victims and society's traditional expectations of men as powerful and aggressive. Male homophobia can also make discussions of sexual abuse, which often involve same-sex assaults, less likely to occur. Men may need help to form a view of themselves that neither exacerbates their feelings of victimization nor imposes unrealistic expectations of unwavering strength. Similarly, traditional societal views of women reinforce stereotypes of female helplessness. Whatever the gender stereotype, both men and women can often benefit from assertiveness training and learning to form healthy self-images that are not based on notions of fear and powerlessness. Some men may find it more difficult to work on these issues, or may be in denial, because of the social stigma around male weakness.

Whether treating individuals with abuse histories in mixed or gender-specific groups, it is important for counselors to avoid having preconceived notions about abusive events. Females may be more often the victims of sexual molestation by males, but sexual abuse is also perpetrated on males by both sexes and on females by other females. Given common expectations, it is especially important not to belittle men's experiences because many men have difficulty expressing uncomfortable emotions associated with abuse. For example, men who were sexually abused as children by females often have significant issues of shame surrounding the abuse. In other cases, the enormous social taboo surrounding the sexual abuse of a son by his father can lead the survivor to feel that he somehow invited the abuse or to question his sexual orientation. Another common scenario is that of men who had distant and unavailable fathers and were abused at young ages (such as 12 or 13 years of age) by older men who sensed their neediness for a male connection during puberty.

The unfortunate truth of child abuse is that any scenario is possible. Both men and women are equally susceptible to the emotional damage that results from the profound betrayal of their trust in the adults who were supposed to take care of them. It is incumbent upon all treatment professionals, therefore, to bring to their work with these individuals sufficient knowledge, sensitivity, and understanding of the unique issues surrounding childhood abuse and neglect.

Self-Help Groups

Many alcohol and drug counselors are committed to the 12-step model; however, that model can be problematic for clients with childhood abuse and neglect. Many survivors believe they do not have any control or power. Therefore, a 12-step approach that asks them to accept their powerlessness might be more harmful than beneficial. The importance given to "surrender to a higher power" can also terrify or anger abuse survivors. They have had personal and very dangerous experiences with submission to human power and have often lost hope in higher spiritual powers that did not protect them in the past. Counselors must be sensitive to and respectful of survivors' needs to avoid this terminology. 12-step organizations that work with this population (e.g., Survivors of Incest Anonymous) have reworded this step to make it less problematic for this population. In general, self-help groups can be tremendous sources of help for clients with all types of associated problems.

Involvement of the Family in Treatment

When adult survivors of child abuse enter treatment, clients' families may have a significant effect on the way in which treatment progresses. Every family has a unique style or unspoken set of rules that is used to maintain equilibrium in the family system. That equilibrium is thrown off balance by changes occurring with any family member. If one part of the family value or belief system changes, all parts of the system change—which may be threatening to some family members. When an outsider, such as the alcohol and drug counselor, tries to work with the problems presented by the client, the tendency in some families is to close ranks and come together to maintain a sense of equilibrium. The dynamics within abusive families may remain secretive, coercive, and manipulative, even if the actual abuse is no longer happening. Often the resistance of families is a way to protect and avoid disclosure, and abusers may still hold a strongly controlling position, even over their young-adult and adult children.

When family members oppose change, it often becomes evident during the course of treatment. The family may minimize the importance of the problem and not support the client's counseling. This is particularly true in families where substance abuse and child abuse are present; the family may be isolated from larger society and be fearful or angry about the counselor's interventions. In some cases, abusive situations may be currently taking place in the family. It is important to note that other family members may not know or want to know about the abuse of another member, whether ongoing or in the past. The counselor should understand that the resistance being encountered is taking place to preserve the family in the only way available to it. Of course, many families welcome change and want their family member to be abstinent; too often the family may be viewed as a potential problem when in fact it could be a great asset. The counselor should talk frankly with the family about the fact that change will be uncomfortable and stressful.

When family therapy is agreed on as a useful component of substance-abuse treatment, it should only be conducted by a licensed mental-health professional with specific training in the area of child abuse and neglect.

Confronting the History of Abuse

When clients' families become involved in treatment, a decision must be made whether and to what degree the subject of abuse will be discussed. This decision is best made between the client and the counselor outside of family sessions. In dealing with clients' current nuclear families, the counselor should explore with clients the possibility of discussing the past abuse within the context of how it affects the clients' substance abuse and current functioning within the family. In any first-time disclosure of abuse, the counselor must take care not to pressure clients to talk about the abuse with their families before they are ready. For the counselor to do so would be to reenact the role of the perpetrator.

Enlisting family members to support a client's treatment may have a positive impact on recovery. In some cases (e.g., when the perpetrator of the abuse is still present in the family), a team review should take place to decide whether to include the family. The team must take into account the client's comfort level and readiness for involving family, as well as her progress thus far in treatment for both substance abuse and mental-health issues and any mandatory reporting guidelines that might apply. Counselors should be very cautious about discussing child abuse issues with family members while the client is still in treatment for substance abuse. Such confrontation may not be considered therapeutic or essential for every client.

Obviously, it is a delicate matter to discuss past abuse in the presence of family members who participated in or were present during it. When such a decision is made, the counselor must bear in mind that he does not, and should not, have the role of confronting the perpetrator. The counselor must avoid taking on the role of rescuer or defender of clients. For the counselor to insert himself into the perpetrator-victim system is to put an end to his therapeutic effectiveness. Nor is the purpose of enlisting family in treatment to allow clients to confront the perpetrator. As in individual sessions with clients alone, the focus must remain on supporting the client's recovery.

A number of problems are associated with accusing family members of abuse of their adult children. One risk is that the accusation will be denied, or the client will be blamed for the abuse, provoking intense emotions and possible relapse. Another problem is political and legal; there has been a strong reaction to accusations of childhood abuse by adults molested as children. Counselors have been accused and sometimes sued for implanting false memories as well as subjecting family members to unexpected accusations when they thought they were going into family therapy in support of their recovering son, daughter, or sibling. This is an unfortunate turn of events for counselors who believe clients and see dealing with these issues as important for recovery. In many cases, mediation is an effective option, but it is not possible with some families.

Deciding Whether to Involve the Family

In most cases, open negotiations with an adult client's family of origin about past abuse should probably not happen until very late in individual therapy, if ever. (For a child or adolescent the situation and issues are quite different, of course.) Substance-dependent clients who have been abused are doubly vulnerable to further hostility and rejection from their families and may respond with either massive anxiety or relapse or both. Involving supportive family members might help with particular issues; for example, a domestic partner can be included in sessions on sexual or emotional intimacy problems.

In general, abused substance-abusing clients benefit most by a strong primary alliance with the therapist and not too much dilution with other relationships. This undivided support and allegiance in a relationship is, after all, what was usually lacking for the clients and what is needed to rebuild the self. Intensive individual therapy is usually the best approach for this type of client. The intended benefits of family therapy are often not worth the potential risks to clients in this unpredictable and emotionally charged situation. Furthermore, it must be emphasized that counselors should take a team approach whenever feasible and not take on more than is appropriate for their level of training, experience, and abilities.

The determination of whether family therapy is effective and appropriate for clients with histories of abuse or neglect depends on a number of factors. Among the most important is whether the history of abuse is known and acknowledged by the family. Other important considerations are clients' feelings and preferences and their current relationships with various members of their families. In evaluating the need for family therapy, providers must also consider clients' personal definitions of family, which may not fit expected norms. Regardless of biological relationships, the issue at hand is to identify the people who are nonthreatening and important in clients' daily functioning.

Before involving clients' families in treatment, the counselor must evaluate clients' tolerance level for the highly charged emotional material that is likely to ensue from taking this step. Ultimately, this decision should be made by the entire treatment team, including a mental-health professional. However, family involvement is often therapeutic for the client and may be a predictor of successful recovery.

Respect for Cultural Norms

The counselor is in the delicate position of trying to gain the cooperation of families and engage clients in a way that does not threaten the family balance. A lack of understanding of clients' culture and specifically the family norms of that culture may hinder this process. In some cultures, someone outside the family may be viewed with distrust and her assistance is considered as interference. Or, in some cultures, calling the father by his first name may violate his authority and alienate him from the treatment process. Being aware of cultural norms that can influence the situation helps the counselor better understand clients and create a framework in which effective therapy can take place.

There is now an influx of immigrant populations to the United States from all over the world, and many come to this country because they have been displaced by war or other traumatic events. It is not possible for a counselor to be aware of all the issues faced by clients. Therefore, it is helpful for the counselor to ask clients and their families to teach him what he needs to know about the values of their culture. Admitting a lack of knowledge and asking specific questions demonstrate respect and are ways in which family members can participate in the treatment process. Families are often willing to discuss these issues, and the counselor gains the information needed to work with the client while building trust.

The Importance of Referrals

Counselors must be careful not to attempt too much when working with clients with a history of severe abuse. Although the best situation is one in which substance abuse and other mental-health issues can be treated together in the same program, programs do not always have the resources to do so. When an assessment of symptoms indicates mental-health problems that are beyond the scope of the counselor's ability to treat, a referral is clearly warranted. Suicidality, self-mutilation, extreme dissociative reactions, and major depression should be treated by a mental-health professional, although that treatment may be concurrent with substance-abuse treatment. The need for a referral, however, is not always so clear.

The treatment provider's first goal for clients is generally to help them stop using substances and maintain abstinence. Clients may wonder or inquire why they are being asked about their childhood in a program for substance abuse and dependence. For the therapeutic process to be effective, both counselors and clients may need to reach a deeper understanding of how the past contributes to present problems. Although the counselor is primarily concerned with substance abuse, she is often in the crucial position to identify clients' other needs, which if not addressed might lead to relapse or escalation of substance use.

The desired outcomes of referral for counseling about childhood abuse issues include the expectation that the referral is actually acted on, but referrals can only be made (and followed up on) with the client's permission. The treatment provider should follow through on the referral process to ensure that it is completed. Once a referral has been made, the mental-health provider can help elicit further information about the client's history of child abuse or neglect. For clients with more severe mental-health problems, the treatment provider's primary concern should be to ensure clients' safety and help minimize the risk of suicidality and relapse.

Mental-Health Treatment Services

Treatment planning for clients with childhood abuse should be a dynamic process that can change as new information is uncovered, taking into account where clients are in the treatment process when the history of abuse is disclosed. What is known by both counselor and clients at the beginning of treatment is often different from what is learned later, as clients' capacity for coherence and clear thinking improves. Clients newly admitted to treatment who have not yet achieved abstinence are not likely to think clearly, to process or synthesize information, or to engage in meaningful self-reflection. Confronting abuse issues at such an early point in treatment may lead to escalation of substance use.

The counselor should prepare clients for mental-health treatment by helping them realize (1) that their history of child abuse or neglect may have contributed to some of their errors in thinking and decision-making, (2) that they may have medicated themselves with substances in order not to deal with their feelings, (3) that they are not alone and resources are available to help them, and (4) they can learn better ways to cope and live a happier life. Regardless of when abuse issues arise in treatment, the counselor should gather information from clients to identify the referral sources that will be most appropriate and helpful. This information helps treatment staff as well, because past abuse may influence a person's chances of recovery and progress through treatment.

Decisions of when and where to refer will vary depending on the availability of local services. When those services are limited or non-existent, treatment providers may have to be creative. Asking clients about possible sources of support—such as those they may have turned to in the past when this issue arose—may turn up resources, such as clergy, teachers, or others in the community.

Case Management and Service Coordination

Case management and coordination of services are key to the provision of integrated or concurrent treatment and of appropriate referrals, especially in the case of referrals for childhood abuse and neglect issues. Once made, such referrals do not mark the end of substance-abuse treatment. On the contrary, treatment for SUDs remains integral in the case management process.

Linkages between treatment providers and mental-health agencies are crucial if the two programs are to understand each other's activities. In the interest of the clients, a case summary should be developed that lists the key issues that need to be addressed in other settings. This not only helps clients but also enhances professional relationships between parties. Ideally, a case manager will coordinate all these services, but often the counselor serves as the coordinator.

The reality of third-party payor systems is that substance-abuse treatment is limited to a finite number of visits. Documentation of child abuse or neglect issues and their effect on the treatment process helps to delineate specific treatment intervention needs and allows for more effective treatment planning. Demonstrating the existence of childhood abuse or neglect and its impact on current dysfunctional behaviors early in treatment supports the complexity of the diagnosis and treatment planning process, thus helping to substantiate the need for greater support to third-party payors. Counselors will often need to substantiate the complexity of a case so that they can begin to formulate a treatment plan. It helps to describe specific behaviors rather than using labels such as "substance abuse" or "childhood abuse and neglect," which will allow for behaviorally based interventions. A mental-health assessment can provide a diagnosis that will be more acceptable for third-party payors.

Working with at-risk clients in today's litigious climate requires that counselors adhere closely to accepted standards and ethics of practice as well as the legal requirements of their position. Working within a multidisciplinary team with adequate supervision ensures that the counselor maintains such standards of care. Team members or colleagues in other agencies can be consulted about treatment issues as well as legal matters concerning reporting requirements and confidentiality.

Recordkeeping

Clients' treatment records are important documents. They provide historical overviews of each client's current status, past experiences, treatment goals, and subsequent progress. Counselors need to record this information in an organized, respectful, and sensitive manner, with the knowledge that others may have access to clients' records. It is best to find a balance in the level of detail recorded. Counselors should make it a practice to document only the factual, observable behavior of clients, and to record statements made by clients and not make judgmental statements about them. It is important to build an efficient means of recordkeeping that follows both federal and state guidelines.

Instances of abuse and neglect that have been revealed must be recorded. To protect the provider, the record should state that the client reported abuse, rather than that the client was abused. When counselors do not record the information they are given, they lose the opportunity of transmitting needed information to future counselors. The message to the client must be that the information is important and needs to be recorded. If not recorded, the counselor is furthering a message of shame and secrecy. Often the information on past trauma or abuse is essential for developing a treatment plan and thus can help strengthen subsequent treatment. The case summary should document such things as clients' status at intake, the diagnosis, course of treatment (including any prescribed medications), status at discharge, the goals met while in treatment, the reason for discharge, and any referrals made. Records should also indicate the extent to which the original goals of the treatment plan were reached. Sufficient notes should be kept for this purpose because the outcome of treatment has important implications for accreditation and funding.

Part Six

Parenting Issues
and Child Abuse Risks

Chapter 46

Family Matters and Child Abuse Risk

Chapter Contents

Section 46.1

Parental Substance Use

This section includes text excerpted from "Parental Substance Use and the Child Welfare System," Child Welfare Information Gateway, U.S. Department of Health and Human Services (HHS), October 2014. Reviewed March 2019.

Many families receiving child welfare services (CWS) are affected by parental substance use. Identifying substance abuse and meeting the complex needs of parents with substance-use disorders (SUDs) and those of their children can be challenging. Over the past two decades, innovative approaches coupled with new research and program evaluation have helped point to new directions for more effective, collaborative, and holistic service delivery to support both parents and children. This section provides child welfare workers and related professionals with information on the intersection of SUDs and child maltreatment and describes strategies for prevention, intervention, and treatment, including examples of effective programs and practices.

Impact of Parental Substance Use on Children

The way parents with SUDs behave and interact with their children can have a multifaceted impact on the children. The effects can be both indirect (e.g., through a chaotic living environment) and direct (e.g., physical or sexual abuse). Parental substance use can affect parenting, prenatal development, and early childhood and adolescent development. It is important to recognize, however, that not all children of parents with substance-use issues will suffer abuse, neglect, or other negative outcomes.

Parenting

A parent's SUD may affect her or his ability to function effectively in a parental role. Ineffective or inconsistent parenting can be due to the following:

- Physical or mental impairments caused by alcohol or other drugs

- Reduced capacity to respond to a child's cues and needs

- Difficulties regulating emotions and controlling anger and impulsivity

- Disruptions in healthy parent-child attachment
- Spending limited funds on alcohol and drugs rather than food or other household needs
- Spending time seeking out, manufacturing, or using alcohol or other drugs
- Incarceration, which can result in inadequate or inappropriate supervision for children
- Estrangement from family and other social supports

Family life for children with one or both parents that abuse drugs or alcohol often can be chaotic and unpredictable. Children's basic needs—including nutrition, supervision, and nurturing—may go unmet, which can result in neglect. These families often experience a number of other problems—such as mental illness, domestic violence, unemployment, and housing instability—that also affect parenting and contribute to high levels of stress. A parent with a SUD may be unable to regulate stress and other emotions, which can lead to impulsive and reactive behavior that may escalate to physical abuse.

Different substances may have different effects on parenting and safety. For example, the threats to a child of a parent who becomes sedated and inattentive after drinking excessively differ from the threats posed by a parent who exhibits aggressive side effects from methamphetamine use. Dangers may be posed not only from the use of illegal drugs, but also, and increasingly, from abuse of prescription drugs (pain relievers, antianxiety medicines, and sleeping pills). Poly-substance use (multiple drugs) may make it difficult to determine the specific and compounded effects on any individual. Further, risks for the child's safety may differ depending upon the level and severity of parental substance use and associated adverse effects.

Prenatal and Infant Development

The effects of parental SUDs on a child can begin before the child is born. Maternal drug and alcohol use during pregnancy has been associated with premature birth, low birth weight, slowed growth, and a variety of physical, emotional, behavioral, and cognitive problems. Research suggests the powerful effects of legal drugs—such as tobacco, as well as illegal drugs—on prenatal and early childhood development.

Fetal alcohol spectrum disorders (FASDs) are a set of conditions that affect an estimated 40,000 infants born each year to mothers who drank alcohol during pregnancy. Children with FASD may experience mild to severe physical, mental, behavioral, and/or learning disabilities, some of which may have lifelong implications (e.g., brain damage, physical defects, attention deficits). In addition, increasing numbers of newborns—approximately 3 per 1,000 hospital births each year—are affected by neonatal abstinence syndrome (NAS), a group of problems that occur in a newborn who was exposed prenatally to addictive illegal or prescription drugs.

The full impact of prenatal substance exposure depends on a number of factors. These include the frequency, timing, and type of substances used by pregnant women; co-occurring environmental deficiencies; and the extent of prenatal care. Research suggests that some of the negative outcomes of prenatal exposure can be improved by supportive home environments and positive parenting practices.

Child and Adolescent Development

Children and youth of parents who use or abuse substances and have parenting difficulties have an increased chance of experiencing a variety of negative outcomes, such as:

- Poor cognitive, social, and emotional development

- Depression, anxiety, and other trauma and mental-health symptoms

- Physical and health issues

- Substance-use problems

Parental substance use can affect the well-being of children and youth in complex ways. For example, an infant who receives inconsistent care and nurturing from a parent engaged in addiction-related behaviors may suffer from attachment difficulties that can then interfere with the growing child's emotional development. Adolescent children of parents with substance-use disorders, particularly those who have experienced child maltreatment and foster care, may turn to substances themselves as a coping mechanism. In addition, children of parents with substance-use issues are more likely to experience trauma and its effects, which include difficulties with concentration and learning, controlling physical and emotional responses to stress, and forming trusting relationships.

Section 46.2

Domestic Violence and Child Abuse

This section includes text excerpted from "Domestic Violence and the Child Welfare System," Child Welfare Information Gateway, U.S. Department of Health and Human Services (HHS), October 2014. Reviewed March 2019.

Domestic violence is a devastating social problem that affects every segment of the population. It is critical for child welfare professionals and other providers who work with children who have experienced abuse to understand the relationship between domestic violence and child maltreatment, as many families experiencing domestic violence also come to the attention of the child welfare system (CWS).

Increasingly, child welfare professionals, domestic violence victim advocates, courts, and other community stakeholders are working together to address the impact of domestic violence on children. This section discusses the extent of the overlap between domestic violence and child welfare, some of the effects of domestic violence on child witnesses, and the trend toward a more collaborative, communitywide response to the issue. It also features promising practices from states and local communities.

Impact of Domestic Violence on Children

Children who have been exposed to domestic violence are more likely than their peers to experience a wide range of difficulties, and the potential effects vary by age and developmental stage. The challenges faced by children and youth exposed to domestic violence generally fall into three categories:

- **Behavioral, social, and emotional problems.** Children in families experiencing domestic violence are more likely than other children to exhibit signs of depression and anxiety; higher levels of anger and/or disobedience; fear and withdrawal; poor peer, sibling, and social relationships; and low self-esteem.

- **Cognitive and attitudinal problems.** Children exposed to domestic violence are more likely than their peers to experience difficulties in school and with concentration and task completion; score lower on assessments of verbal, motor, and cognitive skills; lack conflict resolution skills; and possess limited

problem-solving skills. Children exposed to domestic violence
also are more likely to exhibit pro-violence attitudes.

- **Long-term problems.** In addition to higher rates of
  delinquency and substance use, exposure to domestic violence
  is also one of several adverse childhood experiences (ACEs) that
  have shown to be risk factors for many of the most common
  causes of death in the United States, including alcohol abuse,
  drug abuse, smoking, obesity, and more.

Additional factors that influence the impact of domestic violence
on children include:

- **Nature of the violence.** Children who witness frequent and
  severe forms of violence or fail to observe their caretakers
  resolving conflict may undergo more distress than children who
  witness fewer incidences of physical violence and experience
  positive interactions between their caregivers.

- **Age of the child.** Younger children appear to exhibit higher
  levels of emotional and psychological distress than older
  children. Children five years of age and younger may experience
  developmental regression—the loss of acquired skills—or
  disruptions in eating or sleeping habits. Adolescents may
  exhibit impulsive and/or reckless behavior, such as substance
  use or running away. Age-related differences can result from
  older child's more fully developed cognitive abilities, which
  help them to better understand the violence and select various
  coping strategies to alleviate upsetting symptoms. Additionally,
  because very young children are more likely to have closer
  physical proximity to and stronger emotional dependence on
  their mothers (often the victims of domestic violence), they may
  be more susceptible to and exhibit enhanced trauma symptoms.

- **Elapsed time since exposure.** Children often have heightened
  levels of anxiety and fear immediately after a violent event.
  Fewer observable effects are seen in children as time passes
  after the violent event.

- **Gender.** In general, boys exhibit more externalized behaviors
  (e.g., aggression and acting out), while girls exhibit more
  internalized behaviors (e.g., withdrawal and depression).

Presence of child physical or sexual abuse. Children who witness
domestic violence and are physically or sexually abused are at higher

risk for emotional and psychological maladjustment than children who witness violence and are not abused. Despite these findings, not all children exposed to domestic violence will experience negative effects. Children's risk levels and reactions to domestic violence exist on a continuum; some children demonstrate enormous resiliency, while others show signs of significant maladaptive adjustment. Protective factors, such as social competence, intelligence, high self-esteem, and a supportive relationship with an adult (especially a nonabusive parent), can help protect children from the adverse effects of exposure to domestic violence. It is important for domestic violence, child welfare, and other child-serving professionals to understand the impact of trauma on child development and how to minimize its effects without causing additional trauma.

Section 46.3

Postpartum Depression

This section includes text excerpted from "Moms' Mental Health Matters," *Eunice Kennedy Shriver* National Institute of Child Health and Human Development (NICHD), February 25, 2016.

Pregnancy and a new baby can bring a range of emotions. In fact, many women feel overwhelmed, sad, or anxious at different times during their pregnancy and even after the baby is born. For many women, these feelings go away on their own. But for some women, these emotions are more serious and may stay for some time.

Depression and anxiety that happen during pregnancy or anytime during the first year after the birth of your baby are medical conditions. These feelings are not something you caused by doing or not doing something. And, they can be treated if you seek help.

What Are Depression and Anxiety?

Depression—feeling sad, empty, and/or "down"—and anxiety—feeling nervous, worried, and/or scared—are serious medical conditions that involve the brain and may occur during pregnancy or after birth.

These feelings go beyond what people may experience when they have a bad day or are nervous about an upcoming event. They are also more than just feeling "moody" or having the "baby blues."

Depression and anxiety may get in the way of doing everyday activities, such as taking care of yourself and your baby. They are long lasting and will not go away on their own. But they are treatable, which is why it is important to get help.

What Is Postpartum Depression?

Postpartum depression (PPD) is one name you might hear for depression and anxiety that can happen during and after pregnancy. However, it might not be the best way to describe what women feel.

The word "postpartum" means "after birth," so "postpartum depression" is talking only about depression after the baby is born. For many women, this term is correct: they start feeling depression sometime within the first year after they have the baby.

But research shows that some women start to feel depression while they are still pregnant. You might hear the term "perinatal depression" to describe this situation. The word "perinatal" describes the time during pregnancy or just after birth.

Researchers believe that depression is one of the most common problems women experience during and after pregnancy.

Women may also experience anxiety around the time of pregnancy, beyond just being nervous about having a baby. Anxiety during and after pregnancy is as common as depression and may even happen at the same time as depression. So, you also may hear "perinatal depression and anxiety" or "perinatal mood and anxiety disorders" (PMADs) used to describe what women might feel.

No matter what you call them, depression and anxiety that happen during pregnancy or after birth are real medical conditions, and they affect many women.

How Common Are Depression and Anxiety during Pregnancy or after Birth?

As mentioned above, researchers believe that depression is one of the most common problems women experience during and after pregnancy. According to a national survey, about one in eight women experience postpartum depression after having a baby.

Anxiety during and after pregnancy is as common as depression and may happen at the same time as depression.

You may feel like you are the only person in the world who feels depressed and anxious during pregnancy or after your baby is born, but you are not alone.

Can Depression and Anxiety during Pregnancy or after Birth Affect Your Baby?

Yes—these medical conditions can affect your baby but not directly. Early mother-child bonding is important for your baby's development, and becoming close to your baby is a big part of that bonding. When you have depression or anxiety during pregnancy or after birth, it can be hard to become close to your baby. You may not be able to respond to what your baby needs. And, if there are older children in the house, they may be missing your support as well.

Early treatment is important for you, your baby, and the rest of your family. The sooner you start, the more quickly you will start to feel better.

Can You Prevent Depression or Anxiety during Pregnancy or after Birth?

Currently, there is no known way to prevent depression or anxiety that occurs during pregnancy or after the birth of your baby. But knowing what signs and symptoms to watch for during and after pregnancy can help you prepare and get help quickly. Here is what you can do:

- Find out whether you have factors that put you at greater risk for depression and anxiety during pregnancy and after birth.

- Talk with a healthcare provider about depression and anxiety around pregnancy, and learn what to watch for.

- Learn as much as you can about pregnancy, childbirth, and parenthood so you know what to expect.

- Set realistic expectations for yourself and your family.

- Do things in addition to seeking treatment that may help you feel better.

- Plan ahead. While you are pregnant, think about who can give you support and help when your baby comes. Talk with that person about helping you so that you can both prepare.

Chapter 47

Disciplining Your Child

Chapter Contents

Section 47.1

Setting Structure and Rules

This section includes text excerpted from "Creating
Structure and Rules," Centers for Disease Control and
Prevention (CDC), October 2, 2017.

Does your child have meltdowns when you change from one activity
to another? Do you have trouble getting your child to follow a regular
schedule? Consistent routines and rules help create order and structure your day. Things go more smoothly when you and your child know
what to expect.

Keys to Creating Structure

Some of the key components of your plan should be:

- Consistency, predictability, and follow-through are important for
  creating structure in the home.

- Respond to your child's behavior the same way every time. When
  you are consistent, the behaviors you like will happen more often
  and problem behaviors are less likely to happen.

- Routines and daily schedules help you and your child. You both
  know what to expect each day. Routines can also improve your
  child's behavior and your relationship with your child.

- A family rule is a clear statement about behaviors that are never
  okay, such as hitting and running in the house. You can change
  your child's behavior when there are clear consequences for
  breaking the rule.

- Keep things positive. Reward and praise your child for following
  routines and rules. This makes it more likely that your child will
  follow the routines and rules in the future.

Tips for Creating Structure and Rules
Give Choices

Whenever possible, try to give your child choices. Ask your child,
"Do you want A or B?" ("Do you want the red or the green shirt; the
apple or the banana; this story or that story?") If your child gets upset,
calmly repeat, "Do you want A or B?" If there are two things you need

the child to do, such as getting in the bath and brushing their teeth, let the child choose which one to do first. Giving choices can help your child learn to be more independent, feel like she or he has some control, and reduce struggles.

Establish a Routine

A routine is a set of steps you follow the same way each time. This means that the day's activities are predictable. Morning routines, for example, can help you and your child get ready to leave the house on time. A bedtime routine can help your child sleep better and allow you more time for yourself. A dinnertime routine can help your child eat healthy (no dessert before dinner). If your child knows the routine, you will have fewer tantrums and power struggles during the day.

Prevent Temper Tantrums

Establishing routines can help prevent temper tantrums. Many tantrums occur because children do not know what to expect during the day or do not want to do something they are asked to do. Routines take the guesswork out of the day's activities. It may be helpful to teach your child the routine when you first start using it. A chart or nighttime song that spells out the routine may be helpful.

Be Predictable

Children feel safe and know how to behave when they have a routine and know what to expect. Being predictable in all areas of a child's life can reduce stress and improve children's behavior. Examples include setting and enforcing rules and having a bedtime and mealtime routine.

Wake-Up Times

If you have more than one child, consider staggering wake-up times for children who need to get ready for school or child care in the morning. Wake up the children who need the most help first and then move on to the children who need less help. This can help reduce your frustration in the mornings and get everyone where they need to be on time.

347

Section 47.2

Using Discipline and Consequences

This section includes text excerpted from "Using Discipline and Consequences," Centers for Disease Control and Prevention (CDC), October 2, 2017.

Did you know that what you do right after any of your child's behavior makes a difference? This may be why your child has good behavior some days and not others. Learning how to use discipline and consequences can help you have more good days with your child. It can also help you get behaviors you like to happen more.

Keys to Using Discipline and Consequences

Successful implementation of discipline and consequences depends on the following:

- Use social rewards (such as hugs and kisses) more than material rewards (such as toys or candy). Social rewards can be given often and are more powerful.

- Sticker charts or similar reward programs can help change your child's behavior.

- Ignoring misbehavior means taking away your attention. It helps stop misbehaviors, such as tantrums, whining, and interrupting.

- Want to reduce misbehavior? Distracting your child can help stop misbehaviors. It works by getting your child to think and do something else so he or she does not continue to misbehave.

- Toddlers and preschoolers have short attention spans. Give consequences right after a misbehavior so they can remember what they did that you do not like.

- Use consequences that match your child's age and stage of development.

Tips for Using Discipline and Consequences
Stay Calm

Children pick up on their parents' feelings and actions. When your child is misbehaving or you are disciplining your child, be sure to stay calm.

If you yell or get upset, your child's behavior will likely get worse along with yours. This makes things more difficult and frustrating to handle.

Use Logical Consequences

Consequences for broken rules should be related to the misbehavior when possible. For example, if your child does not follow the house rule of sharing her or his toys, they could lose the toy for a set amount of time.

Other Feelings

Explain to your child how his behaviors make other people feel. Instead of just telling your child to "say you are sorry," tell your child how their behavior makes other people feel. This helps your child understand why they should not misbehave. You will need to do this a lot with young children before they understand.

Be Consistent

Be consistent when using discipline. Follow through with consequences each time a misbehavior occurs. Your child should know that they lose their toy privileges each time they bang it against the window. If you do not follow through, your child may think that they can sometimes get away with misbehaviors, and the misbehaviors will continue.

Explain Family Rules

Explain family rules and consequences to others who care for your child. Take time to explain the family rules and the consequences for breaking the rules to everyone who cares for your child. Make sure they understand that they should enforce the family rules as consistently and predictably as you.

Why Are Discipline and Consequences Important?

From time to time, your child is going to do things you do not like. They will do things that are dangerous. They will do things you do not want them to do again. They will also do a lot of things you like. The consequence, or what happens right after your child's behaviors, makes the behavior more or less likely to happen again. Consequences can be both positive and negative.

Positive and Negative Consequences

Positive consequences show your child that she or he has done something you like. Your child is more likely to repeat the behavior when you use positive consequences. Positive consequences include things, such as rewards, praise, and attention. Use positive consequences as much as possible for behaviors you would like your child to do again.

Negative consequences let your child know you do not like what he or she has done. Your child is less likely to repeat the behavior when you use negative consequences. Negative consequences are also called "discipline." Negative consequences include things, such as ignoring, distraction, loss of a privilege, and time-out. Use negative consequences for behaviors you would like your child to stop. It is a good idea to start with ignoring and distraction, especially for young children. Other consequences may be needed if ignoring and distraction do not work or are not possible. Natural consequences, delay or removal of privileges, and time-out can be used to stop misbehavior. More information about these consequences is provided below.

Ignoring. Children sometimes throw tantrums, whine, and interrupt just to get your attention. When you take away your attention from your child and these misbehaviors, the behaviors often stop. When ignoring, do not make eye contact with your child or talk to him or her. Ignore anything your child does to get your attention.

Distraction

When you distract your child, you get her or him to focus on something else. By doing this, she or he stops the misbehavior. You can use distraction anywhere. You just have to be prepared. Crayons and paper, toys, and small games are things you can keep with you to distract your child. You can also make up games. For example, if your child is whining in the grocery store, you could play the "show me" game. Ask your child to name or point to everything on the aisle that is the color blue or in the shape of a square.

Natural Consequences

Natural consequences are things that happen because of what we do or how we act. If you tell your child to play carefully with a toy, but they continue to bang it, the toy may break. In this case, your child has experienced the natural consequence of playing roughly with the toy. Although it is good for your child to learn from his mistakes, natural consequences should never put the child at risk. Do not allow your child to do anything that could hurt them or others, such as playing with matches or running into the street.

Delay of a Privilege and Logical (Or Common Sense) Consequences

Delaying a privilege means that your child has to wait to get something that they really want. You might tell your child, "After you pick up your toys, you can go out and play," or, "When you take three more bites of your dinner, you can have dessert." Removal of privileges means taking away the items or activities your child enjoys most. For young children, removing privileges is often called "logical (or common sense) consequences." The consequences are logically related to the misbehavior. You might take away toys or crayons that are not handled carefully. You might turn off the TV if your children are arguing about the channel. If your child spills something on purpose, a logical consequence is having your child clean-up the mess.

Time-Out

Time-out removes the child from where they are misbehaving. Time-out puts the child in a place that is free of anything or anyone that might provide attention. If your child hits their sibling, you can give them a time-out. Time-outs, when used the right way, really work at reducing a child's misbehaviors.

Tips on Discipline and Negative Consequences

The negative consequences used to decrease misbehavior should relate to the misbehavior and the seriousness of the misbehavior when possible. If your child is not playing nicely at the park, you can simply take her home. In this case, the negative consequence of going home fits the misbehavior at the park. Negative consequences should never deprive the child of basic essentials, such as food, a bath, or school.

After any consequence your child does not like, go back to being positive with your child. Remember that consequences should be directed at the behavior and not at the person. Avoid saying things like, "You never do anything right." These comments can be damaging to your child's self-esteem and to the parent-child relationship. It was the behavior that was the problem, not the child.

Using Consequences for Misbehaviors

A consequence is what happens immediately after a behavior. Consequences can be both positive and negative. Positive consequences show your child that she or he has done something you like. Your child is more likely to repeat the behavior when you use positive consequences. Negative consequences let your child know you do not like what he or she has done. Your child is less likely to repeat the behavior when you use negative consequences.

The five steps for using consequences to stop misbehavior are listed below.

Step 1: Identify the Misbehavior

What is your child doing that you want to stop? It is important that you and your child are clear about which behaviors are okay and which are not okay. If your child is doing something you do not like and want to stop, let them know by giving a warning that the behavior needs to change, or a consequence will be used.

Be specific when you tell your child what you expect. Saying something such as, "If you do not play nicely, you are going to lose your toys" is vague. You and your child may have different ideas about what "playing nicely" means. State exactly what you want to see your child do. You might say, "If you throw the truck again, I am going to take it away."

Step 2: Give a Warning

Give your child a warning that the behavior needs to change. Let them know they will get a consequence that they do not like if their behavior does not change. Using "If-Then" statements are a good way to give the warning to your child. You might say, "If you do not stop throwing the toy, then I am going to take it away."

Only use a warning if you are willing to follow through with the consequence. Follow through with the consequence every time you give a warning. If you do not, your child will not take the warning seriously. In the warning, be specific about what you expect from your child. If your child is banging pans on the table, you may say, "If you do not play gently with the pans, they will be put away for the rest of the day."

Step 3: Give a Consequence

Once a warning is given, you must always follow-through with a positive or negative consequence. Give a positive consequence if your child did what you asked. This lets them know you like the choice they made. Positive consequences include praise, hugs, pats on the back, or other things. Give a negative consequence if your child did not do what you asked. This lets them know you do not like the choice they made. Ignoring, distraction, time-out, and delay or restriction of privileges are examples of negative consequences. It is a good idea to try ignoring or distracting your child as potential consequences. If these do not work or are not possible, think about the common-sense consequences related to the misbehavior.

Ignoring. When you ignore, you take all your attention away from your child and their behavior. Ignoring usually helps stop behaviors that your child is using to get your attention. This includes behaviors, such as throwing tantrums, whining, and interrupting. When you are ignoring, you do not look at your child or talk to them. Ignore all protests or excuses to get your attention. The general rule is that you ignore the behavior until it stops. Sometimes, this is a long time. You may feel as if it will not stop the behavior. But, if your child is trying to get your attention and you continue ignoring, the behavior will eventually stop. Once you have ignored the misbehavior, you can redirect your child's attention to something else.

Distraction. Distracting your child can also be helpful for managing and preventing misbehaviors. When children are distracted, their attention is redirected to something else. If their attention is on something else, they cannot continue misbehaving. Distraction is easier to use when you plan in advance how you will handle situations that may be hard for your child. For instance, if your child misbehaves when you go out to dinner or on long car trips, bring crayons and paper or small games that can help distract your child. You can also use games like "I spy" to help change your child's attention to a positive activity for the two of you.

Delay of a privilege and logical (or common sense) consequences. Delaying a privilege means that your child has to wait to get something they like. When you remove privileges, you take away things or activities your child likes. For young children, the privileges you remove need to be logically related to the misbehavior. As an example, you might take away a toy your children are fighting over.

Time-out. Time-out takes your child from where the misbehavior is happening. Time-out moves your child to a place free of anything or anyone that might provide attention. Time-outs should be used immediately for misbehaviors. You can use time-outs for not following directions and breaking household rules. Time-outs may also help when your child is doing things that are destructive or dangerous.

Remember that young children have short attention spans. It is the responsibility of parents to make sure a child understands what they did wrong. The consequence should not be excessive. For example, the consequence for throwing a toy could be taking the toy away for a day or part of the day. It may be too much to remove the toy for an entire week. When the child gets the toy back, they will likely have forgotten why it was taken away in the first place. Also, taking away the toy for a week limits your child's chance to show that they can play with their toys the correct way. You will not be able to praise and reward good behaviors if there is not an opportunity.

Step 4: Tell Them Why

Let your child know why the negative consequence is happening. Always follow-through with the consequence. Remember, timing is key. Consequences should occur immediately after the misbehavior. This way, your child clearly understands what they did to get the negative consequence. When using a consequence, you can give a brief explanation to your child. You may say, "Because you hit your brother with your doll, I am taking away your doll for the evening." At that point, the doll should be removed and placed out of the child's reach.

Your child may beg, plead, cry, and tell you what you want to hear once you use the consequence. Your child may also say things such as they hate you or that you are a terrible parent. This should not affect your decision to follow through. If your child throws a tantrum and you give her what she wants, the lesson they learn is "If I cry loud enough, mom/dad will give me what I want." In this case, you have actually rewarded your child for the tantrum and made it more likely that they will throw a tantrum in the future.

Step 5: Go Back to Positive Communication

After the consequence is over, go back to being positive with your child. If a privilege is removed or delayed, you can remind your child of the good behavior you want to see. For example, if you give your child her doll back after a morning time-out, you might say, "You can play with the doll as long as you play gently." Watch for positive behaviors. Give praise and other rewards when your child does the right thing.

Section 47.3

Use of Rewards

This section includes text excerpted from "Use of
Rewards—Using Discipline and Consequences," Centers for
Disease Control and Prevention (CDC), October 2, 2017.

The way you respond right after your child's behaviors makes the
behavior more or less likely to happen again. Behaviors are more likely
to happen again when followed by a positive consequence, such as a
reward. This is true for all behaviors, even those you do not want to
happen again. Rewards are things, such as attention, going to the park,
small toys, or other things your child likes, such as hugs and kisses.

Rewards can be used to encourage your child's good behaviors.
They also help get your child to do more of the things you want them
to do. Rewards that happen right after a behavior are best. Sometimes
rewards cannot be given right away, but they should be given as soon
as possible. Rewards do not work as well when they are given long
after a behavior. This is true especially for toddlers and preschoolers.
Their memory is not as good as it is for older children.

When you first start using rewards, reward the behavior you like
every time it occurs. Tell your child exactly what they did that you
liked and why they are getting the reward. If you do not tell them what
you liked, they will not know what to do next time to be rewarded. You
could say, "I am so happy you put your toys away without being asked.
Now we get to read two extra books before sleepy time!"

Why Are Rewards Important?

Rewards are important for many reasons. First, rewards can be used
to increase self-esteem. Toddlers and preschoolers hear the words "no,"
"do not," "stop," and "quit" many times during the day. This is normal
and one of the ways they learn right from wrong. But when children
hear these things over and over, their self-esteem can begin to suffer.
They may begin to believe they cannot do anything correctly. Rewards
can be used to increase self-esteem. When a child earns a reward, they
know that they have done something good and something you like.

Rewards can also help improve your relationship with your child.
When you give a reward to your child, you and your child are both
happy. You are happy because your child has done something you like.
Your child is also happy because they are getting something they like.

Types of Rewards

There are several types of rewards. Most people think of toys, candy, or other things that cost money as rewards. These are called "material rewards." Another type of reward is a social reward. Social rewards are cheap or free and can be even more powerful than material rewards. They also can be given more often and immediately after behaviors you like. Affection, praise, or attention from you are examples of social rewards.

Examples of social rewards include:

- **Affection.** Rewarding your child with your affection lets him or her know you approve of what he or she did. This includes hugs, kisses, a high five, a smile, a pat on the back, or an arm around the shoulder.

- **Praise.** Praise happens when parents say things, such as "Great job," "Way to go," or "Good boy/girl." These words show approval, but they do not tell children exactly what behavior you liked. Specific (or labeled) praise tells a child exactly what behavior you liked. Examples of labeled praise are:

  1. "Great job playing quietly while I was on the telephone!"

  2. "You were a great helper when you put all your toys in the closet today!"

  3. "Thank you for using your inside voice."

- **Attention and Activities.** Extra time with you or a special activity can be a powerful reward for young children. Some examples include playing a favorite game, reading a story, going to the park, and helping with dinner. Other activities, such as going to the movies, the zoo, or skating, can also be used, but these activities may not always be available or affordable.

Tips for Using Rewards

Using social and material rewards together may increase how quickly your child's behavior changes. You can decrease the use of rewards after your child is doing what you want regularly and consistently.

When using material rewards, the rewards must be something that your child likes or really enjoys. If your child does not like or enjoy the reward, he or she will not be interested in earning it. Praise and attention should always be used with material rewards. Praise and attention play an important role in making the parent-child relationship positive.

When picking rewards, be creative and come up with a variety of rewards to use with each of your children. Remember that all children are different and like different things. What may be rewarding for one child may not be for another. Children will also get bored easily. If they receive the same rewards each time, that reward will be less powerful over time.

When children are younger, small rewards go a long way. A sticker or smiley face and parental attention are usually all that is required to encourage good behaviors. This changes as children get older and other rewards become more important.

Reward Programs

A rewards program is a way to keep track of how often your child does what you like. For young children, a chart is often used. Social and material rewards can be used as part of the reward program. You watch your child's behavior and when you catch him doing what you like, you provide a reward. Rewards could be a sticker, a smiley face, a check mark, or an ink stamp. Praise and attention from you can also be used as the reward. The rewards need to be specific to your child's age, ability level, and preferences.

Chapter 48

Improving Parenting Skills

Chapter Contents

Section 48.1

Building Healthy Relationships with Your Kids

This section includes text excerpted from "Positive Parenting," *NIH News in Health*, National Institutes of Health (NIH), September 2017.

Parents have an important job. Raising kids is both rewarding and challenging. You are likely to get a lot of advice along the way from doctors, family, friends, and even strangers. But every parent and child are unique. Being sensitive and responsive to your kids can help you build positive, healthy relationships together.

"Being a sensitive parent and responding to your kids' cuts across all areas of parenting," says Arizona State University's Dr. Keith Crnic, a parent-child relationship expert. "What it means is recognizing what your child needs at the moment and providing that in an effective way."

This can be especially critical for infants and toddlers, he adds. Strong emotional bonds often develop through sensitive, responsive, and consistent parenting in the first years of life. For instance, holding your baby lovingly and responding to their cries helps build strong bonds.

Building Bonds

Strong emotional bonds help children learn how to manage their own feelings and behaviors and develop self-confidence. They help create a safe base from which they can explore, learn, and relate to others.

Experts call this type of strong connection between children and their caregivers a "secure attachment." Securely attached children are more likely to be able to cope with challenges, such as poverty, family instability, parental stress, and depression.

An analysis shows that about 6 out of 10 children in the United States develop secure attachments to their parents. The 4 out of 10 kids who lack such bonds may avoid their parents when they are upset or resist their parents if they cause them more distress. Studies suggest that this can make kids more prone to serious behavior problems. Researchers have been testing programs to help parents develop behaviors that encourage secure attachment.

Being Available

Modern life is full of elements that can influence your ability to be sensitive and responsive to your child. These include competing priorities, extra work, lack of sleep, and items such as mobile devices. Some experts are concerned about the effects that distracted parenting may have on emotional bonding and children's language development, social interaction, and safety.

If parents are inconsistently available, kids can get distressed and feel hurt, rejected, or ignored. They may have more emotional outbursts and feel alone. They may even stop trying to compete for their parent's attention and start to lose emotional connections to their parents.

"There are times when kids really do need your attention and want your recognition," Crnic explains. Parents need to communicate that their kids are valuable and important, and children need to know that parents care about what they are doing, he says.

It can be tough to respond with sensitivity during tantrums, arguments, or other challenging times with your kids. "If parents respond by being irritable or aggressive themselves, children can mimic that behavior, and a negative cycle then continues to escalate," explains Dr. Carol Metzler, who studies parenting at the Oregon Research Institute.

According to Crnic, kids start to regulate their own emotions and behavior around the age of three. Up until then, they depend on their parents to help them regulate their emotions, whether to calm them or help get them excited. "They are watching you to see how you do it and listening to how you talk to them about it," he explains. "Parents need to be good self-regulators. You are not only trying to regulate your own emotions at the moment but helping your child learn to manage their emotions and behavior."

As kids become better at managing their feelings and behavior, it is important to help them develop coping skills, such as active problem-solving. Such skills can help them feel confident in handling what comes their way.

"When parents engage positively with their children, teaching them the behaviors and skills that they need to cope with the world, children learn to follow rules and regulate their own feelings," Metzler says.

"As parents, we try really hard to protect our kids from the experience of bad things," Crnic explains. "But if you protect them all the time and they are not in situations where they deal with difficult or adverse circumstances, they are not able to develop healthy coping skills."

He encourages you to allow your kids to have more of those experiences and then help them learn how to solve the problems that emerge. Talk through the situation and their feelings. Then work with them to find solutions to put into practice.

Meeting Needs

As children grow up, it is important to remember that giving them what they need does not mean giving them everything they want. "These two things are very different," Crnic explains. "Really hone in on exactly what is going on with your kid in the moment. This is an incredibly important parenting skill, and it is linked to so many great outcomes for kids."

Think about where a child is in life and what skills they need to learn at that time. Perhaps they need help managing emotions, learning how to behave in a certain situation, thinking through a new task, or relating to friends.

"You want to help kids become confident," Crnic says. "You do not want to aim too high where they cannot get there or too low where they have already mastered the skill." Another way to boost confidence while strengthening your relationship is to let your kid take the lead.

"Make some time to spend with your child that is not highly directive, where your child leads the play," advises Dr. John Bates, who studies children's behavior problems at Indiana University Bloomington. "Kids come to expect it and they love it, and it really improves the relationship."

Bates also encourages parents to focus on their child's actual needs instead of sticking to any specific parenting principles.

It is never too late to start building a healthier, more positive relationship with your child, even if things have gotten strained and stressful. "Most importantly, make sure that your child knows that you love them and are on their side," Metzler says. "For older children, let them know that you are genuinely committed to building a stronger relationship with them and helping them be successful."

By being a sensitive and responsive parent, you can help set your kids on a positive path; teach them self-control; reduce the likelihood of troublesome behaviors; and build a warm, caring parent-child relationship.

Section 48.2

Positive Parenting Tips

This section includes text excerpted from "Positive Parenting Tips," Centers for Disease Control and Prevention (CDC), February 6, 2019.

As a parent, you give your children a good start in life—you nurture, protect and guide them. Parenting is a process that prepares your child for independence. As your child grows and develops, there are many things you can do to help your child.

Infants (0 to 1 Year of Age)
Developmental Milestones

Skills, such as taking a first step, smiling for the first time, and waving "bye-bye," are called "developmental milestones." Developmental milestones are things most children can do by a certain age. Children reach milestones in how they play, learn, speak, behave, and move (such as crawling, walking, or jumping).

In the first year, babies learn to focus their vision, reach out, explore, and learn about the things that are around them. Cognitive, or brain, development means the learning process of memory, language, thinking, and reasoning. Learning a language is more than making sounds ("babble"), or saying "ma-ma" and "da-da." Listening, understanding, and knowing the names of people and things are all a part of language development. During this stage, babies also are developing bonds of love and trust with their parents and others as part of social and emotional development. The way parents cuddle, hold, and play with their baby will set the basis for how they will interact with them and others.

Positive Parenting Tips

The following are some things you, as a parent, can do to help your baby during this time:

- Talk to your baby. She or he will find your voice calming.

- Answer when your baby makes sounds by repeating the sounds and adding words. This will help her or him learn to use language.

- Read to your baby. This will help her or him develop and understand language and sounds.

- Sing to your baby and play music. This will help your baby develop a love for music and will help her or his brain development.

- Praise your baby, and give her or him lots of loving attention.

- Spend time cuddling and holding your baby. This will help her or him feel cared for and secure.

- Play with your baby when she or he is alert and relaxed. Watch your baby closely for signs of being tired or fussy so that she or he can take a break from playing.

- Distract your baby with toys, and move her or him to safe areas when she or he starts moving and touching things that she or he should not touch.

- Take care of yourself physically, mentally, and emotionally. Parenting can be hard work. It is easier to enjoy your new baby and be a positive, loving parent when you are feeling good yourself.

Child Safety First

When a baby becomes part of your family, it is time to make sure that your home is a safe place. Look around your home for things that could be dangerous to your baby. As a parent, it is your job to ensure that you create a safe home for your baby. It also is important that you take the necessary steps to make sure that you are mentally and emotionally ready for your new baby. Here are a few tips to keep your baby safe:

- Do not shake your baby, ever. Babies have very weak neck muscles that are not yet able to support their heads. If you shake your baby, you can damage her or his brain or even cause death.

- Make sure you always put your baby to sleep on her or his back to prevent sudden infant death syndrome (commonly known as "SIDS").

- Protect your baby and family from secondhand smoke. Do not allow anyone to smoke in your home.

- Place your baby in a rear-facing car seat in the back seat while she or he is riding in a car.

- Prevent your baby from choking by cutting her or his food into small bites. Also, do not let him or her play with small toys and other things that might be easy to swallow.

- Do not allow your baby to play with anything that might cover her or his face.

- Never carry hot liquids or foods near your baby or while holding her or him.

- Vaccines (shots) are important to protect your child's health and safety. Because children can get serious diseases, it is important that your child get the right shots at the right time. Talk with your child's doctor to make sure that your child is up-to-date on her or his vaccinations.

Healthy Bodies

- Breast milk meets all your baby's needs for about the first 6 months of life. Between 6 and 12 months of age, your baby will learn about new tastes and textures with healthy solid food, but breast milk should still be an important source of nutrition.

- Feed your baby slowly and patiently, encourage your baby to try new tastes but without force, and watch closely to see if she or he is still hungry.

- Breastfeeding is the natural way to feed your baby, but it can be challenging. If you need help, you can call the National Breastfeeding Helpline at 800-994-9662 or get help online at www.womenshealth.gov. You can also call your local WIC Program to see if you qualify for breastfeeding support from health professionals, as well as peer counselors. Or go to www.ilca.org to find an International Board-Certified Lactation Consultant (IBCLC) in your community.

- Keep your baby active. She or he might not be able to run and play like the "big kids" just yet, but there is lots she or he can do to keep her little arms and legs moving throughout the day. Getting down on the floor to move helps your baby become strong, learn, and explore.

- Try not to keep your baby in swings, strollers, bouncer seats, and exercise saucers for too long.

- Limit screen time to a minimum. For children younger than two years of age, the American Academy of Pediatrics (AAP) recommends that it is best if babies do not watch any screen media.

- Make sure your child gets the recommended amount of sleep each night: For infants 4 to 12 months, 12 to 16 hours per 24 hours (including naps) is recommended.

Toddlers (1 to 2 Years of Age)
Developmental Milestones

During the second year, toddlers are moving around more and are aware of themselves and their surroundings. Their desire to explore new objects and people also is increasing. During this stage, toddlers will show greater independence; begin to show defiant behavior; recognize themselves in pictures or a mirror; and imitate the behavior of others, especially adults and older children. Toddlers also should be able to recognize the names of familiar people and objects, form simple phrases and sentences, and follow simple instructions and directions.

Positive Parenting Tips

The following are some of the things you, as a parent, can do to help your toddler during this time:

- Read to your toddler daily.
- Ask her or him to find objects for you or name body parts and objects.
- Play matching games with your toddler, such as shape sorting and simple puzzles.
- Encourage her or him to explore and try new things.
- Help to develop your toddler's language by talking with her or him and adding to words she or he starts. For example, if your toddler says "baba," you can respond, "Yes, you are right—that is a bottle."
- Encourage your child's growing independence by letting her or him help with dressing himself and feeding himself.
- Respond to wanted behaviors more than you punish unwanted behaviors (use only very brief time outs). Always tell or show your child what she or he should do instead.

- Encourage your toddler's curiosity and ability to recognize common objects by taking field trips together to the park or going on a bus ride.

Child Safety First

Because your child is moving around more, she or he will come across more dangers as well. Dangerous situations can happen quickly, so keep a close eye on your child. Here are a few tips to help keep your growing toddler safe:

- Do not leave your toddler near or around water (for example, bathtubs, pools, ponds, lakes, whirlpools, or the ocean) without someone watching him or her. Fence off backyard pools. Drowning is the leading cause of injury and death among this age group.

- Block off stairs with a small gate or fence. Lock doors to dangerous places, such as the garage or basement.

- Ensure that your home is toddler-proof by placing plug covers on all unused electrical outlets.

- Keep kitchen appliances, irons, and heaters out of reach of your toddler. Turn pot handles toward the back of the stove.

- Keep sharp objects, such as scissors, knives, and pens, in a safe place.

- Lock up medicines, household cleaners, and poisons.

- Do not leave your toddler alone in any vehicle (that means a car, truck, or van) even for a few moments.

- Store any guns in a safe place and out of reach.

- Keep your child's car seat rear-facing as long as possible. According to the National Highway Traffic Safety Administration (NHTSA) it is the best way to keep her or him safe. Your child should remain in a rear-facing car seat until they reach the top height or weight limit allowed by the car seat's manufacturer. Once your child outgrows the rear-facing car seat, they are ready to travel in a forward-facing car seat with a harness.

Healthy Bodies

- Give your child water and plain milk instead of sugary drinks. After the first year, when your nursing toddler is eating more and different solid foods, breast milk is still an ideal addition to her or his diet.

- Your toddler might become a very picky and erratic eater. Toddlers need less food because they do not grow as fast. It is best not to battle with her or him over this. Offer a selection of healthy foods, and let her or him choose what she or he wants. Keep trying new foods; it might take time for her or him to learn to like them.

- Limit screen time. For children younger than two years of age, the AAP recommends that it is best if toddlers not watch any screen media.

- Your toddler will seem to be moving continually—running, kicking, climbing, or jumping. Let her or him be active—she or he is developing her or his coordination and becoming strong.

- Make sure your child gets the recommended amount of sleep each night: For toddlers between the ages of 1 and 2, 11 to 14 hours per 24 hours (including naps) is recommended.

Toddlers (2 to 3 Years of Age)
Developmental Milestones

Skills, such as taking turns, playing make believe, and kicking a ball, are called "developmental milestones." Developmental milestones are things most children can do by a certain age. Children reach milestones in how they play, learn, speak, behave, and move (such as jumping, running, or balancing).

Because of children's growing desire to be independent, this stage is often called the "terrible twos." However, this can be an exciting time for parents and toddlers. Toddlers will experience huge thinking, learning, social, and emotional changes that will help them to explore their new world and make sense of it. During this stage, toddlers should be able to follow two- or three-step directions, sort objects by shape and color, imitate the actions of adults and playmates, and express a wide range of emotions.

Positive Parenting Tips

The following are some of the things you, as a parent, can do to help your toddler during this time:

- Set up a special time to read books with your toddler.

- Encourage your child to take part in pretend play.
- Play parade or follow the leader with your toddler.
- Help your child to explore things around him or her by taking him or her on a walk or wagon ride.
- Encourage your child to tell you her or his name and age.
- Teach your child simple songs, such as "Itsy-Bitsy Spider," or other cultural childhood rhymes.
- Give your child attention and praise when she or he follows instructions and shows positive behavior and limit attention for defiant behavior, such as tantrums. Teach your child acceptable ways to show that she or he is upset.

Child Safety First

Because your child is moving around more, she or he will come across more dangers as well. Dangerous situations can happen quickly, so keep a close eye on your child. Here are a few tips to help keep your growing toddler safe:

- Do not leave your toddler near or around water (for example, bathtubs, pools, ponds, lakes, whirlpools, or the ocean) without someone watching her or him. Fence off backyard pools. Drowning is the leading cause of injury and death among this age group.
- Encourage your toddler to sit when eating and to chew her or his food thoroughly to prevent choking.
- Check toys often for loose or broken parts.
- Encourage your toddler not to put pencils or crayons in her or his mouth when coloring or drawing.
- Do not hold hot drinks while your child is sitting on your lap. Sudden movements can cause a spill and might result in your child's being burned.
- Make sure that your child sits in the back seat and is buckled up properly in a car seat with a harness.

Healthy Bodies

- Talk with staff at your child-care provider to see if they serve healthier foods and drinks, and if they limit television and other screen time.

- Your toddler might change what food she or he likes from day to day. It is normal behavior, and it is best not to make an issue of it. Encourage her or him to try new foods by offering her small bites to taste.

- Keep television sets out of your child's bedroom. Limit screen time, including video and electronic games, to no more than 1 to 2 hours per day.

- Encourage free play as much as possible. It helps your toddler stay active and strong and helps her or him develop motor skills.

- Make sure your child gets the recommended amount of sleep each night: For toddlers 1 to 2 years of age, 11 to 14 hours per 24 hours (including naps) is recommended.

Preschoolers (3 to 5 Years of Age)
Developmental Milestones

Skills, such as naming colors, showing affection, and hopping on one foot are called "developmental milestones." Developmental milestones are things most children can do by a certain age. Children reach milestones in how they play, learn, speak, behave, and move (such as crawling, walking, or jumping).

As children grow into early childhood, their world will begin to open up. They will become more independent and begin to focus more on adults and children outside of the family. They will want to explore and ask about the things around them even more. Their interactions with family and those around them will help to shape their personality and their own ways of thinking and moving. During this stage, children should be able to ride a tricycle, use safety scissors, notice a difference between girls and boys, help to dress and undress themselves, play with other children, recall part of a story, and sing a song.

Positive Parenting Tips

The following are some of the things you, as a parent, can do to help your preschooler during this time:

- Continue to read to your child. Nurture her or his love for books by taking him or her to the library or bookstore.

- Let your child help with simple chores.

- Encourage your child to play with other children. This helps her or him to learn the value of sharing and friendship.

- Be clear and consistent when disciplining your child. Explain and show the behavior that you expect from him or her.

- Whenever you tell him or her no, follow up with what she or he should be doing instead.

- Help your child develop good language skills by speaking to her or him in complete sentences and using "grown up" words. Help her or him to use the correct words and phrases.

- Help your child through the steps to solve problems when she or he is upset.

- Give your child a limited number of simple choices (for example, deciding what to wear, when to play, and what to eat for snack).

Child Safety First

As your child becomes more independent and spends more time in the outside world, it is important that you and your child are aware of ways to stay safe. Here are a few tips to protect your child:

- Tell your child why it is important to stay out of traffic. Tell her or him not to play in the street or run after stray balls.

- Be cautious when letting your child ride, her or his tricycle. Keep her or his on the sidewalk and away from the street and always have her or him wear a helmet.

- Check outdoor playground equipment. Make sure there are no loose parts or sharp edges.

- Watch your child at all times, especially when she or he is playing outside.

- Be safe in the water. Teach your child to swim, but watch her or him at all times when she or he is in or around any body of water (this includes kiddie pools).

- Teach your child how to be safe around strangers.

- Keep your child in a forward-facing car seat with a harness until she or he reaches the top height or weight limit allowed by the car seat's manufacturer. Once your child outgrows the forward-facing car seat with a harness, it will be time for him to travel in a booster seat, but still in the back seat of the vehicle.

371

Healthy Bodies

- Eat meals with your child whenever possible. Let your child see you enjoying fruits, vegetables, and whole grains at meals and snacks. Your child should eat and drink only a limited amount of food and beverages that contain added sugars, solid fats, or salt.

- Limit screen time for your child to no more than one to two hours per day of quality programming, at home, school, or child care.

- Provide your child with age-appropriate play equipment, such as balls and plastic bats, but let your preschooler choose what to play. This makes moving and being active fun for your preschooler.

- Make sure your child gets the recommended amount of sleep each night: For preschoolers 3 to 5 years of age, 10 to 13 hours per 24 hours (including naps) is recommended.

Middle Childhood (6 to 8 Years of Age)
Developmental Milestones

Middle childhood brings many changes in a child's life. By this time, children can dress themselves, catch a ball more easily using only their hands, and tie their shoes. Having independence from family becomes more important now. Events, such as starting school, bring children this age into regular contact with the larger world. Friendships become more and more important. Physical, social, and mental skills develop quickly at this time. This is a critical time for children to develop confidence in all areas of life, such as through friends, schoolwork, and sports.

Here is some information on how children develop during middle childhood:

Emotional/Social Changes

Children in this age group might:

- Show more independence from parents and family
- Start to think about the future
- Understand more about her or his place in the world
- Pay more attention to friendships and teamwork
- Want to be liked and accepted by friends

Thinking and Learning

Children in this age group might:

- Show rapid development of mental skills

- Learn better ways to describe experiences and talk about thoughts and feelings

- Have less focus on one's self and more concern for others

Positive Parenting Tips

The following are some things you, as a parent, can do to help your child during this time:

- Show affection for your child. Recognize her or his accomplishments.

- Help your child develop a sense of responsibility—ask her or him to help with household tasks, such as setting the table.

- Talk with your child about school, friends, and things she or he looks forward to in the future.

- Talk with your child about respecting others. Encourage her or him to help people in need.

- Help your child set her or his own achievable goals—she or he will learn to take pride in him- or herself and rely less on approval or reward from others.

- Help your child learn patience by letting others go first or by finishing a task before going out to play. Encourage her or him to think about possible consequences before acting.

- Make clear rules and stick to them, such as how long your child can watch TV or when she or he has to go to bed. Be clear about what behavior is okay and what is not okay.

- Do fun things together as a family, such as playing games, reading, and going to events in your community.

- Get involved with your child's school. Meet the teachers and staff and get to understand their learning goals and how you and the school can work together to help your child do well.

- Continue reading to your child. As your child learns to read, take turns reading to each other.

- Use discipline to guide and protect your child, rather than punishment to make her or him feel bad about her- or himself. Follow up any discussion about what not to do with a discussion of what to do instead.

- Praise your child for good behavior. It is best to focus praise more on what your child does ("you worked hard to figure this out") than on traits she or he cannot change ("you are smart").

- Support your child in taking on new challenges. Encourage her or him to solve problems, such as a disagreement with another child, on her or his own.

- Encourage your child to join school and community groups, such as a team sports, or to take advantage of volunteer opportunities.

Child Safety First

More physical ability and more independence can put children at risk for injuries from falls and other accidents. Motor vehicle crashes are the most common cause of death from unintentional injury among children this age.

- Protect your child properly in the car.

- Teach your child to watch out for traffic and how to be safe when walking to school, riding a bike, and playing outside.

- Make sure your child understands water safety, and always supervise her or him when she or he is swimming or playing near water.

- Supervise your child when she or he is engaged in risky activities, such as climbing.

- Talk with your child about how to ask for help when she or he needs it.

- Keep potentially harmful household products, tools, equipment, and firearms out of your child's reach.

Healthy Bodies

- Parents can help make schools healthier. Work with your child's school to limit access to foods and drinks with added sugar, solid fat, and salt that can be purchased outside the school lunch program.

- Make sure your child has one hour or more of physical activity each day.

- Limit screen time for your child to no more than one to two hours per day of quality programming, at home, school, or afterschool care.

- Practice healthy eating habits and physical activity early. Encourage active play, and be a role model by eating healthy at family mealtimes and having an active lifestyle.

- Make sure your child gets the recommended amount of sleep each night: For school-aged children 6 to 12 years of age, 9 to 12 hours per 24 hours (including naps) is recommended.

Middle Childhood (9 to 11 Years of Age)
Developmental Milestones

Your child's growing independence from the family and an interest in friends might be obvious by now. Healthy friendships are very important to your child's development, but peer pressure can become strong during this time. Children who feel good about themselves are more able to resist negative peer pressure and make better choices for themselves. This is an important time for children to gain a sense of responsibility along with their growing independence. Also, physical changes of puberty might be showing by now, especially for girls. Another big change children need to prepare for during this time is starting middle or junior high school.

Here is some information on how children develop during middle childhood:

Emotional/Social Changes

Children in this age group might:

- Start to form stronger, more complex friendships and peer relationships. It becomes more emotionally important to have friends, especially of the same sex.

- Experience more peer pressure

- Become more aware of her or his body as puberty approaches. Body image and eating problems sometimes start around this age.

375

Thinking and Learning

Children in this age group might:

- Face more academic challenges at school
- Become more independent from the family
- Begin to see the point of view of others more clearly
- Have an increased attention span

Positive Parenting Tips

The following are some things you, as a parent, can do to help your child during this time:

- Spend time with your child. Talk with her or him about her or his friends, her or his accomplishments, and what challenges she or he will face.

- Be involved with your child's school. Go to school events; meet your child's teachers.

- Encourage your child to join school and community groups, such as a sports team, or to be a volunteer for a charity.

- Help your child develop her or his own sense of right and wrong. Talk with him or her about risky things friends might pressure him to do, such as smoking or dangerous physical dares.

- Help your child develop a sense of responsibility—involve your child in household tasks such as cleaning and cooking. Talk with your child about saving and spending money wisely.

- Meet the families of your child's friends.

- Talk with your child about respecting others. Encourage her or him to help people in need. Talk with her or him about what to do when others are not kind or are disrespectful.

- Help your child set her or his own goals. Encourage him or her to think about skills and abilities she or he would like to have and about how to develop them.

- Make clear rules and stick to them. Talk with your child about what you expect from her or him (behavior) when no adults are present. If you provide reasons for rules, it will help her or him to know what to do in most situations.

- Use discipline to guide and protect your child, instead of punishment to make her or him feel badly about him- or herself.

- When using praise, help your child think about her or his own accomplishments. Saying "you must be proud of yourself" rather than simply "I am proud of you" can encourage your child to make good choices when nobody is around to praise her or him.

- Talk with your child about the normal physical and emotional changes of puberty.

- Encourage your child to read every day. Talk with her or him about his homework.

- Be affectionate and honest with your child, and do things together as a family.

Child Safety First

More independence and less adult supervision can put children at risk for injuries from falls and other accidents. Here are a few tips to help protect your child:

- Protect your child in the car. The NHTSA recommends that you keep your child in a booster seat until she or he is big enough to fit in a seat belt properly. Remember: your child should still ride in the back seat until she or he is 12 years of age because it is safer there. Motor vehicle crashes are the most common cause of death from unintentional injury among children of this age.

- Know where your child is and whether a responsible adult is present. Make plans with your child for when she or he will call you, where you can find him or her, and what time you expect her or him home.

- Make sure your child wears a helmet when riding a bike, a skateboard, or using inline skates; riding on a motorcycle, snowmobile, or all-terrain vehicle; or playing contact sports.

- Many children get home from school before their parents get home from work. It is important to have clear rules and plans for your child when she or he is home alone.

Healthy Bodies

- Provide plenty of fruits and vegetables; limit foods high in solid fats, added sugars, or salt, and prepare healthier foods for family meals.

- Keep television sets out of your child's bedroom. Limit screen time, including computers and video games, to no more than one to two hours a day.

- Encourage your child to participate in an hour a day of physical activities that are age appropriate, enjoyable, and offer variety. Just make sure your child is doing three types of activity: aerobic activity, such as running; muscle strengthening, such as climbing, and bone strengthening, such as jumping rope, at least three days per week.

- Make sure your child gets the recommended amount of sleep each night: For school-aged children of the age of 6 to 12 years, 9 to 12 hours per 24 hours (including naps) is recommended.

Young Teens (12 to 14 Years of Age)
Developmental Milestones

This is a time of many physical, mental, emotional, and social changes. Hormones change as puberty begins. Most boys grow facial and pubic hair, and their voices deepen. Most girls grow pubic hair and breasts, and start their period. They might be worried about these changes and how they are looked at by others. This also will be a time when your teen might face peer pressure to use alcohol, tobacco products, drugs, and to have sex. Other challenges can be eating disorders, depression, and family problems. At this age, teens make more of their own choices about friends, sports, studying, and school. They become more independent, with their own personality and interests, although parents are still very important.

Here is some information on how young teens develop:

Emotional/Social Changes

Children in this age group might:

- Show more concern about body image, looks, and clothes

- Focus on themselves; going back and forth between high expectations and lack of confidence

- Experience more moodiness

- Show more interest in and influence by peer groups

- Express less affection toward parents; sometimes might seem rude or short-tempered

- Feel stress from more challenging school work

- Develop eating problems

- Feel a lot of sadness or depression, which can lead to poor grades at school, alcohol or drug use, unsafe sex, and other problems

Thinking and Learning

Children in this age group might:

- Have more ability for complex thought

- Be better able to express feelings through talking

- Develop a stronger sense of right and wrong

Positive Parenting Tips

The following are some things you, as a parent, can do to help your child during this time:

- Be honest and direct with your teen when talking about sensitive subjects, such as drugs, drinking, smoking, and sex.

- Meet and get to know your teen's friends.

- Show an interest in your teen's school life.

- Help your teen make healthy choices while encouraging her or him to make her or his own decisions

- Respect your teen's opinions and take into account her or his thoughts and feelings. It is important that she or he knows you are listening to him or her.

- When there is a conflict, be clear about goals and expectations (such as getting good grades, keeping things clean, and showing respect), but allow your teen's input on how to reach those goals (such as when and how to study or clean).

Child Safety First

You play an important role in keeping your child safe, no matter how old she or he is. Here are a few tips to help protect your child:

- Make sure your teen knows about the importance of wearing seatbelts. Motor vehicle crashes are the leading cause of death among 12- to 14-year-olds.

- Encourage your teen to wear a helmet when riding a bike, a skateboard, or using inline skates; riding on a motorcycle, snowmobile, or all-terrain vehicle; or playing contact sports. Injuries from sports and other activities are common.

- Talk with your teen about the dangers of drugs, drinking, smoking, and risky sexual activity. Ask her or him what she or he knows and thinks about these issues, and share your thoughts and feelings with her or him. Listen to what she or he says and answer her or his questions honestly and directly.

- Talk with your teen about the importance of having friends who are interested in positive activities. Encourage her or him to avoid peers who pressure her or him to make unhealthy choices.

- Know where your teen is and whether an adult is present. Make plans with her or him for when she or he will call you, where you can find her or him, and what time you expect her or him home.

- Set clear rules for your teen when she or he is home alone. Talk about issues, such as having friends at the house, how to handle situations that can be dangerous (emergencies, fire, drugs, sex, etc.), and completing homework or household tasks.

Healthy Bodies

- Encourage your teen to be physically active. She or he might join a team sport or take up an individual sport. Helping with household tasks, such as mowing the lawn, walking the dog, or washing the car, also will keep your teen active.

- Meal time is very important for families. Eating together helps teens make better choices about the foods they eat, promotes healthy weight, and gives your family members time to talk with each other.

- Limit screen time for your child to no more than one to two hours per day of quality programming, at home, school, or afterschool care.

- Make sure your child gets the recommended amount of sleep each night: For teenagers between the ages of 13 and 18 years, 8 to 10 hours per 24 hours (including naps) is recommended.

Teenagers (15 to 17 Years of Age)
Developmental Milestones

This is a time of changes for how teenagers think, feel, and interact with others, and how their bodies grow. Most girls will be physically mature by now, and most will have completed puberty. Boys might still be maturing physically during this time. Your teen might have concerns about her or his body size, shape, or weight. Eating disorders also can be common, especially among girls. During this time, your teen is developing her or his unique personality and opinions. Relationships with friends are still important, yet your teen will have other interests as she or he develops a clear sense of who she or he is. This is also an important time to prepare for more independence and responsibility; many teenagers start working, and many will be leaving home soon after high school.

Here is some information on how teens develop:

Emotional / Social Changes

Children in this age group might:

- Have more interest in romantic relationships and sexuality

- Go through less conflict with parents

- Show more independence from parents

- Have a deeper capacity for caring and sharing and for developing more intimate relationships

- Spend less time with parents and more time with friends

- Feel a lot of sadness or depression, which can lead to poor grades at school, alcohol or drug use, unsafe sex, and other problems

Thinking and Learning

Children in this age group might:

- Learn more defined work habits

- Show more concern about future school and work plans

- Be better able to give reasons for their own choices, including about what is right or wrong

Positive Parenting Tips

The following are some things you, as a parent, can do to help your teen during this time:

- Talk with your teen about her or his concerns, and pay attention to any changes in her or his behavior. Ask her or him if she or he has had suicidal thoughts, particularly if she or he seems sad or depressed. Asking about suicidal thoughts will not cause her or him to have these thoughts, but it will let her or him know that you care about how she or he feels. Seek professional help if necessary.

- Show interest in your teen's school and extracurricular interests and activities and encourage her or him to become involved in activities, such as sports, music, theater, and art.

- Encourage your teen to volunteer and become involved in civic activities in her or his community.

- Compliment your teen and celebrate her or his efforts and accomplishments.

- Show affection for your teen. Spend time together doing things you enjoy.

- Respect your teen's opinion. Listen to her or him without playing down her concerns.

- Encourage your teen to develop solutions to problems or conflicts. Help your teenager learn to make good decisions. Create opportunities for her or him to use his own judgment, and be available for advice and support.

- If your teen engages in interactive Internet media, such as games, chat rooms, and instant messaging, encourage her or him to make good decisions about what she or he posts and the amount of time she spends on these activities.

- If your teen works, use the opportunity to talk about expectations, responsibilities, and other ways of behaving respectfully in a public setting.

- Talk with your teen and help her or him plan ahead for difficult or uncomfortable situations. Discuss what she or he can do if she or he is in a group, and someone is using drugs or under pressure to have sex, or if your child is offered a ride by someone who has been drinking.

- Respect your teen's need for privacy.

- Encourage your teen to get enough sleep and exercise, and to eat healthy, balanced meals.

Safety First

You play an important role in keeping your child safe?no matter how old she or he is. Here are a few ways to help protect your child:

- Talk with your teen about the dangers of driving and how to be safe on the road. You can steer your teen in the right direction. Motor vehicle crashes are the leading cause of death from unintentional injury among teens, yet few teens take measures to reduce their risk of injury.

- Remind your teen to wear a helmet when riding a bike, motorcycle, or all-terrain vehicle. Unintentional injuries resulting from participation in sports and other activities are common.

- Talk with your teen about suicide, and pay attention to warning signs. Suicide is the third leading cause of death among youth between 15 and 24 years of age.

- Talk with your teen about the dangers of drugs, drinking, smoking, and risky sexual activity. Ask her or him what she or he knows and thinks about these issues, and share your feelings with her or him. Listen to what she or he says and answer her or his questions honestly and directly.

- Discuss with your teen the importance of choosing friends who do not act in dangerous or unhealthy ways.

- Know where your teen is and whether a responsible adult is present. Make plans with her or him for when she or he will call you, where you can find her or him, and what time you expect her or him home.

Healthy Bodies

- Encourage your teen to get enough sleep and physical activity, and to eat healthy, balanced meals. Make sure your teen gets one hour or more of physical activity each day.

- Keep television sets out of your teen's bedroom.

- Encourage your teen to have meals with the family. Eating together will help your teen make better choices about the foods she or he eats, promote healthy weight, and give family members time to talk with each other. In addition, a teen who eats meals with the family is more likely to get better grades and less likely to smoke, drink, or use drugs, and also less likely to get into fights, think about suicide, or engage in sexual activity.

- Make sure your child gets the recommended amount of sleep each night: For teenagers 13 to 18 years of age, 8 to 10 hours per 24 hours is recommended.

Section 48.3

Parental Support Groups

This section includes text excerpted from "Parent Support Group Programs," Child Welfare Information Gateway, U.S. Department of Health and Human Services (HHS), November 11, 2016.

The following programs provide information on starting a parent support group.

Birth Parent National Network provides information about a group that works with those who are committed to improving policies for better outcomes for children and families, with a focus on establishing parent leaders who are willing to share their challenges and successes across the country to affect change.

Circle of Parents® is a collaboration of Prevent Child Abuse America and the National Family Support Roundtable, Circle of Parents offers parent self-help support groups to anyone in a parenting role.

Maryland Resource Parent Association offers support to all resource families in Maryland by sharing years of experience, providing input, and giving guidance in areas, such as caregiving, procedures, mental and physical health services, raising teens, and more.

Massachusetts Children's Trust Parenting Education and Support Programs depicts a parenting and education support program that helps parents with young children enhance the knowledge, skills, and confidence to be better parents. The series includes professionally led group sessions that are provided in child-friendly environments.

National Parent Helpline "Find Support" provides links to support services by topic and child's age. The site also provides resources that are for individual states, in printable formats, and in Spanish.

Parents Anonymous® is an international network of accredited organizations that implement community-based, weekly, free-of-charge Parents Anonymous® Groups for parents and other caregivers.

Parent to Parent USA highlights statewide organizations that have parent-to-parent support as a core program and demonstrate a commitment to implementing evidence-based Parent to Parent USA (P2P USA) endorsed practices.

Program for Early Parent Support (PEPS) highlights parent support programs that educate, inform, and create community as parents enter parenthood. Each of the sessions brings parents together to share the joys and challenges of parenthood and develop confidence in their own abilities.

Somebody to Lean On: Connecting with or Creating a Support Group discusses parenting challenges adoptive parents may encounter and the benefits of taking part in a support group with other adoptive families. This publication explains the types of support groups available to adoptive parents in Wisconsin, offers online resources, and describes how to start a support group.

ZERO to THREE® is a national, nonprofit, multidisciplinary organization, with a mission to support the healthy development and well-being of infants, toddlers, and their families by informing, educating, and supporting adults who influence the lives of infants and toddlers.

Chapter 49

Kinship Caregivers, Foster Care, and Adoption

Chapter Contents

Section 49.1

Kinship Caregivers

This section includes text excerpted from "Kinship Caregivers and the Child Welfare System," Child Welfare Information Gateway, U.S. Department of Health and Human Services (HHS), May 2016.

A number of grandparents and other relatives care for children whose own parents are unable to care for them. Sometimes, the arrangement (referred to as "kinship care") is an informal, private arrangement between the parents and relative caregivers. In some cases, guardianship is given to relative caregivers, and child welfare is not involved; in other situations, the local child welfare agency is involved. This section is designed to help kinship caregivers—including grandparents, aunts and uncles, other relatives, and family friends caring for children—work effectively with the child welfare system (CWS).

Different Types of Kinship Care

Children may come to live with their grandparents or other relatives in a number of ways, and only some of these ways involve a child welfare agency. Kinship care arrangements fall roughly into three categories which are discussed below.

Informal Kinship Care

Informal kinship care refers to arrangements made by parents and other family members without any involvement from either the child welfare agency or the juvenile court. A parent may leave children with a grandparent while she or he is sent overseas, or an aunt may care for nephews whose parents are ill or otherwise unable to care for them. In this type of arrangement, the legal custody of the children remains with the parents, and parents can legally take back their children at any time. Kinship caregivers in these circumstances may have difficulty enrolling the children in school, obtaining health insurance, authorizing medical care, and accessing other benefits because they do not have legal custody of the children. However, most states have consent forms that parents can sign to allow kinship caregivers to have some temporary decision-making power regarding the children. Generally, the only type of financial assistance available to kin caregivers in this type of arrangement is the child-only Temporary Assistance for Needy Families (TANF) benefit.

Temporary Guardianship

Parents who are able to plan for their children living temporarily with a relative may consult an attorney about granting temporary guardianship to the relative. Although laws vary from state to state, temporary guardianship often requires an attorney to draw up papers that are presented in court for a judge's approval. Once temporary guardianship is granted, the relative can make decisions, such as medical and educational decisions, for the welfare of the child or children. This works well in cases where the parents initiate the temporary guardianship for the relative. When children have moved in with relatives on an unplanned, emergency basis, and the parents are either unable or unwilling to grant temporary guardianship to the relatives, then options are limited for the kinship caregiver to make legal, medical, and educational decisions affecting the children. The kinship caregiver may want to consult an attorney or legal clinic about options.

Voluntary Kinship Care

Voluntary kinship care refers to situations in which children live with relatives and the child welfare agency is involved, but the state does not take legal custody. In some cases, children have been placed with relatives by a court, and in other cases, an arrangement is made by the child welfare agency with no court involvement. Again, depending on their jurisdiction, parents may be able to sign a state consent form, allowing kinship caregivers to have some temporary decision-making power regarding the children. This type of kinship care covers a wide variety of circumstances and varies greatly from state to state. Some situations that might result in voluntary kinship care include:

- Child welfare workers find signs of abuse or neglect by the parents, but the evidence is insufficient to support taking the children into state legal custody. Instead, caseworkers, parents, and kin work out a voluntary kinship care arrangement in which the children move in with the kin.

- Under the guidance of child welfare workers, parents voluntarily place their children with relatives while they (the parents) receive treatment for substance abuse or mental-health issues.

389

Parents may agree to voluntary placements of their children with a relative in order to prevent the child welfare agency from going to court to pursue involuntary placements. Some jurisdictions will require the parents to sign a voluntary placement agreement with the child welfare agency when the children are placed with relatives.

Formal Kinship Care

Informal kinship care, children are placed in the legal custody of the state by a judge, and the child welfare agency then places the children with kin. In these situations, the child welfare agency, acting on behalf of the state, has legal custody of the children, and relatives have physical custody. The child welfare agency, in collaboration with the family, makes legal decisions about the children, including deciding where they live. The child welfare agency is also responsible for ensuring that the children receive medical care and attend school. If the court has approved visits with parents or siblings, the child welfare agency is responsible for making sure that these visits occur. Informal kinship care, the child's relative caregivers are certified or approved as foster parents and have rights and responsibilities similar to those of non-relative foster parents.

Permanent Families for Children

"Permanency" is a term used by child welfare workers to mean a legally permanent and nurturing family for a child. "Permanency planning" involves time-limited, goal-oriented activities to keep children within their families of origin, including kin, or to place them with other permanent families. Some of the options that might be considered by a court for permanency include reunification, guardianship, and adoption.

Reunification

Reuniting children with a parent or parents is the first choice of child welfare agencies when this option will ensure the safety and well-being of the children and provide a permanent family for them. Family reunification can occur when the judge agrees that the parents have met the goals set out in their service plan, such as the completion of substance-abuse treatment. Each state has different laws, and it is the judge in a review hearing or permanency hearing who makes the decision to give custody of the children back to the parent. The judge bases this decision on evidence from the parent, the child welfare worker, and agency, other adults who may be involved, and, often, the children and the kinship caregiver.

Guardianship

Guardianship is a legal option for permanency, and it may be especially appropriate in kinship care. Federal law encourages states to consider a relative, rather than a nonrelative, when seeking a guardian for a child who cannot return home. When a grandparent or other relative becomes the child's legal guardian, legal custody is transferred from the state to the relative by a court; therefore, in most circumstances, there is no further involvement by the child welfare agency. In guardianship arrangements, parents' parental rights are not terminated. Thus, grandparents or other relatives who become the child's guardian have legal and physical custody, act as the child's parent, and make decisions about the child. Birth parents often retain some visitation or other rights. Guardianship is especially appropriate if the children are older and want to maintain some ties with their parents, or if the grandparent or other relative caregiver prefers not to have the parents' rights terminated (as in adoption) but needs to establish a permanent legal arrangement with the children in order to be able to make education, healthcare, and other decisions for the child.

Most states have subsidized guardianship programs so that guardians continue to receive payments similar to those they received as foster parents. This allows children to have permanent family relationships without causing guardians to lose necessary monthly subsidies. In subsidized guardianship, there is some ongoing involvement of the child welfare agency; although, it is significantly less than in foster care. For instance, the child welfare worker may visit once a year to make sure that the child is still living with the relative and to determine if services are still needed.

Adoption

Some kin caregivers choose to adopt the children in their care. Since adoption is often the agency's preferred permanency plan for children not returning to their parents, relatives may adopt in order to keep children living with biological family members. Adoption assistance (subsidies) may be available to kin families who adopt; however, they would no longer be eligible for temporary assistance child-only grants.

As with foster care and guardianship, the child welfare agency must ensure that the home and prospective adoptive parents meet certain state standards for the safety and well-being of the children. Standards for adoption may be more stringent than those for foster care in some states. These requirements and standards will apply even for kin who have been caring for the children under a foster care arrangement.

Children can be adopted only after the court has terminated all the legal rights of the parents or the parents have voluntarily surrendered all of their parental rights permanently. A court must finalize the adoption. Depending on their age and the state law, courts will often ask the children if they agree to the adoption. For children with special needs who have been in foster care, there may be ongoing adoption assistance (subsidies) available to kin who adopt.

Once the adoption is finalized, the grandparent or other relative becomes the legal parent of the child, and there is generally no further involvement by the child welfare agency, except in circumstances involving adoption assistance.

Conclusion

Kinship care is an excellent option for children and youth who cannot safely remain with their parents. Kinship caregivers can sometimes be confused or frustrated working with an unfamiliar CWS. This may help kin caregivers understand and work with the CWS to provide the best outcomes, including a permanent family, for their relative children.

Section 49.2

Information for Foster Parents Considering Adoption

This section includes text excerpted from "Foster
Parents Considering Adoption," Child Welfare Information
Gateway, U.S. Department of Health and Human
Services (HHS), February 2012. Reviewed March 2019.

If you are a foster parent and are considering adopting a child,
children, or youth currently in your care, you are not alone. In fact,
foster parent adoptions account for more than half the adoptions of
children from foster care. According to the National Adoption and
Foster Care Analysis and Reporting System (AFCARS), in FY 2010,
53 percent of children adopted from foster care were adopted by their
foster parents.

Foster parents who open their hearts and homes to a child in need
may develop relationships as strong as those with their birth children.
Adoption of children and youth by foster parents is increasingly common, and deciding whether adoption is right for you and your family
can raise a lot of questions.

Differences between Foster Parenting and Adopting

There are significant differences between being a foster parent and
an adoptive parent.

Legal Differences

Foster care is intended to be temporary care for children and youth
unable to live with their parents because of neglect, abuse, parent
incarceration, or other issues. However, when reunification with birth
parents or adoption by another relative is not possible, foster parent
adoption becomes a viable option. Adoption is a lifetime legal and
emotional responsibility.

Foster parents have no legal parental rights, but when you adopt
a child, you acquire the same legal rights and responsibilities as parents have for their birth children. The child is no longer in the state's
custody but is a full, legal member of your family.

393

Financial Differences

As a foster parent, you receive a stipend or reimbursement for the care you provide. With adoption, that assistance changes.

One of the misconceptions about adoption is that it is expensive. In reality, foster care adoption is very affordable. You are not expected to carry the financial load alone. In many instances, federal and state assistance programs are available during and after the adoption process. Of children adopted from foster care in 2010, 90 percent received some form of adoption assistance.

Most children and youth in foster care are covered by the federal Medicaid program. Your child also may be eligible for medical assistance from your state after adoption.

Even if families receive adoption assistance or a subsidy, adoptive families are still responsible for everyday financial obligations, such as child care and extracurricular activities.

Full Decision-Making Responsibility

While a child is in foster care, decision making is shared by the agency, foster parents, and perhaps the birth parents. Whereas, when a child is adopted, the adoptive parents take full responsibility for making decisions about issues, such as school enrollment, travel outside the state or country, birth family visitation, and more. While some families may choose to continue to share some decision-making and visitation with the birth family or relatives to benefit the child, the adoptive family has the ultimate decision-making responsibility after the adoption.

Attachment Issues

You likely dealt with, and perhaps continue to deal with, attachment issues after your child or youth joined your family through foster care. Attachment is formed through more than just providing food, shelter, and clothing; it is formed through consistent and predictable interaction—smiles, hugs, conversation, etc.—and it plays an important role in physical, emotional, mental, and psychological development. However, addressing attachment issues is not a linear process. There may be new or recurring issues as your foster child or youth becomes a permanent member of your family. Bear in mind:

- The idea of permanence with a foster/adoptive family and the termination of the birth parents' parental rights may trigger intense grief or a sense of loss.

394

- Bonds with caregivers, even abusive caregivers, are extremely strong. Additionally, past abuse or neglect may be difficult to detect, as children in a temporary environment may not have felt comfortable enough to confide in others.

- Children or youth may experience conflicting feelings between love for the biological family and growing affection for and a sense of security with their foster/adoptive parents.

- Sometimes, children or youth struggle to fully commit to adoption unless they know their birth families are all right and that being adopted is acceptable. Connections and contact between foster/adoptive parents and birth parents can sometimes ease the transition.

- If your child is a regular user of social media, you may want to explore positive ways to use Facebook and other sites to maintain healthy contact between your child and her or his birth family members. Although statistics are not yet available to document the number of adopted people and birth parents who find each other through these sites, anecdotal evidence suggests that it is a growing trend.

Advantages of Foster Parent Adoption

Compared to other kinds of adoption, foster parent adoption offers the advantage of familiarity to the adopting family, the child, and the birth family. You can build on existing relationships because you may already be familiar with the child's personality, family and medical history, education plan, and other important aspects of her or his life. Additionally:

- Foster parents usually know about a child's background and experiences and know what behaviors to expect. If the foster parents have sufficient background information on the child, as well as some knowledge about child development and behavior, they are better able to understand and respond to the child's needs in a positive and appropriate way.

- Foster parents usually have fewer fantasies and fears about the child's birth family because they often have met and know them as real people with real strengths and problems. They may have previously partnered with the birth family to work for the child's return.

- Foster parents have a better understanding of their role and relationship with the agency, and they, hopefully, have a good relationship with their caseworker.

- Some foster parents participate in concurrent planning, in which adoption may be one of the goals. If so, some of the necessary steps toward adoption may have already been taken.

While children and youth benefit the most from foster parent adoption, this type of adoption offers a number of advantages for others as well.

- **Adoptive parents.** One of the biggest advantages of adopting your foster child or youth is seeing your child achieve permanency and complete the placement process. Foster children and youth do not always stay with one family and cannot always be reunited with birth families. When you adopt your foster child, children, or youth, you and the child are granted the permanent protection of your relationship, and you both have a new, permanent family relationship.

- **Children.** Even very young infants may grieve the loss of familiar sights, sounds, smells, and touch of a family when they must move. Being adopted by foster parents means the child or youth will not have to leave familiar foster family members, friends, pets, school, and home. The biggest change for the child is the security that comes with having a permanent family and home.

- **Birth families.** Foster parent adoption also benefits birth families, including siblings and other relatives, by allowing them to know who is permanently caring for their loved one. Depending on the openness of the adoption, birth families may have ongoing contact, and opportunities to maintain relationships and share family histories.

- **Society.** Society as a whole benefit when permanence is attained in lieu of youth aging out of foster care. Many youths transition out of foster care with few connections and little access to support, increasing the risk of negative outcomes, such as jail, homelessness, substance abuse, and teen pregnancy. Research also shows that unemployment and underemployment are two common experiences among former foster youth. For instance:

  - A study of employment by youth who aged out of foster care, youth with a history of foster care who were reunited with their parents, and youth from low-income families found that those who aged out of foster care earned less money than their peers in both of the other groups, and their earnings were well below the poverty line.

- Less than 2 percent of former foster youth obtain a bachelor's degree compared to more than 22 percent of all young people.

Strategies for Foster/Adoptive Families
What Are Some Approaches or Strategies That May Contribute to a Successful Adoption Experience?

All families and children are different, but there are some things you can do to smooth the adoption process.

What the Research Shows

A report from AdoptUSKids explored characteristics of successful adoptions and barriers to adoption of children with special needs by surveying and interviewing adoptive parents, prospective adoptive parents, and adoption professionals. For the purposes of that study, the "special needs" designation referred to children who were over the age of 8, members of sibling groups, had specific ethnic or racial backgrounds, or children for whom agencies had difficulties finding adoptive families. To identify characteristics of successful adoptions, 161 parents who had adopted children around 1 to 14 years earlier, reported on their experiences. Parents volunteered the following factors as contributing to a successful adoption:

- They were committed to the child and the child's adoption into the family.

- They were able to fully integrate the child into the family and not treat the child differently.

- They developed and practiced good parenting skills, including patience, consistency, and flexibility.

- They sought out resources, information, and training when they needed help.

- They had a network of social support.

- They had realistic expectations of the child.

These adoptive parents also reported on post-adoption services and supports. The most common were financial support, such as adoption subsidies and financial help with medical and dental care. The majority of families also noted that services, such as counseling, therapy for the child or family, support groups, and training, were helpful.

Conclusion

It is important to learn as much as possible about the child you want to adopt and the adoption process. Ask your caseworker or agency about resources and trainings, and make sure you are connected with other families and supports. All children deserve loving, permanent homes. Making your family the permanent family for a child, children, or youth currently in your care is a lifetime commitment that requires careful consideration but yields a host of advantages.

Section 49.3

Helping Foster Children Transition into Adoption

This section includes text excerpted from "Helping Your Child Transition from Foster Care to Adoption," Child Welfare Information Gateway, U.S. Department of Health and Human Services (HHS), July 2018.

If you are a foster parent adopting a child, children, or youth currently in your care, you have a pivotal role in helping them adjust to adoption. The adoption process is an ongoing journey that continues well past the day the adoption is finalized. There are several ways you can ease the transition and many supports available to help you in this important work.

This section discusses common issues that come up for children and families during the foster-to-adoption process, how to support your child or youth through the transition, and resources available for help.

Talking with Children about the Transition to Adoption

The transition to adoption is a gradual process for all involved. The adjustment period can be a vulnerable time as your child begins to understand they are a permanent member of your family and will not return to live with their birth family. Some children may feel relief as plans are finalized, while others may feel a deep sense of loss. Listening carefully to your child throughout the adoption process and creating a safe environment for sharing feelings can help build trust and ease the transition.

It is important to share stories in a developmentally appropriate manner about your child's background and/or placement history and how she or he came to be adopted by you. Honor this as an important part of her or his identity. Adopted children and youth often have questions about their birth family and the reasons they are no longer able to live with them. It is essential to validate your child's experiences and feelings and tell the truth, even when it is difficult. There are several ways adoptive parents and siblings can help children or youth adjust to the adoption and feel more secure as a member of the family.

- You can help your child understand that adoption does not have to mean replacing or no longer loving the important people in her or his life. Instead, your child is growing the family that will be a source of love and support.

- Remain truthful as you share information. If your child was adopted at a very young age, perhaps you can let them know— if this was the case—that their birth mother was not able to provide care and asked you and your family to do so.

- Encourage open discussion about the people who matter to your child, and find ways to stay in contact with them.

- Create traditions, activities, events, or anniversaries to recognize and acknowledge the adoption as a milestone for your family. Be sure to listen to and involve your child in planning these events. Many children feel very special on their "adoption day," while others have conflicting feelings of loyalty and loss. It is normal for a child to have mixed feelings.

- Plan regular events and activities where the focus is not on adoption but on building family memories and relationships.

- Develop relationships with other families who may be fostering children or who have adopted children they fostered. It helps to see families that look similar and share common experiences. Sharing common experiences, challenges, and successes may ease the feeling of being isolated or "different."

Children and youth learn best through repetition. Conversation about the differences between foster care and adoption may need to be introduced a number of times before a child fully understands. Integrating these conversations during moments of connection with your child can help foster bonding and attachment, and help her or him explore feelings about adoption and you. Below are some ideas to encourage that process.

- Help your child talk about the perceived difference in her or his own words. Ask open-ended questions, such as, "How do you think being adopted is different from being in foster care?" or "What do you think the biggest difference is, now that you are adopted?"

- Help your child draw analogies to something in her or his life. For instance, you might say, "This is like the time when..."

- To help children understand one of the key differences between foster care and adoption, you might remind them that adoption makes them a "forever" member of your family and that they will always be your child, even when they are grown up. Reading a children's book, such as *Love You Forever* by Robert Munsch, can be helpful.

- An older child may seek to understand her or his personal story and the reasons behind the foster care and adoption. Be honest if you do not have all the details or do not know what happened regarding your child's birth family. You can ask your child or youth about their understanding of the experience. Be aware of your reactions, and make sure you are communicating safety and acceptance with whatever is shared.

Helping Children Understand and Cope

When children or youth spend extended periods in out-of-home care, memories of significant events and people can be lost. Children may lose their sense of self: who they are, where they have lived, the people they have lived with, where they went to school, memories of favorite items (e.g., stuffed animals or blankets), and more. You can help your child review and understand previous life experiences to clarify what happened in the past and help integrate those experiences so your child will have greater self-understanding. Acknowledging your child's past; addressing potential issues of trauma, grief, and loss; and recognizing and embracing racial and cultural identity are all part of a healthy transition process.

Your child may experience a range of emotions and require additional support at different stages. Your child welfare agency, caseworker, or adoption specialist can help you identify appropriate and available services and supports. Many organizations specialize in working with families transitioning to adoption. If you seek counseling or mental-health treatment, it is important to seek a therapist who is competent in adoption-related issues.

Easing the Integration Process

When possible and safe, seek to maintain connections with your child's birth family. Your child or youth comes with a unique story and identity that will always be a part of who they are, regardless of how old they were when they first moved into your home. While children can be resilient and form new attachments to adults who are meeting their needs, recognizing and embracing their past can help them make sense of their personal story and identity and ease the integration process into your family. There are specific steps that can help children integrate existing relationships with the important people in their lives while promoting connections with new family members. Integration can help children cope with the potentially painful realities of separation from their birth family.

Adoption expert Kathryn Donley was the first to describe the five-step integration process:

Step 1. Create an accurate reconstruction of your child's placement history. Creating a "LifeBook" with your child can help them see and understand their own history. LifeBooks, scrapbooks, or memory books are tools used by foster and adoptive parents to help preserve a child's personal history, create a connection with their past, and engage them in a conversation about adoption. They help children and youth answer questions about how they were separated from their birth family and where, ultimately, they belong.

Step 2. Identify the important attachment figures in your child's life by learning who these individuals are and by listening to your child talk about people from previous placements. These attachment figures might be parents, but may also be siblings, former foster parents, pastors, coaches, or extended family members who have a connection with your child. When adoptive parents choose not to talk about birth families, children or youth may sense that the adoptive parents are uncomfortable with their past and feel the loss more intensely.

Step 3. Enlist the support of the most significant attachment figures available; the birth parents, grandparents, relatives, or other important figures in your child's life (e.g., a coach, close family friend, etc.). Even if the birth family is not cooperative regarding a child's adoption permanency goal, there is likely one important person (a teacher, a former neighbor) who will be willing to work with you to make your child's transition a little smoother.

Step 4. Clarify "the permission message." It is necessary for children to hear and feel from people who are important to them that it is okay to love another family. Every effort should be made to ensure those individuals give your adopted child that message.

Step 5. Communicate that permission to the child. Whether the "permission to love your new family" comes in the form of a letter from a close family member or from the birth parent during visits, it is important that children get the message that it is not their fault they are in foster care and that it is all right to love another family. This will go a long way toward helping them relax, and it serves to strengthen the bond with the new family. Help your child or youth understand that they are not replacing their birth family but rather "growing" their family and a support team that will help them through life.

Acknowledging the Past

The following questions may help your child frame past experiences and address current circumstances. The responses may help you figure out how to help your child overcome past traumas and feel more secure in your family.

- Who am I? (exploring identity)

- What happened to me? (exploring issues of loss and/or trauma)

- Where am I going? (new relationships)

- How will I get there? (questions related to relationships)

- When will I know I belong? (connection and safety)

You can help your child answer these questions and understand her or his unique history and current situation. Just because children do not bring up the past does not mean they are not interested or are not still affected by their experiences. What you can do:

- Pay attention to your child's nonverbal cues. If she or he seems quiet and withdrawn, consider what might be going on. You might want to ask if your child is thinking about or missing her or his biological or former foster parents or siblings. Regardless of the answer, this will be a signal to your child that you are willing to explore those feelings.

- You might gently explain that children sometimes feel sad when separated from people they love, and let them know that you care deeply and they are not alone.

- Help your child understand that separation from her or his parents was not because they were bad people, but because they were not able to provide safe care. You can also help your child understand, if developmentally appropriate, that her or his family of origin deserves compassion rather than judgment or scorn. This will demonstrate your empathy and contribute to your child's sense of safety.

- Pay attention to lead-ins for conversation about the past (e.g., a child comments about something they did with their birth family or a former foster family).

Trauma, Grief, and Loss

While it may be difficult to understand the past trauma and losses your child or youth encountered before adoption, all adopted children and youth experience some level of loss when separated from their family of origin. Even if the child has lived in your home for some time and the adoption process has been positive, the finality of the adoption may intensify feelings of loss. Children in foster care often have traumatic histories that affect them in ways that may be difficult for them to put into words and may make it harder for them to form trusting relationships with new family members. The trauma may be greater if the child has experienced multiple foster placements.

Your child may experience a feeling of loss from changes in language, culture, religion, or a separation from her or his siblings. Some of the feelings of loss and grief may be vague—e.g., children know their birth parents and siblings still exist but have no control over their access to them. It is important to be sensitive to how these feelings can affect your child. Minimizing them may result in unresolved grief.

The following resources may be helpful in addressing trauma, grief, and loss:

- The Association for Training and Trauma on Attachment in Children (ATTACh) (www.attach.org) is an international coalition of professionals and families dedicated to promoting attachment and bonding by providing access to relevant resources and materials.

- The Attachment and Trauma Network (ATN) is a national coalition founded by adoptive parents to support families of children who have experienced trauma. ATN maintains a database of attachment and trauma-related resources, attachment and developmental trauma therapists by location, professional organizations, and respite care providers. ATN hosts private, online peer-to-peer support groups (www.attachmenttraumanetwork.org) that are moderated 24/7 by experienced therapeutic parents. ATN will place you in a group that best meets your needs based on the information you provide and the severity of a child's issues.

- Understanding Trauma (www.adoptuskids.org) is a webpage hosted by AdoptUSKids.

Racial and Cultural Identity

If your child has a different racial or cultural identity than you, be aware that a colorblind approach to parenting can limit your child's potential to develop and own their full identity. Experts emphasize the importance of honoring and celebrating your child's racial and cultural heritage. When there is no discussion regarding racial or cultural differences, your child may get the message that conversations around race are off-limits, leading to potential feelings of shame or confusion, and leaving your child to confront her or his reality alone. Your child may also think that racial issues are unimportant or that you do not care.

Promoting Attachment

Attachment is the deep and enduring bond that forms between a child and primary caregiver early in life when a parent is sensitive and responsive to an infant or young child's needs. When this occurs, the child feels valued and trusts the parent. A child who has experienced significant instability and unmet needs early in life often struggles with trust issues and may need to experience a safe, consistent, and unconditionally supportive environment in an adoptive home for some time before feeling safe. As your child's parent, you can promote attachment by confidently asserting your parental role and meeting your child's essential needs for nurturing, safety, and limits. You have made a lifelong commitment with all the rights and responsibilities of parenthood. In addition to assuming a loving, protective, and authoritative parenting role, you can help build your child's sense of belonging by actively seeking similarities between the two of you or other family members (mannerisms, interests, personality traits, or even physical traits).

If your child has experienced abuse and neglect, attachment and connection to your family may take extra time and effort. It is essential to validate your child's feelings at every age and developmental stage. Remember that trust needs to be earned and cannot be rushed—patience is essential.

Infants and Preschool-Age Children

If you have adopted an infant or a young child, consistently offer the kind of physical closeness and attention that she or he may have missed during her or his earliest months and years. Helping your child feel safe, secure, and loved will promote healthy attachment and healing. What you can do:

- Spend as much time with your child as possible, taking leave from work when you can.

- Frequently remind your child how happy you are that she or he has become a part of your family.

- Be aware of your facial expressions. Your eyes are the pathway to connection. Make frequent eye contact and smile often (eye contact may be challenging for children with certain cultural backgrounds or for those who have mental-health issues).

- Your child may need to go back to an earlier developmental stage before she or he can progress developmentally. If needed, rock your child, feed your child with a bottle, play peekaboo, etc. Nurturing your child in the safety of your home environment can help support needed development.

- Be emotionally and physically available to your child (offer frequent hugs, hold hands, cuddle while reading a book or

405

watching TV), or talk affectionately with eye contact, smiles, and frequent praise.

- Play with your child (stacking hands, blowing bubbles, etc.). This lays the foundation for future social and emotional development.

- Use an object, such as a stuffed animal, when you need to be away. Speak to it in front of your child, saying something along the lines of, "Take good care of Spot while I am away. I look forward to hearing about how well things go while I am gone and cannot wait until I get back."

- Affirm your child's feelings (e.g., perhaps a desire to look more like you, particularly in a transracial adoption—acknowledge their wish, tell them their skin color is beautiful, and interact with families that share their heritage)

- Retell your child's story when it feels appropriate, including how she or he came to you. Be aware of how your child is hearing the story, and adjust its telling accordingly. Some children love to hear their story, while others feel protective of the information and find it difficult to hear. Every child is different.

- Talk about future family milestones, including where your child will go to school, to assure her or his of a role in your future.

- Be the primary meal provider during the first six months to enhance the bonding process.

- Your child needs to know that she or he can rely on you. Do not worry about spoiling or overindulging your child.

School-Age Children

School-age children need routine and understanding. With its academic and social challenges, school can be overwhelming for some children. But school can also play an important role in how children perceive their adoption, especially when educators communicate that adoption is a good way to build families. With positive feedback from the school community, children have a better chance of feeling confident and positive about their status. Unfortunately, not all teachers have received training to prepare them to talk about adoption, resulting in silence on the topic. Your child may become aware that there are few, if any, children at their school who are adopted and may be uncomfortable when asked questions by peers or others.

What you can do:

- Talk to your child's teachers and school administrators about adoption and provide them with adoption resources.

- Propose that your school forms a parent committee representing adoptive families and adopted students.

- Offer predictable routines and schedules.

- Affirm and show empathy for whatever your child is feeling.

- Make your home a safe spot for your child's emotions, both positive and negative.

- Help your child construct an adoption story that they are comfortable sharing with peers. C.A.S.E. created the W.I.S.E. UP Powerbook to help children answer awkward questions from classmates and peers.

- Watch for signs that your child may need extra support.

- Look behind your child's behavior—it is a window to how they are feeling.

- Be aware of what your face may be communicating and how your child is responding.

- Play board games, or engage in activities that put you eye-to-eye with your child.

- Do not force a child to make eye contact before she or he is ready

- Provide nurturing physical contact.

- Speak positively about past caregivers and birth parents so your child is not shamed.

- Include your child in planning family activities to reassure them that their feelings matter.

- Encourage self-esteem by providing activities that reflect the child's interests and assign age-appropriate household responsibilities.

- Offer frequent encouragement and praise (e.g., put a note in a lunchbox).

The following are positive signs that attachment is underway:

- Your child is increasing the frequency of eye contact.

- Your child comes to you when distressed.

- How you feel matters to your child.

- Your child looks to you for praise.

- Your child is happy to spend time together.

- Your child prefers you over strangers.

Youth

Because they have likely had multiple disappointments in their lives, older children may take longer to form deep and enduring attachments. The older your child is at the time of adoption, the more likely it is that she or he has experienced not only rejection, but also insecurity related to multiple foster care placements and temporary relationships. She or he may feel unlovable or dispensable as a result and question your commitment and the permanence of the adoption. This can cause your child to actively resist your affection or test you to make sure your love is real and permanent. This may come in the form of angry outbursts or withdrawal. It is important to recognize these behaviors as a process your child needs to work through and not take them personally.

As identity development and separation are a major part of adolescence, your child's interests and tastes may change frequently. These feelings have the potential to overwhelm your child, because her or his developing independence may feel like abandonment and rekindle old feelings associated with the initial separation from the birth family. It is important for your child to feel as though she or he can share these feelings with you or work with a therapist to get through this challenging period. Promoting attachment may be as much about being physically and emotionally available as understanding when to offer space. Involvement with an adoptive parent support group can help you learn how to connect with your youth and "let go" at the same time. What you can do:

- Be available and predictable.

- Allow your youth to express emotions without being judged.

- Talk openly (on their terms) about things that are important to them.

- Help your youth make a LifeBook if there is not one already.

- Point out similarities between the two of you.

- Understand that birth parents might be idealized and that issues of loyalty might surface.

- Help your youth practice how to communicate her or his story with peers.

There are certain steps you can take to help manage difficult behaviors or feelings as they arise:

- Identify when a situation is escalating for your child.

- Recognize what causes these behaviors, and help your child understand these triggers and control their responses.

- Be ready with patience and empathy.

- Move to a private area, if possible, so your child can feel safe.

- Ask your child what she or he may need (do not assume you know)

- Remember this is about your child, not about you. Do not take problem behavior personally.

- Recognize when to give space.

- Seek peer support from other adoptive parents.

- Understand and support your child's growing need for autonomy.

- If you are concerned about certain behaviors, remember that it is always a sign of strength to seek help.

Conclusion

While it may seem easy for a child or youth to transition from foster care to adoption within the same family, in reality, the internal process—for both the child and for families—is much more complicated. Allowing children to "drift" into adoption without actively acknowledging the significant changes up front may lead to difficulties at a later time. Just as your child will need help building attachments to you and your family, you may benefit from the support of adoption-competent therapists and peer counselors to ensure a healthy transition for you and your growing family. Connecting with the post-adoption preservation and support network available in your state—both before and after the adoption has been finalized—will help you with the transition process and beyond.

Adoption is a big step for everyone involved. Keep realistic expectations about yourself, your family, and your child or youth transitioning from foster care. Lastly, recognize that transition can be a lifelong process and there are many organizations, adoption professionals, and supportive services available to help you succeed.

Section 49.4

Sibling Issues in Foster Care and Adoption

This section includes text excerpted from "Sibling Issues in Foster Care and Adoption," Child Welfare Information Gateway, U.S. Department of Health and Human Services (HHS), January 2013. Reviewed March 2019.

Child welfare professionals can make a critical contribution to the well-being of children who enter care by preserving their connections with their brothers and sisters. Approximately two-thirds of children in foster care in the United States have a sibling also in care. For a variety of reasons, many of these siblings are not placed together initially or become separated over time. Foster youth describe this experience as "an extra punishment, a separate loss, and another pain that is not needed."

This section will explore research, intervention strategies, and resources to assist professionals in preserving connections among siblings.

Defining a Sibling Relationship

The identification of siblings can be challenging, especially when children have lived in more than one family. Children's definitions of their siblings often differ from those of caseworkers or official legislative definitions. Children are less formal than adults in their view of who is a brother or sister. Research indicates that biological relatedness was not associated with young children's perceptions of closeness to siblings; being a full, half, or step-sibling did not influence their perception of closeness. Children in foster care may live with and develop ties to children with whom they may or may not have a biological relationship. In child welfare, the term "fictive kin" has been introduced to recognize types of relationships in a child's life where there is no legal or biological tie, but a strong, enduring bond exists.

There are many types of relationships that might be defined as sibling relationships:

- Full or half-siblings, including any children who were relinquished or removed at birth

- Step-siblings

- Adopted children in the same household, not biologically related

- Children born into the family and their foster/adopted siblings

- Other close relatives or non-relatives living in the same kinship home

- Foster children in the same family

- Orphanage mates or group-home mates with a close, enduring relationship

- Children of the partner or former partner of the child's parent

- Individuals conceived from the same sperm or egg donor

While laws and policies may have restrictive definitions of siblings that typically require a biological parent in common, child- and family-centered practice respects cultural values and recognizes close, non-biological relationships as a source of support to the child. In these cases, the child may be one of the best sources of information regarding who is considered a sibling.

Legal Framework for Protecting Sibling Connections

Even when professionals believe that maintaining sibling relationships is in children's best interests, laws and policies must be in place to support these connections, both in foster care and when permanency is achieved. It was not until the mid-1990s that state legislatures and courts-initiated regulations regarding sibling placement and visitation, and in 2004, the Child and Family Services Reviews began to consider efforts to place siblings together. By 2005, sibling placement policies (28 states) and visitation statutes (32 states) had been established in over half the states.

411

State sibling statutes vary considerably in their definitions of sibling relationships, in the scope of activities they regulate, and in whether siblings have legal standing to file suit for access to each other. In 1993, California was one of the first states to pass legislation promoting sibling visitation for foster children, and several additional statutes have expanded legal protections of sibling relationships. The California Welfare and Institutions Code, Section 16002, is recognized by many as offering the strongest statutory protections for the needs of siblings in foster care and adoption among existing state statutes. It liberally defines a "sibling" as a child related to another person by blood, adoption, or affinity through a common legal or biological parent. California's law allows any person, including a dependent child, to petition the court to request sibling visitation, including post-adoption sibling contact or placement with or near a sibling.

Fostering Connections Act

The Fostering Connections to Success and Increasing Adoptions Act of 2008 is the first federal law to address the importance of keeping siblings together. This law requires states to make reasonable efforts to maintain sibling connections in order to receive federal funding. The provisions of section 206 provide that reasonable efforts shall be made:

- To place siblings removed from their home in the same foster care, kinship guardianship, or adoptive placement, unless the state documents that such a joint placement would be contrary to the safety or well-being of any of the siblings

- In the case of siblings removed from their home who are not so jointly placed, to provide for frequent visitation or other ongoing interaction between the siblings, unless that state documents that frequent visitation or other ongoing interaction would be contrary to the safety or well-being of any of the siblings

While the federal government through the Fostering Connections Act has taken a leadership role in mandating reasonable efforts to maintain sibling relationships, it is up to the states to vigorously support these connections. Between 2009 and 2011, 13 states passed statutes regarding sibling placement and visitation, and many others already had such statutes. There is often a gap, however, between what is considered best practice or what the law requires and what happens in day-to-day practice. Ultimately, the state courts will help define reasonable efforts by their decisions as to whether the requirement has been met in specific cases.

Legal scholars assert that there is still a need to fortify statutory protections of siblings' rights to have contact after adoption. The Fostering Connections Act sends a clear message that sibling relationships are critically important to preserve, but it is unclear as to whether the reference to "adoptive placement" in the statute refers to the post-adoption period as well. Mandelbaum recognizes the placement of this phrase after the term "kinship guardianship," which clearly is a permanent arrangement and can infer that "adoptive placement" also refers to the child's life in a permanent adoptive home.

Currently, only a minority of states provide a legal foundation for post-adoption contact between siblings; 7 states—Arkansas, Florida, Illinois (relative adoptions only), Massachusetts, Nevada, Maryland, and South Carolina—allow a court to order post-adoption contact without the consent of adoptive parents, and another 16 states allow for such a court order with the consent of adoptive parents. State-by-state information regarding post-adoption contact agreements can be found in Child Welfare Information Gateway Post-adoption contact agreements between birth and adoptive families (www. childwelfare.gov). These laws pertain not just to sibling contact, but to contact with any birth family member.

Importance of Siblings

Sibling relationships are emotionally powerful and critically important not only in childhood but over the course of a lifetime. As children, siblings form a child's first peer group, and they typically spend more time with each other than with anyone else. Children learn social skills, particularly in sharing and managing conflict, from negotiating with brothers and sisters. Sibling relationships can provide a significant source of continuity throughout a child's lifetime and are likely to be the longest relationships that most people experience.

The nature and importance of sibling relationships vary for individuals, depending on their own circumstances and developmental stage. Typically, there is rivalry in the preschool years; variability in closeness during middle childhood, depending on the level of warmth in the relationship; and less sibling closeness in adolescence, when teens are focused on peers. An extensive body of research addresses issues of birth order, gender, age spacing, and other influences on sibling relationships. Research has demonstrated that warmth in sibling

413

relationships is associated with less loneliness, fewer behavior problems, and higher self-worth.

Marjut Kosonen, a researcher, studied the emotional support and help that siblings provide and found that when they needed help, children would first seek out their mothers but then turn to older siblings for support, even before they would go to their fathers. She also found that for isolated children (as is the case for many children in foster care), sibling support is especially crucial. For these children, an older sibling was often their only perceived source of help.

Sibling Relationships in Abusive or Neglectful Families

In many families involved with child welfare, sibling relationships take on more importance because they can provide the support and nurture that are not consistently provided by parents. For children entering care, siblings can serve as a buffer against the worst effects of harsh circumstances. While sibling relationships—in particular, families experiencing adverse situations—do not always compensate for other deficits, research has validated that, for many children, sibling relationships do promote resilience. For example, a young child's secure attachment to an older sibling can diminish the impact of adverse circumstances, such as parental mental illness, substance abuse, or loss. Adverse circumstances can magnify both the positive and negative qualities of sibling relationships. Some studies have found that the ties between siblings become closer as a result of helping each other through adversity, such a parental divorce.

A study of children's perspectives on their important relationships among 90 children between the ages of 8 and 12 who were or were not in foster care concluded that the foster children's smaller networks of relationships with important persons made siblings proportionally more important. Nearly one-third of the related siblings named by foster children in this study were not known to their social workers—most were half or step-siblings. Kosonen's study also underscores the importance of obtaining children's perspectives on their family relationships. When siblings could not all be placed together, workers often decided to keep those closest in age together, resulting in placements that did not necessarily fit the preferences of the children.

Since children in foster care experience more losses of significant relationships, siblings are often their only source for continuity of important attachments. For children entering care, being with their brothers and sisters promotes a sense of safety and well-being, and being separated from them can trigger grief and anxiety. Therefore, it is especially important to protect these ties that offer support to children removed from their original families.

Benefits of Placing Siblings Together

For children entering care, being with their siblings can enhance their sense of safety and well-being and provide natural, mutual support. This benefit is in contrast to the traumatic consequences of separation, which may include additional loss, grief, and anxiety over their siblings' well-being. Siblings have a shared history, and maintaining their bond provides continuity of identity and belonging. The benefits of keeping brothers and sisters together are most clearly evidenced from the perspectives of youth themselves.

Children's Perspective

It is essential for professionals to be able to understand children's experiences from the child's perspective in order to be able to grasp the critical importance of maintaining sibling connections whenever possible. A North Carolina publication for foster and adoptive families sponsored an essay contest for foster children to write, "Why are your siblings important to you?" Below are just a few of their entries:

- "My sister is only three years old, but she has a big heart with me in it. Jayden is braver than me—she is not scared of the dark like me. When I was left alone in a big house all I had was my sister to keep me company till someone returned. I love her"— Joseph, age 7

- "(When they) moved us and placed us all in different homes I felt as if God was punishing me for something. It broke my heart."— Arlene, age 16

- "The group home that we went to forever changed our relationship. Nothing has been the same. I see them and it feels like I don't even know them at all. I raised my little sister from infancy and I see her now and she's almost a stranger to me. At one point, I could not even talk to any of them at all."—Cierra, age 17

When youth in foster care unite to work toward protecting the rights of children entering out-of-home care, keeping brothers and sisters together is invariably near the top of their list; for example, a New

England Youth Coalition (NEYC) joined with the New England Association of Child Welfare Commissioners and Directors (NEACWCD) in the summer of 2012 to develop a regional Siblings' Bill of Rights. Youth advocates in states across the country have sponsored similar efforts.

Studies that directly seek the perspective of foster children are relatively rare, but those that have done so consistently underscore the overwhelming importance of protecting sibling relationships. Folman, a researcher, who interviewed 90 children (between the ages of 8 and 14) about their memories of their initial removal, reported that many children did not know they were being separated from siblings until they were dropped off at different houses, nor did they know how to contact each other. In describing their distress at separation, she wrote, "All sense of family, of comfort, of familiarity and of belonging was gone and there was no one except strangers."

Not only is the support of siblings helpful in the immediate adjustment to the trauma of placement, but this contact continues to offer support to the child over the course of their time in care and into adulthood. Mary Herrick and Wendy Piccus are child welfare professionals who themselves spent considerable time in care. They poignantly described the central themes related to the value of sibling connections for children in foster care, illustrated by their own experiences.

For some siblings in care, their separation or infrequent visiting can cause their relationships to wither, sometimes to the point of permanent estrangement. Maintaining these relationships is important for the future, as well as the present. Youth who age out of foster care report the value of sibling connections; for example, a Midwest study of over 600 foster alumni found that youth were most likely to identify a sibling as a family member they felt close to—59 percent felt very close, and 23 percent felt somewhat close to a sibling.

Moreover, a Texas study of adult foster alumni found that those who had greater access to their siblings and reported stronger relationships with them during childhood had higher levels of social support, self-esteem, and income, as well as stronger adult- sibling relationships than those who did not.

Research on Outcomes of Placing Sibs Together

Research on sibling placement patterns has confronted methodological challenges and developed more sophisticated research designs; however, there are differences in findings across studies. When significant differences are found between siblings placed in different patterns, they typically favor siblings placed totally or partially with each other over those placed completely separately.

Joint sibling placements can increase the likelihood of achieving permanency. Several studies have found that placing siblings in the same foster home is associated with a significantly higher rate of family reunification. Another research finding revealed that children placed with the same number of siblings consistently throughout foster care had greater chances for adoption or subsidized guardianship than those placed alone. Some studies find that children placed with their siblings also experience more stability and fewer disruptions in care than those who were separated.

Conversely, some studies have found that separated siblings in foster care or adoption are at higher risk for negative adjustment outcomes, including running away and higher levels of behavior problems, evidenced in some studies but not all. Another study found that girls separated from all of their siblings are at the greatest risk for poor mental health and socialization. Finally, a recent study based on the National Study of Child and Adolescent Well-Being (NSCAW) did not find that separated siblings were reported to have more behavior problems but did find that teachers reported lower academic performance for separated siblings (either partially or totally) than for those placed together.

Barriers to Placing Siblings Together

Past research indicates that a substantial proportion of children in foster care who had siblings in care were not placed with all of those siblings, but this proportion varied significantly across studies. Two California studies published in the past decade with large samples of 10,000 or more children indicated that somewhere between 23 and 46 percent of siblings were placed with all their siblings in their initial placements, and about two-thirds were placed with at least one sibling. Also, an analysis of placements of more than 168,000 foster youth with siblings in care in New York city over a 15-year period revealed that initial placement status was a strong determinant of sibling placement over time. 78 percent of those siblings entering care together were placed all together, but those entering care longer than 6 months apart were at the highest risk of being separated. This study is one of the only ones that followed siblings to see how many placements were still intact 4 years after admission. The authors found that of those initially placed together, 79 percent were still intact 4 years later. Some of those initially separated came together; among sibling groups that were completely separated in their initial placement, 51 percent were intact at the end of 4 years.

It is possible that the percentage of sibling groups placed together initially has improved since the passage of the Fostering Connections Act.

Factors Associated with Placing Siblings Apart

Besides entering foster care at different times, a number of other demographic and situational factors are associated with the likelihood that siblings are placed in the same foster home. These include:

- Size of sibling group—larger groups are more often split

- Age gap—wide age span leads to splitting

- Differences in the needs of siblings

- Type of placement—siblings placed with kin are more likely to be together, and those in group care are less likely

- Behavior problems—a sibling with a behavior problem is more likely to be removed

- Organizational policies and procedures

- Adequacy of placement resources and supports

- Agency rules regarding the maximum number of children who can be placed in a foster home

In many, if not most, cases of sibling separation, brothers and sisters are separated because the system cannot accommodate the best interests of children, rather than for any child-centered reason. For example, a researcher interviewed caseworkers of adolescents in care who were separated from their siblings, asking for all the reasons and the most important reason. While 19 percent did not know the reason, the most common of all reasons given was "could not find a placement for all" (33%).

Beliefs Associated with Placing Siblings Apart

Beliefs and attitudes of foster parents, workers, agency personnel, and therapists also contribute to separating siblings. In a study of foster parents' and workers' views on placing siblings, over half of the foster mothers (55%) did not believe it was easier for a foster child to fit into the foster family if placed with siblings. As explained by one foster parent, "the siblings depend on one another too much, and shut other people out." Approximately 45 percent of foster parents believed that children placed with siblings were easier to foster because they felt more secure having their siblings with them.

In this same study, over half the caseworkers indicated that it was difficult to find foster parents willing to accept sibling groups. Most caseworkers also believed that the presence of siblings made it harder for the foster parents to incorporate the child into the family. However, the vast majority of caseworkers personally believed in the county policy of placing children with their siblings, unless separation was in the best interests of the child.

Recommendations of therapists may be the basis of some placements. However, best practice indicates that the therapist should have experience with siblings in child welfare and that the same therapist should see all of the siblings in order to make a recommendation that is beneficial for the group. Some clinical judgments that have been used to justify separating siblings in the past are not necessarily best practice, including the following:

- There is too much conflict or rivalry between particular siblings to keep them together.

- The special needs of a single child require a separate placement.

- An older child is too involved in taking care of a younger brother or sister.

- A sibling born after older siblings have been removed from the home can be considered separately for purposes of permanency goals, because the children do not have an established relationship.

In many of these cases, therapy and services will help all the siblings, and the benefits of being together will outweigh those of being separated.

Practices for Keeping Siblings Together in Placements

Decisions regarding sibling placement may be more straightforward when siblings come into care at the same time, and the sibling group is small. When the sibling group is large, enters care at very different times, or individual siblings have extraordinary needs, caseworkers face more challenges.

Initial Assessment of Sibling Relationships

During intake, workers need to complete a thorough assessment of sibling relationships and individual children, including the experience and feelings of each child. If separate placements must be made for very large sibling groups, this assessment will help the worker make decisions about which sibling relationships are most essential to the well-being of specific children. They should talk with children individually and ask age-appropriate questions, such as:

- Which sibling do you enjoy spending time with?

- Which sibling enjoys spending time with you?

- Who will play a game with you?

- Which sibling do you turn to when you are afraid or hurt?

- Which sibling turns to you when she or he is afraid or hurt?

Groza, Maschmeier, Jamison, and Piccola of Mandel School of Applied Social Sciences, Case Western Reserve University, offer an assessment tool for making decisions regarding the placement of siblings. The factors include the degree, duration, quality, and intensity of the sibling relationships; any safety risks associated with placement; possible long-term benefits; the family's ability to meet the needs of all siblings; and the children's preferences.

In completing assessments, it is important to recognize that sibling relationships vary greatly in both positive and negative qualities. In evaluating the quality of sibling relationships, the worker will want to look for warmth or affection between siblings, rivalry and hostility, interdependence, and relative power and status in the relationship, as well as determining how much time the siblings have spent together.

Strategies for Placing Siblings Together

Agency practices, along with the individual circumstances of each sibling group, will affect whether or not siblings are placed together. The following are practice strategies designed to address the needs of sibling groups:

- Designate certain foster home resources for large sibling groups and offer incentives to hold them open for these placements.

- Recruit families specifically to care for sibling groups through community outreach, the media, special events, faith-based organizations, photo listings, and websites.

- Provide training for caseworkers, foster, and adoptive parents on the importance of preserving sibling connections and the impact of sibling loss on children.

- Have contracts with private agencies to offer a specialized foster care program designed specifically for large sibling groups. Examples of these include the Hull House Neighbor to Neighbor program in Chicago (www.cebc4cw.org), Neighbor to Family in Florida (neighbortofamily.org), and the Jewish Child Care Association Sibling Boarding Home program in New York. The last program has three apartments staffed by foster parents for large sibling groups of up to seven or eight children, with an assistant cook and child care counselors for relief.

- If efforts are being made to recruit an adoptive family for a sibling group, list them as a group with a picture of the entire sibling group.

- Have a system in place to track the location and status of all siblings.

- Seek kinship placements first, because they are generally more open to taking a sibling group and because such placements offer the further advantage of preserving family connections.

- Conduct a thorough social work assessment of the sibling group as a whole, as well as of each individual child, and include children in discussions.

- Assign all siblings to the same caseworker, no matter when they enter care.

- If siblings must be separated in an emergency placement, provide for a review within the first week to plan for reunification.

- At regular case reviews, discuss sibling issues and include children or youth in these discussions.

- Provide sufficient resources for foster families who take in large sibling groups and may need additional household items and services.

- Ensure that information about siblings is included in each child's LifeBook.

- Conduct yearly interviews with adoptive parents of separated siblings to assess:

  - If visits between and among the siblings are continuing, how often, for how long, and of what quality

  - If visits have discontinued, for what reason(s) and what would it take to re-establish connections

When Siblings Cannot Live in the Same Home

Despite supportive policies or a caseworker's best efforts, a number of situations may lead to siblings being placed separately. This initial separation can lead to permanent separation if an agency does not make ongoing, concerted efforts to place the children together. Both policy and practice should promote ongoing efforts to reunite separated siblings. Common dilemmas regarding separated siblings include the following:

- An infant may come into care and be placed in a foster home before workers have determined that the infant has siblings already in foster care or in adoptive homes. The foster parents of the infant may then argue against the removal of the infant from their home. To avoid this dilemma, agencies should establish whether or not any infant or child coming into care has siblings already in placement. If so, strong efforts should be made to place the infant with siblings.

- In some cases of separated siblings, foster parents may want to adopt only the sibling placed with them. Workers are put in the untenable position of choosing the lesser of two evils—allowing the child to be adopted without her or his siblings or keeping the child in foster care until a family can be found who will adopt all of the siblings. To reduce the likelihood of this situation, foster parents should always be told at the time of placement that reuniting siblings is a top priority of the agency. Whatever decision is made, there should be provisions for maintaining connections with both the foster parents and siblings.

- A similar dilemma occurs when a sibling group placement disrupts because the foster parents cannot handle one of the sibling's behavior, but they want to continue parenting the others. The worker must decide whether to remove just the one child or the entire sibling group. An alternative would be to have a temporary specialized placement for the sibling with behavior problems if the foster parents are willing to work toward reintegrating this child into their family.

When a Sibling Is Abusive

Research identifies sibling assault as one of the most common forms of victimization in families generally, and more than 50 percent of children and adolescents have acted toward a sibling with severe violence. Whenever there is a concern that one sibling poses a safety risk to another, a thorough assessment needs to occur. Physical aggression within the normal range of sibling relationships needs to be differentiated from physical abuse or victimization of a weaker sibling. Distinctions need to be made between sexually reactive behavior (inappropriate sexual touching or fondling between children close in age) and sexual abuse by a more powerful sibling of another. Also, the severity of the abusive behavior needs to be assessed and a determination made as to whether the safety risks are moderate and can be managed through closer supervision, therapeutic parenting, and clinical treatment to change behaviors. If there is significant physical or sexual abuse that does not respond to treatment, or if the risk of recurrence is high, the abusing sibling most likely needs to be moved to another placement.

Victimization of one sibling by another should not be ignored. Research indicates that the impact of sexual abuse by a sibling is just as harmful to the victim as sexual abuse by a parent or stepparent. In fact, one study found that penetration occurred more commonly in sibling incest (71%), than in incest between a father or stepfather and a child (35%). Hence, children should be protected from abuse by a sibling just as they are protected from abuse by caretakers. In some cases, it may be possible to work toward reunification after a period of treatment for the offending sibling.

Maintaining Ties between Separated Siblings

When siblings cannot be placed together, facilitating regular contact is critical to maintaining these relationships. Regular contact may even affect permanency outcomes. Findings from the Child and Family Services Reviews (CFSR) conducted in all states found a significant association between visiting with parents and siblings and both permanency and well-being outcomes. Ultimately, workers and foster or adoptive parents have to understand the importance of sibling contact for the children for whom they are responsible in order to maintain their commitment to making these contacts happen. Caregivers play a crucial gatekeeping role in regulating contact between siblings, particularly after adoption, and sometimes they limit contact with the intent of protecting themselves or the child from what they view as negative influences or painful experiences. Sometimes, supporting and sustaining sibling visits requires clinical interventions, including both sibling therapy and clinically supervised visits, in order to address dysfunctional patterns that have developed in their relationships. A project called "Sibling Kinnections" developed a clinical visiting model to address barriers to visiting, such as anxiety or behavioral problems of individual children, miscommunication among their respective foster or adoptive parents, and parental concerns about the effect of visits on specific children.

Facebook and other social media make it much easier for siblings to both find and communicate with one another, regardless of the adults' feelings or concerns.

Strategies for Preserving Sibling Ties in Separate Placements

Some promising practices from the field suggest ways to maintain ties among separated siblings.

- Place siblings with kinship caregivers who have an established personal relationship. Even when siblings cannot be placed in the same home, they are more apt to keep in close contact if they are each placed with a relative.

- Place nearby. Placing siblings in the same neighborhood or school district ensures that they will be able to see each other regularly. Also, keeping children in their same schools contributes to better educational outcomes.

- Arrange for regular visits. Frequent visits help to preserve sibling bonds. The Children's Bureau Guidance on the Fostering Connections Act (www.acf.hhs.gov) allows agencies to set standards for the frequency of visits but designates that these should be at least monthly. Some state statutes specify contact twice a month, and at least three states (Alabama, Missouri, and Utah) require weekly visits, although many others do not specify frequency. Also, visits with birth parents can be arranged to occur at a time when all the siblings can be together.

- Arrange other forms of contact. If the distance between siblings is great, workers need to assist foster and adoptive families in maintaining frequent contacts through letters, email, social media, cards, and phone calls. Make sure that children have full contact information for all their siblings. For instance, providing older siblings with calling cards may facilitate sibling communication.

- Involve families in planning. The adults in the siblings' families should be involved with the worker in developing a plan for ongoing contact. This meeting should include working through any barriers to visits, and the plan needs to be reviewed and revised as needed, at least yearly. Sometimes, there are value differences between families or differences in rules that cause parental discomfort with visits. Such differences need to be discussed and resolved.

- Plan joint outings or camp experiences. Siblings may be able to spend time together in a joint activity or at summer or weekend camps, including camps specifically for siblings or through short-term outings. Such camp experiences help siblings build and maintain their relationships.

- Arrange for joint respite care. Families caring for siblings may be able to provide babysitting or respite care for each other, thus giving the siblings another opportunity to spend time together.

- Help children with emotions. Sometimes sibling visits stir up emotional issues in children, such as the intense feelings they may experience when visiting birth parents. Children need to be helped to express and work through these feelings; this does not mean visits should not occur. Visits should provide some opportunities for joint LifeBook work with siblings. If siblings are in therapy, they should be seeing the same therapist, and it may be possible to schedule appointments either jointly or back to back. Children may also need help with feelings of guilt if they have been removed from an abusive home while other siblings were left behind or born later.

- Encourage sustained contact. Sustaining sibling contact often requires a unique understanding and commitment from parents. Many adoptive parents recognize the importance of their adopted children having contact with siblings living with their birth families or other adoptive families. Some families even travel across the country or to other countries to give their children the opportunity to get to know their siblings. Some states offset the costs of such visits through their adoption subsidy plans. The earlier these relationships can begin, the more children can use these opportunities to work through adoption identity issues that may arise, and the sooner they can develop truly meaningful relationships with siblings.

Many states have adoption registries that can help adult siblings separated by foster care or adoption re-establish contact later in life. The caseworker needs to make sure that all pertinent information on each sibling is entered in the registry at the time of each child's adoption.

Sibling Issues within the Foster or Adoptive Family

Facilitating healthy attachments and interactions among all siblings in foster and adoptive families, including all birth, foster, and adopted children, is an essential therapeutic goal. A single family may contain birth and foster children as well as adopted children coming from different backgrounds or types of adoptions. Negative interaction patterns can result when children have different statuses in their families or special needs that require an inordinate amount of parental attention, create stress for other family members, or both.

Other dynamics lead to tensions as well; for example, one adopted child may have extensive information about her or his background, as well as ongoing contact with birth relatives, while another may have neither of these. Or an adopted child who maintains contact with her or his siblings who are still living with the birth family may have difficulty integrating into the adopted family.

More than a dozen research studies have explored the experiences of birth children in foster families, but less attention has been paid to siblings in adoptive families. Birth children often report positive benefits of sharing their home with foster children but also report a range of difficulties, such as competing for parents' time and attention; loss of family closeness; difficulties dealing with some foster siblings' behavior problems, including having possessions stolen or fear of physical aggression; a high level of stress in the family; different expectations or discipline between birth and foster children; loss and worry when a foster sibling leaves the family; and others. Studies also show that birth children often do not communicate their feelings and concerns fully to their parents, and cope independently or through isolating themselves.

Two social workers in Minnesota developed a model for preparing and supporting children already in families when older children are adopted. The model was developed after the agency experienced an adoption disruption related to other children in the family. This model advocate having a social worker assigned to the sibling group who meets with them at strategic points. It is essential to prepare children for both the positive and negative changes in the family that are likely after a new placement and to assist parents in developing strategies to communicate and cope with their children's needs.

Some important strategies for parents and workers in addressing the needs of all children in the family include:

- Encourage children to share their thoughts and feelings; empathize with and do not minimize their concerns.

- Provide opportunities for fun and positive interactions between children to promote attachment.

- Promote reciprocity between children in the family; for example, if a child destroys the property of another, find a way for the child to make up for the loss, such as earning the money to replace the item.

- Find ways for parents to have meaningful one-on-one time with each child.

- Teach children skills to resolve their own disputes to the extent possible.

- Develop a support group for siblings, either informally or through an agency.

- Seek professional help for serious sibling conflicts.

Section 49.5

Parenting a Child Who Has Been Sexually Abused: A Guide for Foster Parents

This section includes text excerpted from "Parenting a Child or Youth Who Has Been Sexually Abused: A Guide for Foster and Adoptive Parents," Child Welfare Information Gateway, U.S. Department of Health and Human Services (HHS), December 2018.

As a parent or caregiver of a child or youth who has a known or suspected history of being sexually abused, you may feel confused about the impact of the abuse and uncertain about how you can help. It may be comforting to know that most children and youth who have been abused do not go on to abuse others, and many live happy, healthy, successful lives. At the same time, all children and youth who have been abused need to feel safe and loved in nurturing homes. As a parent or caregiver, you can play a central role in your child's healing process, as well as in building resilience, which strengthens your child's ability to adapt to or cope with adversity.

This section discusses how you can help children and youth in your care by educating yourself about child sexual abuse, understanding the impact of the abuse, establishing guidelines for safety and privacy in your family, and seeking help if you need it. Reading this section alone will not guarantee that you will know what to do in every circumstance, but you can use it as a resource for some of the potential challenges and rewards that lie ahead.

Educating Yourself

One of the most useful steps you can take to help your child is to educate yourself about both sexual abuse and healthy sexual development in children. With this information, you will more easily recognize behaviors possibly associated with past or current abuse and avoid uncertainty if your child or youth shows uncommon sexual behaviors. Most importantly, you may gain confidence in supporting your child or youth through a variety of sensitive questions or situations that may arise. This section covers signs and behaviors that may suggest sexual abuse in children and youth, as well as common healthy sexual development behaviors.

What Is Child Sexual Abuse?

The National Child Traumatic Stress Network (NCTSN) defines "child sexual abuse" as the following:

"Any interaction between a child and an adult (or another child) in which the child is used for the sexual stimulation of the perpetrator or an observer. Sexual abuse can include both touching and nontouching behaviors. Nontouching behaviors can include: voyeurism (trying to look at a child's naked body), exhibitionism, or exposing the child to pornography. Children of all ages, races, ethnicities, and economic backgrounds may experience sexual abuse. Child sexual abuse affects both girls and boys in all kinds of neighborhoods and communities."

Signs of Sexual Abuse

If you are parenting a child or youth who has been removed from her or his family, you may not know whether she or he has been sexually abused. Child welfare agencies are required to share all known information about a child's history with her or his caregiver. However, past records of abuse may not exist, and young children or children who are nonverbal may be unable to tell you about being abused. Children and youth with disabilities, many of whom cannot interpret or articulate abusive experiences, are at significantly higher risk of sexual abuse than their peers without disabilities. Moreover, many children do not reveal past abuse until they feel safe. For these reasons, foster or adoptive parents or kinship caregivers are sometimes the first to learn that a child has been sexually abused. Therefore, knowing the signs and behaviors of abuse is critical.

Children who have been sexually abused, may also act out—that is, express feelings or sexual impulses that are odd, excessive, aggressive, or explicit. Although no one specific sign or behavior proves that sexual abuse has occurred, the Table 49.1 provides examples of potential warning signs of abuse.

These red flags do not always indicate that your child or youth has experienced sexual abuse. Rather, these actions may reflect an underlying issue, such as physical or emotional abuse or unintentional exposure to sexual content. Regardless, a trained professional who specializes in working with children who have been sexually abused should assess whether there is an underlying concern.

429

Table 49.1. Signs and Behaviors That May Suggest Sexual Abuse in Children and Youth

Younger Children	Older Children and Youth	Both Children and Youth
• Imitation of sexual acts with toys or other objects, such as stuffed animals • Behavior of a much younger child, such as wetting the bed or sucking a thumb • Refusal to take off clothing at appropriate times (e.g., bathing, going to bed) • Sexually transmitted infections (STIs) (especially in children who have not yet started puberty)	• Unhealthy eating patterns or unusual weight gain or weight loss • Anxiety or depression • Changes in self-care or paying less attention to hygiene • Self-harming behaviors or suicidal thoughts • Alcohol or drug use • Running away • STIs or pregnancy • High-risk sexual behavior • Suddenly having money	• Explicit sexual knowledge beyond the child's developmental stage • Sexual fixation indicated by language or drawings • Nightmares, trouble sleeping, or fear of the dark • Sudden or extreme mood swings (e.g., rage, fear, anger, crying, or withdrawal) • References to a new, older friend • Unexplained avoidance of certain people, places, or activities • Pain, itching, or bleeding in genital areas

Healthy Sexual Development in Children and Youth

At each developmental stage, children show a range of healthy sexual behaviors and curiosity. Children's behaviors and curiosity may develop gradually, based on their development, and may be influenced by factors, such as what they observe and the guidance they receive from parents and caregivers. Understanding healthy sexual development can provide a context in which to consider signs and behaviors of possible abuse. The table lists common behaviors considered healthy for most children and youth, according to their developmental phases.

Table 49.2. Common Sexual Development Behaviors in Children and Youth

Younger Children	Older Children and Youth
• Curiosity about their bodies, occasional masturbation in public and private	• Adherence to social norms around masturbation likely occurs in private
• Consensual, playful exploration of their bodies with children of similar age	• Shared sexual behaviors with peers of a similar age may take place
• Questions about sexuality, such as "Where do babies come from?"	• Interest in adult bodies on TV or in the media
• Lack of inhibition about nudity, particularly under age five	• Understanding of pregnancy, human immunodeficiency viruses (HIV), and other sexually transmitted infections (STIs)
• Use of slang to describe body parts and jokes about bodily functions	• Capacity to learn about intimate, long-term, loving relationships and healthy versus unhealthy relationships

Establishing Family Guidelines for Safety and Privacy

Establishing family guidelines for safety and privacy is critical, as survivors of sexual abuse are vulnerable to later abuse. Some children and youth who have been sexually abused have heightened sensitivities to situations that involve physical contact, evoke sexual innuendo, or include implicit or explicit sexual content. Practicing some of the following guidelines may make your home a comfortable place for children or youth who have been abused. It may also reduce your vulnerability to abuse allegations by children living with you.

- Respect every family member's comfort level with touching, hugging, and kissing. Encourage children and adults to respect the comfort and privacy of others.

- Be cautious with playful touch, such as play fighting and tickling. This type of play may be uncomfortable or trigger memories of sexual abuse.

- Be mindful that some children who have experienced sexual abuse may not have healthy boundaries. Teach your children and the entire family about healthy age-appropriate boundaries.

431

- Teach children and youth the importance of privacy. Remind children to knock before entering bathrooms and bedrooms and model privacy and respect.

- Keep adult sexuality private. Adult caretakers need to pay special attention to intimacy and sexuality when young children with a history of sexual abuse are around.

Other family guidelines for safety and privacy include supervising and monitoring children's play. If you know that your child has a history of sexual abuse, supervise and monitor her or his play with siblings or other children in your home. Some children require constant supervision; they cannot be left alone with younger children for even a moment. Consider placing locks or bells on bedroom doors so that you can track a child's movements at night. Other measures, such as audio and visual monitors or installing door alarms, can also help ensure safety.

If your teen has a history of sexual abuse, maintaining open communication is advisable. Knowing who your youth is with and what she or he is doing and setting clear expectations for check-ins can enhance communication and mitigate high-risk behavior.

Practicing responses to children and youth who exhibit sexual behavior issues prepares you to help children develop self-awareness and learn to respect others. Encourage your children to talk to you or another trusted adult if they want to engage in inappropriate sexual behavior, and let them know it is okay to talk about the feelings they are having. For children and youth who have been abused, you can say, "Just like it was not okay for so-and-so to touch your private parts, it is not okay for you to touch other people's private parts." You might also give clear directives, such as "We don't use that language in this house!" or "I'd like you to use different words so that we can really hear what you're saying."

If your child has demonstrated inappropriate touching or sexually aggressive behaviors, you may need to take additional steps, such as creating a family safety plan, to help ensure safety for your child as well as her or his peers. Consider how these tips may apply to your situation:

- **With friends.** If your child has known issues with touching other children, you will need to ensure constant supervision by informing other caregivers when she or he is playing with friends, whether at your home or theirs. You should be able to see your child at all times when she or he is with other children. Constant supervision will help to ensure safety for all children and prevent texually aggressive behaviors from becoming a habit. Sleepovers may not be a good idea when children have touching issues.

- **At school.** Working closely with the school to set up a safety plan for children or youth with aggressive sexual behaviors ensures an appropriate level of supervision and protects everyone involved. The plan should address concerns such as bathrooms and locker rooms, lunch, recess, transitions between classes, field trips, and other situations. Children or youth who have been sexually abused should not be alone with one teacher. At least one additional teacher should be in the room.

- **In the community.** Setting up a safety plan with coaches, camp counselors, and other adults who are monitoring your child also may be useful. Children with sexual behavior concerns should not be given authoritative roles over other children. If your child has these issues, do not ask her or him to watch over younger children at any time. If your child or youth is focused on specific individuals, make sure she or he is not alone or placed together in small groups.

Even as sexual behaviors diminish, continue to look for changes over time. These sexual behaviors can reemerge as children develop, so do not be discouraged if this occurs. Because sexual behavior may be a reaction to stress, it is also important to remove stressors from the child's life as much as possible.

Seeking Help

Responding to the needs of a child or youth who has been sexually abused may involve the entire family and will likely affect family relationships. Mental-health professionals (e.g., counselors, therapists, or social workers) can help your family cope with reactions, thoughts, and feelings about the abuse. Look for a mental-health professional with a background in sexual abuse, child development, and child trauma. Before agreeing to work with a particular provider, ask questions about the person's background, experience, and approach to treating children.

Counseling for Parents and Children

Working with a specialized mental-health professional as soon as issues arise can help you determine if your child's behavior is cause for concern. Specialists can also provide guidance in responding to

433

your child's difficulties; offer suggestions for how to talk with her or him; and offer suggestions for creating structured, safe, and nurturing environments.

Many mental-health professionals begin with a thorough assessment exploring how a child or youth functions in various areas of life. The specialist will want to know about the following:

- Past stressors (e.g., history of abuse, frequent moves, and other losses)

- Current stressors (e.g., a medical problem or learning disability)

- Emotional state (e.g., Is the child or youth usually happy or anxious?)

- Coping strategies (e.g., Does the child withdraw or act out when angry or sad?)

- Friendships (e.g., Does the child have challenges making or maintaining friends?)

- Strengths (e.g., Is the youth creative, athletic, organized?)

- Communication skills (e.g., Can the child communicate appropriately for her or his age?)

- Attachments to adults in her or his life (e.g., Does the child seem comfortable around adults?)

- Activities (e.g., time spent watching TV, using the Internet, playing video games)

After a thorough assessment, the professional will decide if the child and family could benefit from therapy. A child's social worker can help you understand your child's assessments and select the most appropriate form of therapy. The social worker will assist you in finding a therapist with the right credentials for your child and family as well as help you understand insurance coverage and payment plans.

Not all children who have been abused require therapy. For those who do, the mental-health professional will develop a plan tailored to the child and to the family's strengths. This plan may include one or more of the following types of therapy:

- **Individual therapy.** The style of therapy will depend on the child's age and the therapist's training. Some therapists use creative techniques (e.g., art, play, and music therapy) to help children or youth who are uncomfortable talking about their experiences.

- **Group therapy.** Meeting in groups with other children or youth who have been sexually abused or who have developed sexual behavior issues can help children understand themselves; feel less alone; and learn new skills through play, role-playing, discussion, and games.

- **Family therapy.** Many therapists will see children and parents together to support positive parent-child communication and to guide parents in learning new skills that will help their children feel better and support healthy behaviors.

Regardless of whether therapy for the family is advised, parents should stay involved in their child's treatment plan and therapy sessions. Skilled professionals will always seek to involve the parents by asking for and sharing information. Parents can benefit from professionals who understand the parenting needs of a child who has experienced sexual abuse.

Some forms of therapy are designed for dealing with trauma in general and posttraumatic stress disorder (PTSD) specifically.

- **Trauma-informed therapy.** This therapy acknowledges the impact of trauma and recognizes that even a child who is not old enough to remember a traumatic event may still experience its effects. Trauma-informed therapy focuses on processing traumatic memories and experiences so they become tolerable.

- **PTSD therapy.** Children and youth who are coping with symptoms of PTSD may be dealing with flashbacks and nightmares. They may be easily frightened and experience outbursts of anger and negative thoughts and distorted feelings. Approaches, such as cognitive processing therapy, eye movement desensitization and reprocessing, and group therapy can reduce symptoms of PTSD.

Several evidence-based programs have been found useful for treating children who have been sexually abused and their families. Websites with descriptions include the following:

- The California Evidence-Based Clearinghouse for Child Welfare lists programs for the treatment of sexual behavior issues in adolescents and in children.

- NCTSN includes information about trauma-informed treatment for sexual abuse.

Where to Find and What to Look For in a Mental-Health Professional

Finding an experienced mental-health professional who specializes in treating children who have been sexually abused is key to getting the help your family needs. Some communities have special programs for treating children who have been sexually abused (e.g., child advocacy centers and child protection teams). The organizations and resources below also may provide specialists in your community.

- Stop It Now!

- Child advocacy centers

- Rape crisis or sexual assault centers

- Child abuse hotlines

- NCTSN maintains a list of its members that specialize in research and/or treatment

- Nonprofit service providers serving families of missing or exploited children

- Hospitals with child and adolescent protection centers

- Crime-victim assistance programs in a law enforcement agency or in a prosecutor or district attorney's office

- Group mental-health private practices with a specialization in trauma services

- Family court services, including court-appointed special advocate groups or guardians ad litem

- American Academy of Child and Adolescent Psychiatry (AACAP)

- American Psychological Association (APA)

Therapy for children who have been sexually abused is specialized work. When selecting a mental-health professional, look for the following:

- An advanced degree in a recognized mental-health specialties, such as psychiatry (M.D.), psychology (Ph.D. or Psy.D.), social work (M.S.W.), counseling (L.P.C.), marriage and family therapy (M.F.T.), or psychiatric nursing (R.N.)

- Licensure to practice as a mental-health professional in your state

- Special training in treating child sexual abuse and the dynamics of abuse, how abuse affects children and adults, and the use of goal-oriented treatment plans

- Knowledge about the legal issues involved in child sexual abuse, especially the laws about reporting child sexual victimization, procedures used by law enforcement and protective services, evidence collection, and expert testimony in your state

- A willingness to collaborate with other professionals involved in your family's care

Your Child Welfare Agency

If you are a caregiver or parent, or if you are seeking to adopt a child, you may wish to talk with your social worker about what you discover about your child's history and any behaviors that worry you. Sharing your concerns will help your social worker assist you and your family. If your child or youth exhibits sexual behavior issues toward other children, be aware that you may also be required to report these to child protective services to comply with mandated reporting laws in your jurisdiction.

Conclusion

As the parent of a child or youth who has been or may have been sexually abused, you have an opportunity to provide comfort and security as well as help her or him build resilience and effective coping strategies for the trauma they have or may have endured. Creating a structured, safe, and nurturing home is the greatest gift that you can give to all of your children. Seek help when you need it, share your successes with your social worker or other community supports, and remember that a healthy relationship with your children allows them to begin and advance the healing process.

Section 49.6

Questions to Ask Your Adoption Agency or Organization

This section includes text excerpted from "Obtaining
Background Information on Your Prospective Adopted Child," Child
Welfare Information Gateway, U.S. Department of Health and
Human Services (HHS), October 2018.

Asking questions will help you obtain the information you need to get a better understanding of your prospective child. You may also request a child's case file to obtain written personal records or social history. Your questions and the information you receive will largely depend on the child's age and the type of adoption. For example, if you are considering the adoption of a newborn or infant, the birth parents' health history and birth mother's medical care during the pregnancy and delivery will be most important and more likely to be available. With an older child, information on the child's social, trauma, developmental, placement, educational, and mental-health histories is essential.

If your prospective child has been in foster care, you will want to know as much as possible about the child's placement history and experiences. Detailed information may be more difficult to come by in inter-country adoptions. Being informed about a child's placement history and any prior maltreatment will give you a better understanding of the child's social history and how that might affect behavior and adjustment. This can help you understand incidents or events that might trigger emotional reactions. Trauma from prior abuse and neglect can affect a child's physical, emotional, and cognitive health into adulthood.

As you consider adoption, keeping your family's needs in mind is essential. How much information do you need to make this important decision confidently? Even if little or no prenatal information is available, observing the child and accessing whatever records are available will help to inform your decision. The following questions may help to guide your decision.

About the child:

- What are the child's nicknames, personality characteristics, strengths, interests, preferences, skills, hobbies, etc.?

- What is the child's understanding of her or his story? What would a child with this history believe about her/ himself?

- How will this child likely view parents/caretakers/the world?

- What types of behaviors can we expect from a child with this history? What special skills and/or resources will be needed to raise this child? Do we have them and/or can they be learned?

- How will this child fit in with our family?

- Does the child resemble anyone in her or his birth family? If so, whom?

Social and Placement History

- Why did the birth parents make an adoption plan, or why was the child removed from her or his birth family?

- Did the child experience abuse or neglect? At what age(s)? Who was the perpetrator and what happened?

- At what age did the child enter care, and for what reason?

- How many placements have the child experienced? Where and with whom were the placements, and what does the child remember?

- What were the relationships of the caregivers with the child? Is there available contact information for former caregivers to learn more about the child?

- Where has the child attended school?

- What are the results of any educational testing?

- What are the past and existing relationships with people she or he has lived with?

- How has the child handled visits with birth family members or former caregivers in the past?

Developmental Milestones

- Has there been a failure to thrive? A problem with feeding or swallowing?

- Have there been any issues with the child's gross or fine motor skills?

- At what age did baby talk begin? When did the child first use words, and when did she or he begin to combine words and sentences?

- Has the child experienced inconsistent language gains (e.g., had the skill but then lost it)?

- At what age did the child first sit? Crawl? Walk?

- At what age did the child become potty-trained?

- How are the child's self-help skills, and when did they develop (e.g., feeding, dressing, bathing)?

- Does the child have any special educational needs or abilities?

Physical, Behavioral, and Emotional Health

- Does the child have a history of significant medical issues? If so, what are they and how have they been treated?

- Are records available from any physician or hospital visits?

- What is the child's current need for medical, dental, or mental healthcare?

- Is there an available therapy history? If so, is a list of current and past providers available?

- Has the child been diagnosed with a psychiatric disorder?

- How much did the child cry as an infant or toddler?

- How does the child self-regulate? Is she or he able to self-soothe?

- What types of behavioral outbursts or temper tantrums does the child exhibit?

- Describe the child's fears, concerns, or triggers.

- Describe the child's social skills.

- How does the child respond to direction and/or criticism?

- How does the child handle transitions?

About the child's family:

- What is the family's racial, ethnic, cultural, and religious background?

- Is the family's physical and mental-health history available?

- What information is available regarding family members and recent contact? Are photos available?

- Are there siblings in foster care or those who have been privately adopted, or is there an adoption history for them?

- Is there a family history of neglect or emotional, sexual, or physical abuse?

- Is the father known and/or involved with the family?

- What is the educational background of the birth parents and siblings?

- Are there available letters, videos, or photos from the birth family?

- Are there specific connections that are important to maintain?

Prenatal History

- At what age did the child's mother give birth?

- What was the mother's health like during her pregnancy? What was the health of each parent at the time of the child's birth?

- What was the child's condition at birth?

- How many children does the mother currently have?

- Were maternal rights ever terminated? If so, with which child(ren) and why (find or ask to see the court order, if available)?

- Is there a maternal history of alcohol, prescription drugs, or other substance use?

School-Aged Children

- Are the child's language abilities and vocabulary consistent with her or his peers?

- How are the child's social skills?

- How does the child take direction?

- Is the child currently receiving educational supports (e.g., such as an Individualized Education Program)?

Chapter 50

Parenting a Child Who Has Experienced Trauma

Children who have experienced traumatic events need to feel safe and loved. All parents want to provide this kind of nurturing home for their children. However, when parents do not have an understanding of the effects of trauma, they may misinterpret their child's behavior and end up feeling frustrated or resentful. Their attempts to address troubling behavior may be ineffective or, in some cases, even harmful. This chapter discusses the nature of trauma, its effects on children and youth, and ways to help your child. By increasing your understanding of trauma, you can help support your child's healing, your relationship with her or him, and your family as a whole.

What Is Trauma?

Trauma is an emotional response to an intense event that threatens or causes harm. The harm can be physical or emotional, real or perceived, and it can threaten the child or someone close to him or her. Trauma can be the result of a single event, or it can result from

---

This chapter includes text excerpted from "Parenting a Child Who Has Experienced Trauma," Child Welfare Information Gateway, U.S. Department of Health and Human Services (HHS), November 2014. Reviewed March 2019.

exposure to multiple events over time. Potentially traumatic events may include:

- Abuse (physical, sexual, or emotional)

- Neglect

- Effects of poverty (such as homelessness or not having enough to eat)

- Being separated from loved ones

- Bullying

- Witnessing harm to a loved one or pet (e.g., domestic or community violence)

- Natural disasters or accidents

- Unpredictable parental behavior due to addiction or mental illness

For many children, being in the child welfare system becomes another traumatic event. This is true of the child's first separation from his or her home and family, as well as any additional placements.

The Impact of Untreated Trauma

Children are resilient. Some stress in their lives (e.g., leaving caregivers for a day at school, riding a bike for the first time, feeling nervous before a game or performance) helps their brains to grow and new skills to develop. However, by definition, trauma occurs when a stressful experience (such as being abused, neglected, or bullied) overwhelms the child's natural ability to cope. These events cause a "fight, flight, or freeze" response, resulting in changes in the body—such as faster heart rate and higher blood pressure—as well as changes in how the brain perceives and responds to the world. In many cases, a child's body and brain recover quickly from a potentially traumatic experience with no lasting harm. However, for other children, trauma interferes with normal development and can have long-lasting effects.

Factors that determine the impact of traumatic events include the following:

- **Age.** Younger children are more vulnerable. Even infants and toddlers who are too young to talk about what happened retain lasting "sense memories" of traumatic events that can affect their well-being into adulthood.

444

- **Frequency.** Experiencing the same type of traumatic event multiple times, or multiple types of traumatic events, is more harmful than a single event.

- **Relationships.** Children with positive relationships with healthy caregivers are more likely to recover.

- **Coping skills.** Intelligence, physical health, and self-esteem help children cope.

- **Perception.** How much danger the child thinks he or she is in, or the amount of fear the child feels at the time, is a significant factor.

- **Sensitivity.** Every child is different—some are naturally more sensitive than others.

The effects of trauma vary depending on the child and the type of traumatic events experienced. The right kind of help can reduce or even eliminate many of these negative consequences.

Understanding Your Child's Behavior

When children have experienced trauma, particularly multiple traumatic events over an extended period of time, their bodies, brains, and nervous systems adapt in an effort to protect them. This might result in behaviors such as increased aggression, distrusting or disobeying adults, or even dissociation (feeling disconnected from reality). When children are in danger, these behaviors may be important for their survival. However, once children are moved to a safer environment, their brains and bodies may not recognize that the danger has passed. These protective behaviors, or habits, have grown strong from frequent use (just as a muscle that is used regularly grows bigger and stronger). It takes time and retraining to help those "survival muscles" learn that they are not needed in their new situation (your home), and that they can relax. It might be helpful to remember that your child's troublesome behavior may be a learned response to stress—it may even be what kept your child alive in a very unsafe situation. It will take time and patience for your child's body and brain to learn to respond in ways that are more appropriate for his or her current, safe environment.

Trauma Triggers

When your child is behaving in a way that is unexpected and seems irrational or extreme, he or she may be experiencing a trauma trigger.

445

A trigger is some aspect of a traumatic event that occurs in a completely different situation but reminds the child of the original event. Examples may be sounds, smells, feelings, places, postures, tones of voice, or even emotions. Youth who have experienced traumatic events may reenact past patterns when they feel unsafe or encounter a trigger. Depending on whether the child has a "fight," "flight," or "freeze" response, the child may appear to be throwing a tantrum, willfully not listening, or defying you. However, responses to triggers are best thought of as reflexes—they are not deliberate or planned. When children's bodies and brains are overwhelmed by a traumatic memory, they are not able to consider the consequences of their behavior or its effect on others.

Symptoms by Age

The age ranges are merely guidelines. For many children who have experienced trauma, their development lags behind their age in calendar years. It may be normal for your child to exhibit behaviors that are more common in younger children.

These signs alone do not necessarily indicate that your child has experienced trauma. However, if symptoms are more severe or longer lasting than is typical for children the same age, or if they interfere with your child's ability to succeed at home or in school, it is important to seek help.

Trauma and Mental Health

Trauma symptoms that are more severe or disruptive to a child's ability to function at home or at school may overlap with specific mental-health diagnoses. This may be one reason why nearly 80 percent of children aging out of foster care have received a mental-health diagnosis.

Children who have difficulty concentrating may be diagnosed with attention deficit hyperactivity disorder (ADHD).

Children who appear anxious or easily overwhelmed by emotions may be diagnosed with anxiety or depression.

Children who have trouble with the unexpected may respond by trying to control every situation or by showing extreme reactions to change. In some cases, these behaviors may be labeled oppositional defiant disorder (ODD) or intermittent explosive disorder (IED).

Dissociation in response to a trauma trigger may be viewed as defiance of authority, or it may be diagnosed as depression, ADHD (inattentive type), or even a developmental delay.

It may be necessary to treat these diagnoses with traditional mental-health approaches (including the use of medications, where indicated) in the short term. However, treating the underlying cause by addressing the child's experience of trauma will be more effective in the long run.

Helping Your Child

Although childhood trauma can have serious, lasting effects, there is hope. With the help of supportive, caring adults, children can and do recover. Consider the following tips:

- **Identify trauma triggers.** Something you are doing or saying, or something harmless in your home, may be triggering your child without either of you realizing it. It is important to watch for patterns of behavior and reactions that do not seem to "fit" the situation. What distracts your child, makes him or her anxious, or results in a tantrum or outburst? Help your child avoid situations that trigger traumatic memories, at least until more healing has occurred.

- **Be emotionally and physically available.** Some traumatized children act in ways that keep adults at a distance (whether they mean to or not). Provide attention, comfort, and encouragement in ways your child will accept. Younger children may want extra hugs or cuddling; for older youth, this might just mean spending time together as a family. Follow their lead and be patient if children seem needy.

- **Respond, do not react.** Your reactions may trigger a child or youth who is already feeling overwhelmed. (Some children are even uncomfortable being looked at directly for too long.) When your child is upset, do what you can to keep calm: Lower your voice, acknowledge your child's feelings, and be reassuring and honest.

- **Avoid physical punishment.** This may make an abused child's stress or feeling of panic even worse. Parents need to set reasonable and consistent limits and expectations and use praise for desirable behaviors.

- **Do not take behavior personally.** Allow the child to feel his or her feelings without judgment. Help him or her find words and other acceptable ways of expressing feelings, and offer praise when these are used.

447

- **Listen.** Do not avoid difficult topics or uncomfortable conversations. (But don't force children to talk before they are ready.) Let children know that it is normal to have many feelings after a traumatic experience. Take their reactions seriously, correct any misinformation about the traumatic event, and reassure them that what happened was not their fault.

- **Help your child learn to relax.** Encourage your child to practice slow breathing, listen to calming music, or say positive things.

- **Be consistent and predictable.** Develop a regular routine for meals, playtime, and bedtime. Prepare your child in advance for changes or new experiences.

- **Be patient.** Everyone heals differently from trauma, and trust does not develop overnight. Respecting each child's own course of recovery is important.

- **Allow some control.** Reasonable, age-appropriate choices encourage a child or youth's sense of having control of his or her own life.

- **Encourage self-esteem.** Positive experiences can help children recover from trauma and increase resilience. Examples include mastering a new skill; feeling a sense of belonging to a community, group, or cause; setting and achieving goals, and being of service to others.

Seeking Treatment

If your child's symptoms last more than a few weeks, or if they are getting worse rather than better, it is time to ask for help. Mental-health counseling or therapy by a professional trained to recognize and treat trauma in children can help address the root cause of your child's behavior and promote healing. A therapist or behavioral specialist might be able to help you understand your child and respond more effectively. At times, medications may be necessary to control symptoms and improve your child's ability to learn new skills. Begin by asking your caseworker or agency whether your child has been screened for trauma. If you know that your child experienced trauma, ask whether he or she has had a formal mental-health assessment by a professional who is aware of trauma's effects. Ideally, this assessment (including both strengths and needs) should be repeated periodically to help you and your child's therapist monitor progress. Once your child has been assessed and it has been determined that treatment is needed, ask about treatment options.

However, they are not all available in every community. Consult with your child's caseworker about the availability of trauma-focused treatment where you live. Timely, effective mental and behavioral health interventions may help in the following ways:

- Increase your child's feelings of safety

- Teach your child how to manage emotions, particularly when faced with trauma triggers

- Help your child develop a positive view of him- or herself

- Give your child a greater sense of control over his/her own life

- Improve your child's relationships—with family members and others

It is important to look for a provider who understands and has specific training in trauma. Most providers will agree to a brief interview in their office or over the phone, to determine whether they are a good fit for your needs.

Helping Yourself and Your Family

Parenting a child or youth who has experienced trauma can be difficult. Families can sometimes feel isolated as if no one else understands what they are going through. This can put a strain not only on your relationship with your child but with other family members, as well (including your spouse or partner). Learning about what your child experienced may even act as a trigger for you if you have your own trauma history that is not fully healed. Being affected by someone else's trauma is sometimes called "secondary trauma."

to take good care of your child, you must take good care of yourself. Here are some things you can do:

- **Be honest about your expectations for your child and your relationship.** Having realistic expectations about parenting a child with a history of trauma increases the chances for a healthy relationship.

- **Celebrate small victories.** Take note of the improvements your child has made.

- **Do not take your child's difficulties personally.** Your child's struggles are a result of the trauma he or she experienced; they are not a sign of your failure as a parent.

- **Take care of yourself.** Make time for things you enjoy doing that support your physical, emotional, and spiritual health.

- **Focus on your own healing.** If you have experienced trauma, it will be important for you to pursue your own healing, separate from your child.

- **Seek support.** Your circle of support may include friends, family, and professional support if needed. Do not be afraid to ask about resources available from the child welfare system, such as a caseworker or support groups.

Conclusion

Trauma can affect children's behavior in ways that may be confusing or distressing for caregivers. It can impact the long-term health and well-being of the child and his or her family members. However, with understanding, care, and proper treatment (when necessary), all members of the family can heal and thrive after a traumatic event.

Chapter 51

Parenting Children and Youth Who Have Experienced Abuse or Neglect

Children and youth who have been abused or neglected need safe, stable, and nurturing relationships and environments to recover from the trauma they have experienced. If you are parenting a child or youth with a history of abuse or neglect, you might have questions about the impacts and how you can help your child heal. This chapter is intended to help parents (birth, foster, and adoptive) and other caregivers better understand the challenges of caring for a child or youth who have experienced maltreatment and learn about available resources for support.

Child Abuse and Neglect and Its Effects

Knowing about abuse and neglect (also known as "child maltreatment") and their effects will help you respond to the needs of your child or youth while building trust, a sense of safety, and support in your relationship. How you respond to your child's maltreatment

---

This chapter includes text excerpted from "Parenting Children and Youth Who Have Experienced Abuse or Neglect," Child Welfare Information Gateway, U.S. Department of Health and Human Services (HHS), November 2018.

will depend on what you know about his or her history and the type of abuse or neglect experienced. The first step toward understanding how to best parent your child or youth is learning what child maltreatment is.

Child maltreatment falls into four main groups:

- Physical abuse refers to a nonaccidental physical injury (from hitting, kicking, or burning, for example) caused by a parent, caregiver, or trusted adult with whom the child has regular contact, such as a teacher, babysitter, or coach.

- Sexual abuse refers to forcing or coercing a child or youth to engage in sexual activity, including exploitation through pornography.

- Emotional abuse is a pattern of behavior that hurts the emotional development or sense of self-worth of a child or youth (for example, constant criticism, threats, or sarcasm; belittling, shaming, or withholding love).

- Neglect is the failure of a parent or caregiver to protect a child or youth from harm or provide basic needs (for example, food, shelter, supervision, medical care, education, or emotional nurturing).

According to the U.S. Centers for Disease Control and Prevention (CDC) children and youth who have experienced abuse or neglect are at higher risk for poor long-term health, impaired mental health, and negative social consequences than those who have not experienced child maltreatment. Examples of poor health outcomes include high blood pressure, delays in physical and emotional development, depression or anxiety, and attachment disorders. Abuse or neglect can impair healthy development by negatively affecting the way a child's brain develops. Maltreatment can delay or alter how he or she is able to process information and respond emotionally, see right from wrong, anticipate the consequences of actions, and learn from mistakes. The effects of maltreatment can be long-term, occur immediately or years after the abuse, and may depend on several factors, including the following:

- The age of the child or youth at the time of the abuse or neglect

- Whether the maltreatment happened once or was ongoing

- Who abused or neglected the child or youth (for example, a parent or other caregiver)

- Whether a nurturing person was in the child or youth's life

- The type and severity of the maltreatment

While child abuse and neglect can leave physical and emotional scars, it can also cause trauma and toxic stress. Trauma occurs when someone directly experiences injury or threat of injury or witnesses an event that threatens or causes serious harm to themselves or a loved one. According to the Center on the Developing Child at Harvard University, toxic stress can occur when a child lacks a supportive parent or other adult and experiences strong, frequent, or ongoing adversity, such as physical or emotional abuse, chronic neglect, caregiver substance use or mental illness, or exposure to violence. Responses to trauma experienced by children and youth may vary; some children may be reluctant to trust, some may act out, and some may withdraw from family and friends.

How Can I Help My Child or Youth Heal?

This section explores strategies for helping your child or youth build resilience after experiencing abuse or neglect. It also discusses protective factors and capacities that parents can develop to help prevent future child maltreatment or retraumatization.

Building Resilience and Promoting Protective Factors and Protective Capacities

Although exposure to abuse or neglect increases the risk of negative psychological, social, and emotional short- and long-term outcomes, your child's resilience may protect him or her from developing poor physical or mental-health issues. According to the American Psychological Association, resilience in children and youth enables them to thrive in spite of their adverse circumstances. It involves behaviors, thoughts, and actions that can be learned over time and can be nurtured through positive and healthy relationships with parents and other caregivers and adults who guide them in healthy problem-solving strategies. As with any skill, resilience must be developed. You can help your child or youth build resilience if you:

- **Model a positive outlook.** When faced with a problem, show your child or youth that the problem is only for a short time and that things will get better. Children and youth learn from your ability to bounce back from and work through tough situations.

- **Build confidence.** Let your child or youth know when he or she does something well, such as demonstrating kindness or honesty.

- **Express support.** Express love, empathy, and support verbally and physically. Express your love through words, notes, and hugs.

- **Build connections.** Create bonds with friends and family that can support your child or youth during challenges and teach him or her to consider other people's feelings.

- **Allow children to express their feelings.** Teach them how to identify and describe their feelings and commend them for expressing feelings of hurt or sadness without acting out.

- **Be consistent.** If you say you will be there, be there. If you say you'll listen to concerns, listen. This will help teach your child or youth that people can be trusted.

- **Be patient.** Children's reactions to trauma vary as widely as the types of trauma one can experience. There is not a one-size-fits-all solution.

- **Teach your child or youth the importance of healthy behaviors.** Have open and honest talks about the dangers of drugs and alcohol, smoking, and sexually inappropriate behavior. Teach your child the importance of eating properly and exercising.

The healing process does not always follow a clear, straight path. After experiencing trauma or maltreatment, resilience takes time to develop. Steps you can take to help your child or youth heal include the following:

- Address your child's physical safety first by assuring him or her that no one will physically touch or harm them. This will help your child or youth develop feelings of trust and openness to psychological and emotional healing.

- Address the past as the past. Help your child or youth identify elements of his or her current life that are different from the past. Use this as a chance to discuss expectations and personal boundaries—limits set in relationships that protect our sense of self. To encourage feelings of belonging and attachment, provide regular routines around mealtime, naps, and bedtime; talk with your child or youth about the importance of feelings, and teach him or her to solve problems in age-appropriate ways.

As children and youth can be resilient, so can parents. By increasing your own resiliency, you will help to improve your child or youth's long-term well-being. As you develop these skills, you build protective factors, which are elements or tools that help to reduce the negative effects of child maltreatment and the trauma resulting from it.

Protective Factors

Issues, such as substance use, poverty, parental stress, and lack of parental supervision, present risks (also known as "risk factors") that can increase your child's chances of developing poor health, experiencing abuse or neglect, or other negative outcomes. Protective factors, such as strong social connections and solid parent-child attachments, may buffer the effect of risks and help children, youth, and families manage difficult circumstances and fare better in school, work, and life. Building protective factors to support children and youth who have experienced child abuse and neglect can also help increase their resilience.

Protective Capacities

As a parent, you also have the potential to protect your children. These abilities, known as protective capacities, develop over time. Improving your own mental and emotional well-being will help you to develop these protective capacities, which will then better enable you to help your child or youth build resilience and reduce the risk of experiencing harm, including abuse or neglect. Protective capacities can be categorized as mental, emotional, or behavioral.

- **Mental protective capacity:** Your knowledge, understanding, and perceptions of your child or youth

- **Emotional protective capacity:** Your feelings and attitudes toward, and identification with, your child or youth

- **Behavioral protective capacity:** Your actions and behaviors toward your child or youth

Building a Strong Relationship with Your Child or Youth

A child's earliest relationships are some of the most important. Attachment refers to the relationship that develops as a result of a caregiver's sensitive attention to a child and the child's responses to the caregiver. A strong and secure emotional bond between children and their caregivers is critical for children's physical, social, and emotional development, including their ability to form trusting relationships and to exhibit positive behaviors. Helping parents learn and practice the nurturing skills that lead to strong, secure attachments is a well-supported pathway to positive outcomes for children.

If children lack an attachment to a caring adult, receive inconsistent nurturing, or experience harsh punishment, the consequences can affect their lifelong health, well-being, and relationships with others. In some cases, children may lack a strong attachment because their parents work multiple jobs to provide for them, so less time is spent together building a strong and secure emotional bond. Parents may need additional support and resources to address this issue.

To help build a secure relationship with your child or youth:

- **Be available.** Provide consistent support to build feelings of trust and safety.

- **Be supportive and empathic.** Comfort your child or youth when he or she is upset, modeling appropriate displays of affection and building self-esteem.

- **Be encouraging.** Listen and be involved and interested in your child's activities. Stay aware of his or her interests and friends and stay actively supportive.

Developing Caring Discipline Techniques

As part of normal development, children and youth act out on occasion and challenge the authority of parents or caregivers. Toddlers throw tantrums. Children whine. Teenagers argue. To help a child learn from these natural behaviors, parents need sound techniques for handling them.

Positive discipline techniques teach children and youth the difference between acceptable and unacceptable behavior and help a child internalize self-control, self-discipline, and self-respect. Children should always know that you love, support, and respect them, even when you correct their unacceptable behavior.

When parents are angry or feel frustrated they may use unpleasant or painful methods—physical or emotional—in reaction to and for the purpose of discouraging behavior. A child who is misbehaving can be frustrating but using physical force or other abusive techniques to teach a lesson is never appropriate.

For children and youth who have experienced abuse or neglect, using physical force or other abusive techniques could elicit memories of past trauma or cause retraumatization. How harmful a method is may depend not only on the punishment chosen but also on the abuse or neglect your child or youth experienced. For example, sending your child to bed hungry could retraumatize them if they have had previously experienced neglect by being denied food.

Other factors, such as lack of sleep and a poor diet, can also impair a child's ability to make good choices or to show self-control. Before disciplining a child for misbehaving, consider whether he or she is tired, hungry, or reacting to an underlying issue like fear or anxiety. Try to engage your child or youth in a quiet activity that will provide needed rest or decrease anxiety or offer a snack or an early meal to ease his or her hunger.

Positive Discipline Tips and Techniques

Positive discipline that works at one age may not work at another. Children change as they go through their developmental stages, so using age-appropriate discipline when parenting a child or youth who has experienced abuse or neglect is important in promoting healthy development and preventing retraumatization. Allow your child or youth to learn at his or her own pace. Break tasks into small, manageable steps that will provide a sense of success and accomplishment.

Where Can I Find Support?

Recovering from abuse and neglect is a journey that affects the entire family. Parents and caregivers need support to learn as much as they can about child maltreatment. Developing your parenting skills can go a long way toward promoting your child's well-being and building a healthy family.

Parent Education and Training

Parent education programs offer ways to handle demanding situations and enhance problem-solving skills. These support and training programs are geared toward reinforcing your positive parenting skills and teaching you effective strategies to reduce the occurrence of your child's misbehavior. Parent education programs can be online or in-person, involve one-to-one instruction, or take place in a group setting. Whether you prefer a course with direct instruction, videos, or another format, successful programs:

- Promote positive family interaction

- Involve fathers

- Use interactive training techniques

- Offer opportunities to practice new skills

- Teach emotional communication skills

- Encourage peer support

Therapy and Support Groups

Dealing with the effects of maltreatment can be challenging. You and your family may wish to seek support from a professional. Therapy and support groups can provide children, youth, and caregivers with the skills necessary to build healthy relationships, overcome past trauma, and prevent reoccurring or future trauma.

Therapists best suited to assist with parenting children and youth who have experienced abuse or neglect should:

- Be trained and knowledgeable about the impact of trauma on children, youth, and families

- Allow and encourage your participation in treatment

- Not restrain a child or youth or intrude on his or her physical space, as children and youth who have been maltreated need to develop clear boundaries to feel safe and prevent retraumatization

If you are an adoptive parent, it is important that the therapist you seek fits the needs of your family and is "adoption competent."

Conclusion

If you are the parent or caregiver of a child or youth who has experienced abuse and neglect, helping him or her through that trauma can be daunting, but there are resources available to help. It is important to remember that many children and youth who have been abused or neglected do not grow up to abuse others and can live happy and healthy lives. You and your family play an important role in your child's healing. The more you know about child maltreatment and the services available for support, the better prepared you will be to help your child through this difficult time.

Chapter 52

Parenting after Domestic Violence

When one person in a relationship uses any kind of abuse to control the other, this is domestic violence. You may have recently left a relationship that is abusive, or you may still be in one. Your children may have heard or seen the abuse, or they may have been targets themselves.

Living with domestic violence takes a toll on all family members. Your children may still feel afraid, even if the danger is past. But with your help, they can find ways to cope with stress, be safe, and heal.

What You Might Be Seeing

Some children living with abuse do not show signs of stress. Others struggle at home, at school, or in the community.

You may notice increased fear or anger, clinging, difficulty sleeping, or tantrums. If the abuse goes on for a long time, children can experience more serious problems, such as depression or anxiety, skipping school, or using drugs.

This chapter includes text excerpted from "Parenting after Domestic Violence," Child Welfare Information Gateway, U.S. Department of Health and Human Services (HHS), 2019.

What You Can Do

A strong relationship with a caring, nonviolent parent is important to help your children grow up in a positive way. You can help them by taking the following steps:

- **Plan for safety.** If you are still in an abusive situation, make a safety plan with your children. Teach them how to call 911, where to go for help, and never to get in the middle of an adult fight. Local domestic violence advocates can help you plan.

- **Take care of yourself.** Finding ways to cope with your own stress is good for you and for your children. Make time to connect with friends, exercise, listen to music, take a bath, or do something else that helps you relax and refocus.

- **Help your children feel secure.** Keep your kids close to you when you can, and give them lots of eye contact, kisses, and hugs. Play together, even if just for a few minutes at a time. Provide routines, such as bedtime reading and regular meal times.

- **Stay calm.** Children who have lived with violence will sometimes act in ways that make life more chaotic. Set clear limits and follow through, but keep your voice calm. Get help if you need it.

- **Talk about it.** Be willing to listen to your children talk about what has happened and how they feel. Tell them the truth when they ask questions. Reassure them that you are working to keep your family safe.

- **Help your children develop relationships.** Positive relationships with peers and other supportive adults can help your children manage stress and stay strong and happy.

- **Celebrate their strengths.** Find the things your children are good at. Encourage them in school and other activities.

Remember, you are the most important person in your children's lives. Your children need to know that you are there for them, you love them, and you will do all you can to keep them safe.

If you are in danger, contact 911 for emergency police assistance.

Chapter 53

Leaving Your Child Home Alone

All parents eventually face the decision to leave their child home alone for the first time. Whether they are just running to the store for a few minutes or working during after-school hours, parents need to be sure their child has the skills and maturity to handle the situation safely. Being trusted to stay home alone can be a positive experience for a child who is mature and well prepared and can boost the child's confidence and promote independence and responsibility. However, children face real risks when left unsupervised. Those risks, as well as a child's comfort level and ability to deal with challenges, must be considered. This chapter provides some tips to help parents and caregivers when making this important decision.

What to Consider before Leaving Your Child Home Alone

When deciding whether to leave a child home alone, you will want to consider your child's physical, mental, developmental, and emotional well-being; his or her willingness to stay home alone; and laws and policies in your state regarding this issue. There are many resources you can consult for guidance.

This chapter includes text excerpted from "Leaving Your Child Home Alone," Child Welfare Information Gateway, U.S. Department of Health and Human Services (HHS), December 2018.

463

Depending on the laws and child protective policies in your area, leaving a young child unsupervised may be considered neglect, especially if doing so places the child in danger. If you are concerned about a child who appears to be neglected or inadequately supervised, contact your local child protective services (CPS) agency. If you need help contacting your local CPS agency, call the Childhelp® National Child Abuse Hotline at 800-422-4453.

Some parents look to the law for help in deciding when it is appropriate to leave a child home alone. Only three states currently have laws regarding a minimum age for leaving a child home alone: Illinois, 14 years of age; Maryland, 8 years of age; and Oregon, 10 years of age. Many states' child protection laws classify "failing to provide adequate supervision of a child" as child neglect, but most of these States do not provide any detail on what is considered "adequate supervision." In some states, leaving a child without supervision at an inappropriate age or in inappropriate circumstances may be considered neglect after considering factors that may put the child at risk of harm, such as the child's age, mental ability, and physical condition; the length of the parent's absence; and the home environment. Instead, many states offer nonbinding guidelines for parents that can assist them in determining when it is appropriate for them to leave their child home alone. For information on laws and guidelines in your state, contact your local CPS agency.

Age and Maturity

There is no agreed-upon age when a child can stay home alone safely. Because children mature at different rates, you should not base your decision on age alone. You may want to evaluate your child's maturity and how he or she has demonstrated responsible behavior in the past. The following questions may help:

- Is your child physically and mentally able to care for him- or herself?

- Does your child obey rules and make good decisions?

- How does your child respond to unfamiliar or stressful situations?

- Does your child feel comfortable or fearful about being home alone?

For children with developmental or intellectual disabilities who are not able to stay home alone, parents may be able to arrange supervised options that support independence while maintaining safety and well-being.

Circumstances

When and how a child is left home alone can make a difference to his or her safety and success. You may want to consider the following questions:

- How long will your child be left home alone at one time? Will it be during the day, evening, or night? Will the child need to fix a meal? If so, is there food that can be prepared without using a stove to minimize the risk of fires or burns?

- How often will the child be expected to care for him or herself?

- How many children are being left home alone? Children who seem ready to stay home alone may not necessarily be ready to care for younger siblings.

- Is your home safe and free of hazards? Hazards can include nonworking smoke alarms; improperly stored cleaning chemicals, firearms, and medication; unsecured furniture, pools, unlocked alcohol, etc.

- How safe is your neighborhood? Is there a high incidence of crime?

- Does your child know how to lock or secure the doors? Does your child have a key to your home or a plan if he or she gets locked out?

- Does your child know what to do if a visitor comes to the door?

- Are there other adults nearby the home (e.g., friend, family, or neighbor) who you trust and can offer immediate assistance if there is an emergency or your child becomes fearful?

- Can you or a trusted, nearby adult be easily contacted by the child?

Safety Skills

In addition to age and maturity, your child will need to master some specific skills before being able to stay home alone safely. In particular, your child needs to know what to do and whom to contact in an emergency situation. This information should be written out in a way the child can understand and stored in an easily accessible place. Knowledge of basic first aid, such as how to check for breathing, assist with choking, and treat burns, also is useful. You may want to consider enrolling your child in a safety course such as one offered by the American Red Cross.

Make sure that there is easy access to first aid supplies at home in case they are needed. The following questions also may help:

- Does your family have a safety plan for emergencies? Can your child follow this plan?

- Does your child know his or her full name, address, and phone number?

- Does your child know where you are and how to contact you at all times?

- Does your child know the full names and contact information of other trusted adults and know to call 911 in case of emergency?

Even if your child demonstrates knowledge of all this information, it is wise to have it written out in an easily accessible place. The Red Cross has created a pediatric first aid reference guide and a safety tip sheet that outline steps parents and children can take to make being home alone safer and less stressful.

Youth Babysitting Other Children

In households with more than one child, one of the challenges can be deciding when the elder child, who may be ready to stay home alone, can supervise his or her younger sibling(s). While there is no clear-cut answer, consider asking your child the same questions for staying home alone, in addition to the following:

- Are you comfortable handling being in charge without abusing it?

- Are you able to calmly handle any emergency or other problems that arise?

- Are you willing to be responsible for the safety of your sibling(s)?

Other things to consider are the age of the younger sibling(s), sibling dynamics, and if the younger sibling(s) have any special needs. Consider having your child prepare with a course through your local Red Cross or YMCA. The Red Cross offers resource materials and online and in-person babysitting and child care courses for those 11 years of age and older. These 4-hour courses cover basic child care, what to do in emergencies, and more. They also offer courses in first aid and CPR.

Communication

As cell phones are more widely used as the primary method of contact, landlines are becoming rarer. If your house does not have a landline and your child does not have his or her own cell phone, parents need to consider how their child will be able to communicate in case of an emergency.

If you have reliable Internet access at home, an iPod, iPad, other tablet, or computer are additional options to consider as means of communication. These often have features such as FaceTime, Messaging, Skype, or similar apps and may allow you to communicate with your child. However, these applications cannot make emergency phone calls to 911. Another option is to get your child an inexpensive mobile phone to use while they are alone. Many retail outlets offer inexpensive phones with limited features, sometimes called a "dumb phone," that could be a good fit for this purpose. Your choice will differ depending on your circumstances, but the importance of having reliable communication cannot be overstated.

When deciding which forms of communication to use, consider these questions:

- Does your child know how to use a computer or tablet?

- Does your child know how to use a phone (cell or landline)?

- If there is an emergency, does your child know who to contact and how to do so (e.g., call 911)?

In addition, parents should establish clear guidelines for their children regarding the use of technology, such as social media and the Internet. Parents should teach their child safe Internet behaviors, including not giving out personal information, and that talking to people in a chat room or on social media is the same as talking with strangers.

Suggestions for Parents

Once you have determined that your child is ready to stay home alone, the following suggestions may help you to prepare your child and to feel more comfortable about leaving him or her home alone:

- **Have a trial period.** Leave the child home alone for a short time while staying close to home. This is a good way to see how he or she will manage.

- **Roleplay.** Act out possible situations to help your child learn what to do, such as how to manage visitors who come to the door or how to answer phone calls in a way that does not reveal that a parent is not at home.

- **Establish rules.** Make sure your child knows what is (and is not) allowed when you are not home. Set clear limits on the use of television, computers and other electronic devices, and the Internet.

- **Discuss emergencies.** What does the child consider an emergency? What does the parent consider an emergency? Have a code word that the parent and child can use in the event of any emergency.

- **Check-in.** Call your child while you are away to see how it is going, or let them know they will have a trusted neighbor or friend check in on them.

- **Talk about it.** Encourage your child to share his or her feelings with you about staying home alone. Have this conversation before leaving your child and then, when you return, talk with your child about his or her experiences and feelings while you were away. This is particularly important when your child is first beginning to stay home alone, but a quick check-in is always helpful after being away.

- **Don't overdo it.** Even a mature, responsible child should not be home alone too much. Consider other options, such as programs offered by schools, community centers, youth organizations, or faith-based organizations, to help keep your child connected and involved.

- **Follow up.** After a child is left home alone, talk about his or her experience. How did he or she feel about it? Was your child nervous? Did anything unexpected come up? If the child was watching a younger sibling, ask how he or she felt about doing so.

Part Seven

Additional Help and Information

Chapter 54

Glossary of Terms Related to Child Abuse

abandonment: A situation in which the child has been left by the parent(s), the parent's identity or whereabouts are unknown, the child suffers serious harm, or the parent has failed to maintain contact with the child or to provide reasonable support for a specified period of time.

abusive head trauma: A term used to describe the constellation of signs and symptoms resulting from violent shaking or shaking and impacting of the head of an infant or small child.

adoption: The social, emotional, and legal process through which children who will not be raised by their birth parents become full and permanent legal members of another family while maintaining genetic and psychological connections to their birth family.

adoption services: Services or activities provided to assist in bringing about the adoption of a child.

adoptive parent: A person with the legal relation of parent to a child not related by birth, with the same mutual rights and obligations that exist between children and their birth parents.

alcohol abuse: Compulsive use of alcohol that is not of a temporary nature. Applies to infants addicted at birth, or who are victims of fetal

---

This glossary contains terms excerpted from documents produced by several sources deemed reliable.

alcohol syndrome, or who may suffer other disabilities due to the use of alcohol during pregnancy.

alleged perpetrator: An individual who reports an alleged incident of child abuse or neglect in which she/he caused or knowingly allowed the maltreatment of a child.

assessment: The ongoing practice of informing decision-making by identifying, considering, and weighing factors that impact children, youth, and their families. Assessment occurs from the time children and families come to the attention of the child welfare system and continues until case closure.

behavior problem: Behavior of the child in the school and/or community that adversely affects socialization, learning, growth, and moral development. May include adjudicated or nonadjudicated behavior problems. Includes running away from home or a placement.

behavioral health: A state of mental/emotional being and/or choices and actions that affect wellness. Substance abuse and misuse, as well as serious psychological distress, suicide, and mental illness, are examples of some behavioral health problems.

biological parent: The birth mother or father of the child rather than the adoptive or foster parent or the stepparent.

birth mother: An individual's biological mother, after an adoption has occurred. Prior to an adoption decision and legal adoption, birth mother is referred to as a pregnant woman, or expectant mother.

birth parent: An individual's biological mother or father, after an adoption has occurred. Prior to an adoption decision and legal adoption, birth parents are referred to as a child's parents or expectant parents.

bonding: The process of developing lasting emotional ties with one's immediate caregivers; seen as the first and primary developmental achievement of a human being and central to a person's ability to relate to others throughout life.

caregiver: One who provides for the physical, emotional, and social needs of a dependent person. The term most often applies to parents or parent surrogates, child care and nursery workers, healthcare specialists, and relatives caring for children, elderly, or ill family members.

case management: Coordination and monitoring of services on behalf of a client. In general, the role of the case manager does not involve the provision of direct services but the monitoring of services to assure that they are relevant to the client, delivered in a useful way, and effective in meeting the goals of the case plan. A key element of case management in child welfare is the ongoing assessment of the client's needs and progress in services.

child: A person less than 18 years of age or considered to be a minor under state law.

child abuse and neglect: Defined by the Child Abuse Prevention and Treatment Act (CAPTA) as any recent act or failure to act on the part of a parent or caretaker that results in death, serious physical or emotional harm, sexual abuse, or exploitation, or an act or failure to act that presents an imminent risk of serious harm. Child abuse and neglect are defined by federal and state laws.

Child Abuse Prevention and Treatment Act (CAPTA): The key federal legislation addressing child abuse and neglect.

child protective services (CPS): The social services agency designated (in most states) to receive reports, conduct investigations and assessments, and provide intervention and treatment services to children and families in which child maltreatment has occurred. Frequently, this agency is located within larger public social service agencies, such as departments of social services.

child victim: A child for whom an incident of abuse or neglect has been substantiated or indicated by an investigation or assessment. A state may include some children with other dispositions as victims.

corporal punishment: Inflicting physical pain for the purpose of punishment in an effort to discipline a child.

court action: Legal action initiated by a representative of the child protective services (CPS) agency on behalf of the child. This includes, for instance, authorization to place the child, filing for temporary custody, dependency, or termination of parental rights. It does not include criminal proceedings against a perpetrator.

court-appointed special advocate (CASA): A person, usually a volunteer appointed by the court, who serves to ensure that the needs and interests of a child in child protection judicial proceedings are fully protected.

custody: Refers to the legal right to make decisions about children, including where they live. Parents have legal custody of their children unless they voluntarily give custody to someone else or a court takes this right away and gives it to someone else. For instance, a court may give legal custody to a relative or to a child welfare agency. Whoever has legal custody can enroll the children in school, give permission for medical care, and give other legal consents.

cycle of abuse: A generational pattern of abusive behavior that can occur when children who have either experienced maltreatment or witnessed violence between their parents or caregivers learn violent behavior and learn to consider it appropriate.

developmental disability: A diverse group of severe chronic conditions caused by mental and/or physical impairments. People with developmental disabilities may have problems with major life activities such as language, mobility, learning, self-help, and independent living.

discipline: Training that develops self-control, self-sufficiency, and orderly conduct. Discipline is based on respect for an individual's capability and is not to be confused with punishment.

domestic violence: A pattern of assaultive and/or coercive behaviors, including physical, sexual, and psychological attacks, as well as economic coercion, that adults or adolescents use against their intimate partners. Intimate partners include spouses, sexual partners, parents, children, siblings, extended family members, and dating relationships.

drug abuse: Compulsive use of drugs that is not of a temporary nature. Applies to infants addicted at birth.

educational neglect: Failure to ensure that a child's educational needs are met. Such neglect may involve permitting chronic truancy, failure to enroll a child in school, or inattention to special education needs.

emotional maltreatment: Type of maltreatment that refers to acts or omissions, other than physical abuse or sexual abuse, that caused, or could have caused, conduct, cognitive, affective, or other mental disorders. Includes emotional neglect, psychological abuse, mental injury, etc. Frequently occurs as verbal abuse or excessive demands on a child's performance and may cause the child to have a negative self-image and disturbed behavior.

emotional neglect: Failure to provide adequate nurturing and affection or the refusal/delay in ensuring that a child receives needed treatment for emotional or behavioral problems. Emotional neglect may also involve exposure to chronic or extreme domestic violence.

family: A group of two or more persons related by birth, marriage, adoption, or emotional ties.

family preservation services: Short-term, family-focused, and community-based services designed to help families cope with significant stresses or problems that interfere with their ability to nurture their children. The goal of family preservation services (FPS) is to maintain children with their families or to reunify the family, whenever it can be done safely. These services are applicable to families at risk of disruption/out-of-home placement across systems and may be provided to different types of families—birth or biological families, kinship families, foster families, and adoptive families—to help them address major challenges, stabilize the family, and enhance family functioning.

fetal alcohol spectrum disorders (FASDs): A group of conditions that can occur in a person whose mother drank alcohol during pregnancy. These effects can include physical problems and problems with behavior and learning. Often, a person with an FASD has a mix of these problems.

foster care: Twenty-four-hour substitute care for children placed away from their parents or guardians and for whom the state agency has placement and care responsibility. This includes, but is not limited to, family foster homes, foster homes of relatives, group homes, emergency shelters, residential facilities, child care institutions, and preadoptive homes regardless of whether the facility is licensed and whether payments are made by the state or local agency for the care of the child, or whether there is federal matching of any payments made.

foster children: Child who has been placed in the state's or county's legal custody because the child's custodial parents/guardians are unable to provide a safe family home due to abuse, neglect, or an inability to care for the child.

foster parent: Individual licensed to provide a home for orphaned, abused, neglected, delinquent or disabled children, usually with the approval of the government or a social service agency. May be a relative or a nonrelative.

group home: Residence intended to meet the needs of children who are unable to live in a family setting and do not need a more intensive residential service. Homes normally house 4 to 12 children in a setting that offers the potential for the full use of community resources, including employment, healthcare, education, and recreational opportunities. Desired outcomes of group home programs include full incorporation of the child into the community, return of the child to her or his family or other permanent family, and/or acquisition by the child of the skills necessary for independent living.

guardian ad litem (GAL): A lawyer or layperson who represents a child in juvenile or family court. Usually this person considers the best interest of the child and may perform a variety of roles, including those of independent investigator, advocate, advisor, and guardian for the child. A layperson who serves in this role is sometimes known as a court-appointed special advocate (CASA).

guardianship: The transfer of parental responsibility and legal authority for a minor child to an adult caregiver who intends to provide permanent care for the child. This can be done without terminating the parental rights of the child's parents. Transferring legal responsibility removes the child from the child welfare system, allows the caregiver to make important decisions on the child's behalf, and establishes a long-term caregiver for the child. In subsidized guardianship, the guardian is provided with a monthly subsidy for the care and support of the child.

inadequate housing: A risk factor related to substandard, over-crowded, or unsafe housing conditions, including homelessness.

incest: Sexual intercourse between persons who are closely related by blood. In the United States, incest is prohibited by many state laws as well as cultural tradition.

intervention: An action intended to modify an outcome; a set of techniques and therapies practiced in counseling.

investigation: The gathering and assessment of objective information to determine if a child has been or is at risk of being maltreated. Generally includes face-to-face contact with the victim and results in a disposition as to whether the alleged report is substantiated or not.

juvenile and family court: Court that specializes in areas such as child maltreatment, domestic violence, juvenile delinquency, divorce, child custody, and child support. These courts were established in most states to resolve conflict and to otherwise intervene in the lives of families in a manner that promotes the best interest of children.

juvenile delinquency: A federal criminal violation committed prior to one's eighteenth birthday.

kinship care: Kinship care is the full time care, nurturing, and protection of a child by relatives, members of their tribe or clan, godparents, stepparents, or any adult who has a kinship bond with the child. This definition is designed to be inclusive and respectful of cultural values and ties of affection. It allows a child to grow to adulthood in a family environment.

learning disability: A disorder in basic psychological processes involved in understanding or using language, spoken or written, that may manifest itself in an imperfect ability to listen, think, speak, read, write, spell or use mathematical calculations. The term includes conditions such as perceptual disability, brain injury, minimal brain dysfunction, dyslexia, and developmental aphasia.

maltreatment: An act or failure to act by a parent, caretaker, or other person as defined under state law which results in physical abuse, neglect, medical neglect, sexual abuse, emotional abuse, or an act or failure to act which presents an imminent risk of serious harm to a child.

mandated reporter: Individuals required by state statutes to report suspected child abuse and neglect to the proper authorities (usually child protective services or law enforcement agencies). Mandated reporters typically include educators and other school personnel, healthcare and mental-health professionals, social workers, child care providers, and law enforcement officers or others who have frequent contact with children and families. Some states identify all citizens as mandated reporters.

medical neglect: A type of maltreatment caused by failure by the caretaker to provide for the appropriate healthcare of the child although financially able to do so, or offered financial or other means to do so.

mental-health services: Beneficial activities which aim to overcome issues involving emotional disturbance or maladaptive behavior adversely affecting socialization, learning, or development. Usually provided by public or private mental health agencies and includes both residential and nonresidential activities.

minor: *See* child

out-of-home care: Also called foster care, including family foster care, kinship care, treatment foster care, and residential and group care. Out-of-home care encompasses the placements and services provided to children and families when children must be removed from their homes because of child safety concerns, as a result of serious parent-child conflict, or to treat serious physical or behavioral health conditions that cannot be addressed within the family.

parent: The birth mother/father, adoptive mother/father, or step mother/father of the child.

parent–child interaction therapy (PCIT): A family-centered treatment approach proven effective for abused and at-risk children ages 2 to 12 and their biological or foster caregivers. A key activity is the therapist's role in coaching the parent to interact more positively with the child.

parental rights: The legal rights and corresponding legal obligations that go along with being the parent of a child.

perpetrator: The person who has been determined to have caused or knowingly allowed the maltreatment of the child.

physical abuse: Child abuse that results in physical injury to a child. This may include, burning, hitting, punching, shaking, kicking, beating, or otherwise harming a child. Although an injury resulting from physical abuse is not accidental, the parent or caregiver may not have intended to hurt the child. The injury may have resulted from severe discipline, including injurious spanking, or physical punishment that is inappropriate to the child's age or condition. The injury may be the result of a single episode or of repeated episodes and can range in severity from minor marks and bruising to death.

physical neglect: Failure to provide for a child's basic survival needs, such as nutrition, clothing, shelter, hygiene, and medical care. Physical neglect may also involve inadequate supervision of a child and other forms of reckless disregard of the child's safety and welfare.

prenatal substance exposure: Fetal exposure to maternal drug and alcohol use that can significantly increase the risk for developmental and neurological disabilities in the child. The effects can cause severe neurological damage and growth retardation in the substance-exposed newborn.

preventive services: Beneficial activities aimed at preventing child abuse and neglect. Such activities may be directed at specific populations identified as being at increased risk of becoming abusive and may be designed to increase the strength and stability of families, to increase parents' confidence and competence in their parenting abilities, and to afford children a stable and supportive environment.

protective factor: Strengths and resources that appear to mediate or serve as a buffer against risk factors that contribute to maltreatment. These factors may strengthen the parent-child relationships, ability to cope with stress, and capacity to provide for children. Protective factors include nurturing and attachment, knowledge of parenting and of child and youth development, parental resilience, social connections, and concrete supports for parents.

relinquishment: Voluntary termination or release of all parental rights and duties that legally frees a child to be adopted. This is sometimes referred to as a surrender or as making an adoption plan for one's child.

resilience: The ability to adapt well to adversity, trauma, tragedy, threats, or even significant sources of stress. Parental resilience is considered a protective factor in child abuse and neglect prevention. Resilience in children enables them to thrive, mature, and increase competence in the midst of adverse circumstances. Resilience can be fostered and developed in children as it involves behaviors, thoughts, and actions that can be learned over time and is impacted by positive and healthy relationships with parents, caregivers, and other adults.

respite care: Child care offered for designated periods of time to allow a caregiver to tend to other family members; alleviate a work, job, health, or housing crisis; or take a break from the stress of caring for a seriously ill child. Respite for foster and adoptive parents is a preventive measure that enhances quality of care for the child, gives the caregiver a deserved and necessary break, and ensures healthy and stable placements for children.

risk: In child welfare, the likelihood that a child will be maltreated in the future. A risk assessment is a measure of the likelihood that a child will be maltreated in the future, frequently through the use of checklists, matrices, scales, and other methods of measurement.

risk factor: Behaviors and conditions present in the child, parent, or family that will likely contribute to child maltreatment occurring in the future. Major risk factors include substance abuse, domestic/family violence, and mental-health problems.

safe haven: When applied to legislation, refers to the policy in which a parent can relinquish a child, usually a newborn, to lawfully designated places such as a hospital. When a child is surrendered in this way, the parent is protected from criminal prosecution. The scope and specifications of the rule vary widely across the states.

safety plan: A casework document developed when it is determined that a child is in imminent or potential risk of serious harm. In the safety plan, the caseworker targets the factors that are causing or contributing to the risk of imminent serious harm to the child and identifies, along with the family, the interventions that will control the safety factors and assure the child's protection.

sexual abuse: According to the Child Abuse Prevention and Treatment Act (CAPTA), the employment, use, persuasion, inducement, entice-ment, or coercion of any child to engage in, or assist any other person to engage in, any sexually explicit conduct or simulation of such conduct for the purpose of producing a visual depiction of such conduct; or the rape, and in cases of caretaker or interfamilial relationships, statutory rape, molestation, prostitution, or other form of sexual exploitation of children, or incest with children.

shaken baby syndrome: The collection of signs and symptoms resulting from the violent shaking of an infant or small child. The consequences of less severe cases may not be brought to the attention of medical professionals and may never be diagnosed. In severe cases that usually result in death or severe neurological consequences, the child usually becomes immediately unconscious and suffers rapidly escalating, life-threatening central nervous system dysfunction.

sibling abuse: The physical, emotional, or sexual maltreatment of a child by a brother or sister.

substantiated: An investigation disposition concluding that the alle-gation of child maltreatment or risk of maltreatment was supported or founded by state law or state policy. A child protective services determination means that credible evidence exists that child abuse or neglect has occurred.

Temporary Assistance for Needy Families (TANF): A program that provides assistance and work opportunities to needy families by granting states the federal funds and wide flexibility to develop and implement their own welfare programs. The focus of the program is to help move recipients into work and to turn welfare into a program of temporary assistance.

unsubstantiated: Not substantiated. An investigation disposition that determines that there is not sufficient evidence under state law or policy to conclude that a child has been maltreated or is at risk of maltreatment. A child protective services determination means that credible evidence does not exist that child abuse or neglect has occurred.

visitation: Scheduled contact among a child in out-of-home care and his or her family members. The purpose of visitation is to maintain family attachments, reduce the sense of abandonment that children may experience during placement, and prepare for permanency.

well-being: The result of meeting a child's educational, emotional, and physical and mental health needs. Well-being is achieved when families have the capacity to provide for the needs of their children or when families are receiving the support and services needed to adequately meet the needs of their children.

youth development: A process that prepares young people to meet the challenges of adolescence and adulthood through a coordinated, progressive series of activities and experiences that help them to become socially, morally, emotionally, physically, and cognitively competent.

Chapter 55

Where to Report Child Abuse

Alabama
Phone: 334-242-1310
Website: dhr.alabama.gov/
contact/Contact_Us.aspx
Additional information: Visit the
website above for information on
reporting or call Childhelp (800-
422-4453) for assistance.

Alaska
Toll-Free: 800-478-4444
Website: dhss.alaska.gov/ocs/
Pages/default.aspx

Arizona
Toll-Free: 888-SOS-CHILD
(888-767-2445)
Website: dcs.az.gov/
report-child-abuse-or-neglect

Colorado
Toll-Free: 844-CO-4-KIDS
(844-264-5437)
Website: www.colorado.gov/
pacific/cdhs/news/colorado-child-
abuse-neglect-hotline-1-844-
co-4-kids-enters-its-third-year-
significant-changes

Connecticut
Toll-Free: 800-842-2288
Toll-Free TDD: 800-624-5518
Website: portal.ct.gov/DCF/1-
DCF/Reporting-Child-Abuse-
and-Neglect

Delaware
Toll-Free: 800-292-9582
Website: kids.delaware.gov/
services/crisis.shtml

Resources in this chapter were compiled from several sources deemed reliable;
all contact information was verified and updated in March 2019.

District of Columbia
Phone: 202-671-SAFE
(202-671-7233)
Website: cfsa.dc.gov/service/
report-child-abuse-and-neglect

Florida
Toll-Free: 800-96-ABUSE
(800-962-2873)
Website: www.dcf.state.fl.us/
abuse

Georgia
Toll-Free: 855-GA-CHILD
(855-422-4453)
Website: dfcs.dhs.georgia.gov/
child-abuse-neglect

Hawaii
Toll-Free: 888-380-3088
Website: humanservices.hawaii.
gov

Idaho
Toll-Free: 855-552-KIDS
(855-552-5437)
Website: healthandwelfare.
idaho.gov/ContactUs/tabid/127/
Default.aspx

Illinois
Toll-Free: 800-25-ABUSE
(800-252-2873)
Website: www.state.il.us/dcfs/
child/index.shtml

Indiana
Toll-Free: 800-800-5556
Website: www.in.gov/dcs/2971.
htm

Iowa
Toll-Free: 800-362-2178
Website: dhs.iowa.gov/
report-abuse-and-fraud

Kansas
Toll-Free: 800-922-5330
Website: www.dcf.ks.gov/Pages/
Default.aspx

Kentucky
Toll-Free: 877-KYSAFE1
(877-597-2331)
Website: chfs.ky.gov/Pages/
contact.aspx

Louisiana
Toll-Free: 855-4LA-KIDS
(855-452-5437)
Website: dss.louisiana.gov/
index.cfm?md=pagebuilder&
tmp=home&pid=109

Maine
Toll-Free: 800-452-1999
Toll-Free TTY: 800-963-9490
Website: www.maine.gov/dhhs/
phone2.htm

Massachusetts
Toll-Free: 800-792-5200
Website: www.mass.gov/how-to/
report-child-abuse-or-neglect

Michigan
Toll-Free: 855-444-3911
Website: www.michigan.
gov/mdhhs/0,5885,7-339-
73971_7119_50648_7193---,00.
html

Minnesota
Phone: 651-431-4661
Website: mn.gov/dhs/people-we-serve/children-and-families/services/child-protection/contact-us
Additional information: Visit the website above for information on reporting or call Childhelp (800-422-4453) for assistance.

Missouri
Toll-Free: 800-392-3738
Website: dss.mo.gov/cd/can.htm

Montana
Toll-Free: 866-820-5437
Website: www.dphhs.mt.gov/cfsd/index.shtml

Nebraska
Toll-Free: 800-652-1999
Website: dhhs.ne.gov/children_family_services/Pages/children_family_services.aspx

Nevada
Toll-Free: 800-992-5757
Website: dcfs.nv.gov/Programs/CWS/CPS/CPS

New Hampshire
Toll-Free: 800-894-5533
Toll-Free TDD: 800-735-2964
Fax: 603-271-6565
Website: www.dhhs.state.nh.us/dcyf/cps/contact.htm

New Jersey
Toll-Free: 877-NJ-ABUSE (877-652-2873)
Toll-Free TDD/TTY: 800-835-5510
Website: www.nj.gov/dcf/about/divisions/dcpp

New Mexico
Toll-Free: 855-333-SAFE (855-333-7233)
Website: cyfd.org/child-abuse-neglect

New York
Toll-Free: 800-342-3720
Toll-Free TDD/TTY: 800-638-5163
Website: www.ocfs.state.ny.us/main/cps

North Carolina
Toll-Free: 800-662-7030
Website: www2.ncdhhs.gov/dss/cps
Additional information: Visit the website above for information on reporting or call Childhelp (800-422-4453) for assistance.

North Dakota
Website: www.nd.gov/dhs/services/childfamily/cps/#reporting
Additional information: Visit the website above for information on reporting or call Childhelp (800-422-4453) for assistance.

Ohio
Toll-Free: 855-OH-CHILD
(855-642-4453)
Website: jfs.ohio.gov/ocf/
childprotectiveservices.stm
Additional information: Contact
the county Public Children
Services Agency or call
Childhelp (800-422-4453) for
assistance.

Oklahoma
Toll-Free: 800-522-3511
Website: www.okdhs.org/
services/cps/Pages/default.aspx

Oregon
Phone: 503-945-5600
Website: www.oregon.gov/DHS/
CHILDREN/CHILD-ABUSE/
Pages/index.aspx
Additional information: Visit the
website above for information on
reporting or call Childhelp (800-
422-4453) for assistance.

Pennsylvania
Toll-Free: 800-932-0313
Toll-Free TDD: 866-872-1677
Website: keepkidssafe.pa.gov/
laws/index.htm

Puerto Rico
Toll-Free: 800-981-8333
Website: www2.pr.gov/
Directorios/Pages/L%C3%ADnea
sdeAyudaparaEmergencias.aspx

Rhode Island
Toll-Free: 800-RI-CHILD
(800-742-4453)
Website: www.dcyf.ri.gov/child_
welfare/index.php

South Carolina
Phone: 803-898-7318
Website: dss.sc.gov/content/
customers/protection/cps/ index.
aspx
Additional information: Visit the
website above for information on
reporting or call Childhelp (800-
422-4453) for assistance.

South Dakota
Phone: 605-773-3165
Website: dss.sd.gov/
childprotection

Tennessee
Toll-Free: 877-237-0004 or 877-
54ABUSE (877-542-2873)
Website: www.tn.gov/dcs/
program-areas/child-safety/
reporting/child-abuse.html

Utah
Toll-Free: 855-323-3237
Website: health.utah.gov/
telephone-hotlines

Vermont
Toll-Free: 800-649-5285
Website: dcf.vermont.gov/
prevention

Virginia
Toll-Free: 800-552-7096
Website: www.dss.virginia.gov/
family/cps/index.html

Washington
Toll-Free: 866-END-HARM
(866-363-4276)
Website: www.dcyf.wa.gov/
contact-us

West Virginia
Toll-Free: 800-352-6513
Website: www.wvdhhr.org/
report.asp

Wisconsin
Phone: 608-422-7000
Website: dcf.wisconsin.gov/
children/CPS/cpswimap.htm
Additional information: Visit the
website above for information on
reporting or call Childhelp (800-
422-4453) for assistance.

Wyoming
Toll-Free: 800-457-3659
Website: dfsweb.wyo.
gov/social-services/
child-protective-services
Additional information: Visit the
website above for information on
reporting or call Childhelp (800-
422-4453) for assistance.

Chapter 56

A Directory of Organizations Dedicated to Promoting Healthy Families

Adult Survivors of Child Abuse (ASCA)
The Morris Center
P.O. Box 281535
San Francisco, CA 94128
Website: www.ascasupport.org
E-mail: info@ascasupport.com

Advocates for Youth
1325 G St. N.W.
Ste. 980
Washington, DC 20005
Phone: 202-419-3420
Fax: 202-419-1448
Website: www.
advocatesforyouth.org
E-mail: info@advocatesforyouth.
org

American Academy of Pediatrics (AAP)
141 N.W. Point Blvd.
Elk Grove Village
IL 60007-1098
Toll-Free: 800-433-9016
Phone: 847-434-4000
Fax: 847-434-8000
Website: aap.org
E-mail: commun@aap.org

Resources in this chapter were compiled from several sources deemed reliable; all contact information was verified and updated in March 2019.

American Humane Association
1400 16th St. N.W.
Ste. 360
Washington, DC 20036
Toll-Free: 800-227-4645
Phone: 303-792-9900
Website: www.americanhumane.
org
E-mail: info@americanhumane.
org

American Professional Society on the Abuse of Children (APSAC)
1706 E. Broad St.
Columbus, OH 43203
Toll-Free: 877-402-7722
Phone: 614-827-1321
Website: www.apsac.org
E-mail: info@apsac.org

Association for Play Therapy (APT)
401 Clovis Ave.
Ste. 107
Clovis, CA 93612
Phone: 559-298-3400
Fax: 559-298-3410
Website: www.a4pt.org
E-mail: info@a4pt.org

Association for the Treatment of Sexual Abusers (ATSA)
4900 S.W. Griffith Dr., Ste. 274
Beaverton, OR 97005
Phone: 503-643-1023
Fax: 503-643-5084
Website: www.atsa.com
E-mail: atsa@atsa.com

AVANCE, Inc.
118 N. Medina St.
San Antonio, TX 78207
Phone: 210-270-4630
Fax: 210-270-4636
Website: www.avance.org
E-mail: info@avance.org

Center for Violence and Injury Prevention (CVIP)
1 Brookings Dr.
CB 1196
St. Louis, MO 63130
Phone: 314-935-8129
Website: cvip.wustl.edu/
about-us/contact-us
E-mail: bcvip@wustl.edu

Chadwick Center for Children and Families
3020 Children's Way, MC 5016
San Diego, CA 92123
Phone: 858-966-4011
Fax: 858-966-8535
Website: www.chadwickcenter.
com/contact-us
E-mail: chadwickcenter@rchsd.
org

Chapel Hill Training-Outreach Project, Inc. (CHTOP)
800 Eastowne Dr.
Ste. 105
Chapel Hill, NC 27514
Phone: 919-490-5577
TDD: 919-490-5577
Fax: 919-490-4905
Website: chtop.org

Child AbuseWatch.NET
One Child International, Inc.
590 S.W. Ninth Terr.
Ste. 2
Pompano Beach, FL 33069
Website: www.abusewatch.net
E-mail: info@abusewatch.net

Child Lures Prevention
5166 Shelburne Rd.
Shelburne, VT 05482
Toll-Free: 800-552-2197
Phone: 802-985-8458
Fax: 802-985-8418
Website: www.
childluresprevention.com
E-mail: info@
childluresprevention.com

Child Molestation Research and Prevention Institute (CMRPI)
2515 Santa Clara Ave.
Ste. 208
Alameda, CA 94501
Toll-Free: 888-7730-8368
Phone: 510-740-1410
Website: www.
childmolestationprevention.org
E-mail: contact@
childmolestationprevention.org

Child Welfare Information Gateway
Children's Bureau/ACYF
330 C St. S.W.
Washington, DC 20201
Toll-Free: 800-394-3366
Fax: 703-225-2357
Website: www.childwelfare.gov
E-mail: info@childwelfare.gov

Child Welfare League of America (CWLA)
727 15th St. N.W.
12th Fl.
Washington, DC 20005
Phone: 202-688-4200
Fax: 202-833-1689
Website: www.cwla.org
E-mail: cwla@cwla.org

Childhelp USA
4350 E. Camelback Rd.
Bldg. F250
Phoenix, AZ 85018
Toll-Free: 800-4-A-CHILD
(800-422-4453)
Phone: 480-922-8212
Toll-Free TDD: 800-2-A-CHILD
(800-222-4453)
Fax: 480-922-7061
Website: www.childhelp.org
E-mail: khackley@childhelp.org

Children Without a Voice USA (CWAV)
P.O. Box 4351
Alpharetta, GA 30023
Website: www.cwavusa.org/
privacy-policy
E-mail: email@
childrenwithoutavoiceusa.org

Children's Trust Massachusetts
55 Court St.
Fourth Fl.
Boston, MA 02108
Phone: 617-727-8957
Fax: 617-727-8997
Website: www.childrenstrustma.
org/about-us/contact-us
E-mail: info@childrenstrustma.org

491

Circle of Parents
2100 S. Marshall Blvd.
Ste. 305
Chicago, IL 60623
Phone: 773-257-0111
Fax: 773-277-0715
Website: www.circleofparents.
org
E-mail: CSavage@
circleofparents.org

**Committee for Children
(CFC)**
2815 Second Ave., Ste. 400
Seattle, WA 98121
Toll-Free: 800-634-4449
Phone: 206-343-1223
Fax: 206-438-6765
Website: www.cfchildren.org
E-mail: info@cfchildren.org

**Computer Science and
Telecommunications Board
(CSTB)**
The National Academies
500 Fifth St. N.W.
Washington, DC 20001
Phone: 202-334-2605
Fax: 202-334-2318
Website: www.cstb.org
E-mail: cstb@nas.edu

**Cooperative Extension
System (CES), United States
Department of Agriculture**
National Institute of Food and
Agriculture (NIFA)
1400 Independence Ave. S.W.
Stop 2201
Washington, DC 20250-2201
Website: nifa.usda.gov/
Extension

**Court Appointed Special
Advocates for Children
(CASA)**
100 W.Harrison St., N. Tower
Ste. 500
Seattle, WA 98119
Toll-Free: 800-628-3233
Website: www.casaforchildren.
org
E-mail: executiveoffice@
casaforchildren.org

**Crime Victims' Institute
(CVI)**
College of Criminal Justice,
Sam Houston State University
(SHSU)
P.O. Box 2180
Huntsville, TX 77341-2180
Phone: 936-294-3100
Fax: 936-294-4296
Website: www.
crimevictimsinstitute.org
E-mail: crimevictims@shsu.edu

Darkness to Light
7 Radcliffe St.
Ste. 200
Charleston, SC 29403
Toll-Free: 866-FOR-LIGHT
(866-367-5444)
Phone: 843-513-1616
Website: www.d2l.org
E-mail: Facilitatorsupport@D2L.
org

Doris Duke Charitable Foundation (DDCF)
650 Fifth Ave.
19th Fl.
New York, NY 10019
Phone: 212-974-7000
Fax: 212-974-7590
Website: www.ddcf.org
E-mail: webmaster@ddcf.org

Every Child Matters Education Fund (ECM)
660 Pennsylvania Ave. S.E.
Ste. 303
Washington, DC 20003
Phone: 202-223-8177
Fax: 202-223-8499
Website: www.everychildmatters.org
E-mail: info@everychildmatters.org

FaithTrust Institute
2414 S.W. Andover St.
Ste. D208
Seattle, WA 98106
Toll-Free: 877-860-2255
Phone: 206-634-1903
Fax: 206-634-0115
Website: www.faithtrustinstitute.org
E-mail: info@faithtrustinstitute.org

Fight Crime: Invest in Kids
1212 New York Ave. N.W.
Ste. 300
Washington, DC 20005
Phone: 202-464-7005
Fax: 202-776-0110
Website: www.fightcrime.org
E-mail: info@fightcrime.org

Future of Children
267 Wallace Hall
Princeton University
Princeton, NJ 08544
Phone: 609-258-5894
Website: www.princeton.edu/futureofchildren
E-mail: foc@princeton.edu

General Federation of Women's Clubs (GFWC)
1734 N St. N.W.
Washington, DC 20036-2990
Toll-Free: 800-443-4392
Phone: 202-347-3168
Fax: 202-835-0246
Website: www.gfwc.org
E-mail: gfwc@gfwc.org

Healthy Families America (HFA)
200 S. Wabash,
10th Fl.
Chicago, IL 60604
Phone: 312-663-3520
Fax: 312-939-8962
Website: healthyfamiliesamerica.org
E-mail: hfamail@preventchildabuse.org

International Center for Assault Prevention (ICAP)
107 Gilbreth Pkwy, Ste. 200
Mullica Hill, NJ 08062
Toll-Free: 800-258-3189
Phone: 856-582-7000
Fax: 856-582-3588
Website: www.internationalcap.org
E-mail: childassaultprevention@gmail.com

International Initiative to End Child Labor (IIECL)
1016 S. Wayne St., Ste. 702
Arlington, VA 22204
Phone: 703-328-3401
Website: www.endchildlabor.org
E-mail: IIECL@endchildlabor.org

International Society for Prevention of Child Abuse and Neglect (ISPCAN)
12200 E. Iliff Ave., Ste. 103
Aurora, CO 80014
Phone: 720-449-6010
Fax: 720-449-6012
Website: www.ispcan.org
E-mail: resources@ispcan.org

Jacob Wetterling Resource Center (JWRC)
2324 University Ave. W.
Ste. 105
St. Paul, MN 55114
Toll-Free: 800-325-HOPE
(800-325-4673)
Phone: 651-714-4673
Fax: 651-714-9098
Website: www.gundersenhealth.org/ncptc/jacob-wetterling-resource-center
E-mail: admin@ncptc-jwrc.org

Kempe Foundation
The Gary Pavilion at Children's Hospital Colorado, Anschutz Medical Campus
13123 E. 16th Ave., B390
Aurora, CO 80045
Phone: 303-864-5300
Website: www.kempe.org
E-mail: questions@kempe.org

Kidpower Teenpower Fullpower International
P.O. Box 1212
Santa Cruz, CA 95061
Toll-Free: 800-467-6997
Website: www.kidpower.org
E-mail: safety@kidpower.org

Liberty House
2685 Fourth St. N.E.
Salem, OR 97301
Toll-Free: 866-303-4643
Phone: 503-540-0288
Website: libertyhousecenter.org
E-mail: kwolfer@libertyhousecenter.org

Maternal Infant Health Outreach Worker (MIHOW)
Center for Community Health Solutions
461 21st Ave. S.
Nashville, TN 37240
Phone: 615-322-4184
Fax: 615-343-0325
Website: www.mihow.org
E-mail: mihow@vanderbilt.edu

National Alliance of Children's Trust and Prevention Funds
P.O. Box 15206
Seattle, WA 98115
Phone: 206-526-1221
Fax: 206-526-0220
Website: www.ctfalliance.org
E-mail: info@ctfalliance.org

National Association of State Mental Health Program Directors (NASMHPD)
66 Canal Center Plaza
Ste. 302
Alexandria, VA 22314
Phone: 703-739-9333
Fax: 703-548-9517
Website: www.nasmhpd.org

National Center for Mental Health Promotion and Youth Violence Prevention
Education Development Center, Inc. (EDC)
43 Foundry Ave.
Waltham, MA 02453
Phone: 617-969-7100
TTY: 617-964-5448
Fax: 617-969-5979
Website: www.edc.org/contact
E-mail: contact@edc.org

National Center for Missing and Exploited Children (NCMEC)
Charles B. Wang International Children's Bldg.
699 Prince St.
Alexandria, VA 22314-3175
Toll-Free: 800-THE-LOST
(800-843-5678)
Phone: 703-224-2150
Fax: 703-224-2122
Website: www.missingkids.com

National Center on Shaken Baby Syndrome (NCSBS)
1433 N. 1075 W.
Ste. 110
Farmington, UT 84025
Phone: 801-447-9360
Fax: 801-447-9364
Website: www.dontshake.org
E-mail: mail@dontshake.org

National Child Protection Training Center (NCPTC)
Winona State University Campus
P.O. Box 5838
175 W. Mark St.
Winona, MN 55987
Toll-Free: 800-342-5978
Phone: 507-457-5000
Website: www.winona.edu

National Children's Advocacy Center (NCAC)
210 Pratt Ave. N.E.
Huntsville, AL 35801
Phone: 256-533-KIDS
(256-533-5437)
Fax: 256-534-6883
Website: www.nationalcac.org

National Children's Alliance (NCA)
516 C St. N.E.
Washington, DC 20002
Toll-Free: 800-239-9950
Phone: 202-548-0090
Fax: 202-548-0099
Website: www.
nationalchildrensalliance.org

National Coalition to Prevent Child Sexual Abuse and Exploitation
Website: www.preventtogether. org
E-mail: PreventTogether@gmail. com

National Council on Child Abuse and Family Violence (NCCAFV)
1025 Connecticut Ave. N.W.
Ste. 1000
Washington, DC 20036
Phone: 202-429-6695
Fax: 202-521-3479
Website: www.nccafv.org
E-mail: info@nccafv.org

National Indian Child Welfare Association (NICWA)
5100 S.W. Macadam Ave.
Ste. 300
Portland, OR 97239
Phone: 503-222-4044
Fax: 503-222-4007
Website: www.nicwa.org
E-mail: info@nicwa.org

National Parent Helpline
250 W.First St.
Ste. 250
Claremont, CA 91711
Toll-Free: 855-4-A-PARENT
(855-427-2736)
Phone: 909-621-6184
Website: www.
nationalparenthelpline.org
E-mail: info@
nationalparenthelpline.org

Office for Victims of Crime (OVC)
U.S. Department of Justice (DOJ)
810 Seventh St. N.W.
Second Fl.
Washington, DC 20531
Toll-Free: 800-363-0441
Phone: 202-307-5983
Fax: 202-514-6383
Website: www.ovc.gov
E-mail: itverp@usdoj.gov

Parents Anonymous, Inc.
250 W. First St.
Ste. 250
Claremont, CA 91711
Phone: 909-621-6184
Fax: 909-621-0614
Website: www.
parentsanonymous.org

Parents for Megan's Law and the Crime Victims Center (CVC)
100 Comac St.
Ronkonkoma, NY 11779
Toll-Free: 888-ASK-PFML
(888-275-7365)
Phone: 631-689-2672
Website: www.
parentsformeganslaw.org/
welcome.jsp
E-mail: pfmeganslaw@aol.com

Prevent Child Abuse America
228 S. Wabash Ave.
10th Fl.
Chicago, IL 60604
Toll-Free: 800-Children
(800-244-5373)
Phone: 312-663-3520
Fax: 312-939-8962
Website: www.
preventchildabuse.org
E-mail: info@preventchildabuse.
org

Rape, Abuse and Incest National Network (RAINN)
2000 L St. N.W.
Ste. 406
Washington, DC 20036
Toll-Free: 800-656-HOPE
(800-656-4673)
Phone: 202-544-3064
Fax: 202-544-3556
Website: www.rainn.org
E-mail: info@rainn.org

Safe Child Program
Coalition for Children, Inc.
P.O. Box 6304
Denver, CO 80206
Phone: 303-320-6328
Fax: 303-809-6328
Website: www.safechild.org
E-mail: info@safechild.org

Safe4Athletes
P.O. Box 650
Santa Monica, CA 90406
Toll-Free: 855-SAFE-4-AA
(855-723-3422)
Website: safe4athletes.org
E-mail: info@safe4athletes.org

Safer Society Foundation, Inc.
P.O. Box 340
Brandon, VT 05733-0340
Phone: 802-247-3132
Fax: 802-247-4233
Website: www.safersociety.org
E-mail: info@safersociety.org

Sexuality Information and Education Council of the United States (SIECUS)
1012 14th St. N.W.
Ste. 1108
Washington, DC 20005
Phone: 202-265-2405
Fax: 212-819-9776
Website: www.siecus.org
E-mail: info@siecus.org

Stop It Now!
351 Pleasant St.
Ste. B-319
Northampton, MA 01060
Toll-Free: 888-PREVENT
(888-773-8368)
Phone: 413-587-3500
Fax: 413-587-3505
Website: www.StopItNow.org
E-mail: info@stopitnow.org

Substance Abuse and Mental Health Services Administration (SAMHSA)
SAMHSA's Public Engagement Platform
P.O. Box 2345
Rockville, MD 20847-2345
Toll-Free: 877-SAMHSA-7 (877-726-4727)
Phone: 240-221-4036
Toll-Free TTY: 800-487-4889
Fax: 240-221-4292
Website: store.samhsa.gov

Survivors of Incest Anonymous (SIA)
World Service Office (WSO)
P.O. Box 7078
Pittsburgh, PA 15212
Toll-Free: 877-742-9761
Phone: 410-893-3322
Website: www.siawso.org

Index

Index

501

intimate partner violence (IPV),
continued
perpetration 5
teen dating violence 114
intimidation, cognitive behavioral
therapy (CBT) 296
investigation
Child Abuse Prevention and
Treatment Act (CAPTA) 265
child exploitation 35
child maltreatment 22
child welfare system 279
childhood sexual abuse 191
defined 476
online sexual exploitation 160
physical abuse 84
physical consequences 66
reporting child abuse 294
involuntary servitude
child labor trafficking 36
physical abuse 8
Iowa, child abuse reporting
contact 484
IPV *see* intimate partner violence
IY *see* Incredible Years

J

Jacob Wetterling Resource Center
(JWRC), contact 494
Justice for Victims of Trafficking Act
of 2015, child neglect 13
juvenile and family court,
defined 476
juvenile delinquency
behavioral consequences 68
defined 476
juvenile justice
Child Abuse Prevention and
Treatment Act (CAPTA) 266
child exploitation 35
child maltreatment 240
fatality 26

K

Kansas, child abuse reporting
contact 484
Kempe Foundation, contact 494

Kentucky, child abuse reporting
contact 484
kicking
child maltreatment 222
physical abuse 8, 82
Kidpower Teenpower, contact 494
kinship care, defined 476
kinship caregivers, overview 388–92
"Kinship Caregivers and the Child
Welfare System" (HHS) 388n

L

labeled praise, social rewards 356
lack of attachment, emotional
maltreatment 81
LEA *see* law enforcement agency
"Learn the Warning Signs—
Recognizing Sexual Abuse"
(DOJ) 225n
learning disability
defined 477
educational neglect 132
learning problems, child abuse 78
"Leaving Your Child Home Alone"
(HHS) 463n
legal custody, kinship caregivers 388
legislation
child maltreatment 20
child neglect 125
child welfare system 278
incest 105
infant safe haven laws 261
Liberty House, contact 494
life-threatening conditions, neglect 9
live coaching, parent–child interaction
therapy (PCIT) 306
"Long-Term Consequences of
Child Abuse and Neglect"
(HHS) 65n
long-term psychological effects, sibling
abuse 47
Louisiana, child abuse reporting
contact 484

M

magnetic resonance imaging (MRI),
shaken baby syndrome (SBS) 99

technology
  babysitting 467
  child exploitation 110
  overview 141–59
  sex offender registration act 270
  sexual abuse prevention 228
teen dating violence, overview 113–5
"Teen Dating Violence" (CDC) 113n
Temporary Assistance for Needy
  Families (TANF)
  cross-system collaboration 240
  defined 480
  economic consequences 69
  kinship care 389
temporary guardianship,
  described 389
Tennessee, child abuse reporting
  contact 486
termination of parental rights,
  relinquishment 263
terrible twos, parenting skills 368
tertiary prevention programs, quality
  programs 236
threats
  behavioral therapy 297
  parenting 337
  school safety 244
"Through Our Eyes: Children,
  Violence, and Trauma" (DOJ) 31n
time-out
  childhood maltreatment 167
  described 351
  discipline and consequences 350
  misbehavior and consequences 353
  parenting 366
  therapeutic approach 301
toxic stress
  abuse or neglect 453
  child abuse 222
  child maltreatment 62
  prevention program 239
trafficking of minors, abuse 8
Trafficking Victims Protection Act
  (TVPA), child labor 36
trauma
  abuse and mental health 209
  abuse and neglect 453, 458
  abuse survivors 322
  adoption 403

trauma, *continued*
  bullying 56
  child abuse 66
  child neglect 14, 126
  chronic fatigue syndrome 181
  cognitive behavioral therapy
    (CBT) 297
  head trauma 93
  human trafficking 42
  incest 106
  male survivors 193
  maltreatment 83
  parental risk factors 250
  parental substance use 338
  parenting 443
  physical abuse 302
  posttraumatic stress disorder
    (PTSD) 200
  sexual abuse 433
  violence 31
trauma history
  bullying 56
  mental health 449
trauma-informed care, online sexual
  exploitation 160
traumatic events
  child abuse 327
  parenting 443
  posttraumatic stress disorder
    (PTSD) 200
treatment planning
  adult survivors 317
  mental health 330
  Munchausen syndrome 96
Triple P—Positive Parenting Program
  (Triple P), defined 217
truancy
  consequences 68
  overview 131–4
12-step approach, treatment
  techniques 321

U

Unaccompanied Refugee Minors
  (URM) Program, child labor
  trafficking 39
"Understanding the Effects
  of Maltreatment on Brain
  Development" (HHS) 62n